DESIGNED
TO KILL

DESIGNED TO KILL

Major Arthur Hogben

PSL

Patrick Stephens
Wellingborough, Northamptonshire

First published in 1987

British Library Cataloguing in Publication Data

Hogben, Arthur
Designed to kill : the history of British
bomb disposal.
1. Bomb reconnaissance—Great Britain
I. Title
358'.2 EM HV6640

ISBN 0-85059-865-6

Patrick Stephens Limited is part of the
Thorsons Publishing Group

Printed and bound in Great Britain

1 3 5 7 9 10 8 6 4 2

Contents

Foreword

by Major-General The Viscount Monckton of
Brenchley, CB, OBE, MC, DL

There has long been a need for a full history of British bomb disposal. This history needed to cover its formation, war and peacetime work without being too technical. This book is the result of hard work and research by the author, Major Arthur Hogben, who is uniquely qualified for the task. He has spent much of his Service career in bomb disposal both in the Army and in Joint Service appointments. In 1974 he was awarded the Queen's Gallantry Medal for bomb disposal work in the East End of London.

The history of the operations in many countries reveals the humour and the tragedies in this most dangerous form of service. Cold, calm courage was the necessary requirement and this was obvious in so many of the events described in this book.

Television highlights some of the work in Northern Ireland, Britain and elsewhere. Few, however, realize the difference between this work and ordinary Service life. The soldier, sailor or airman is only sometimes on active service and rarely in action. The bomb disposal units are always on active service and often in action.

As an old soldier, a brother Man of Kent and a friend of the author I hope many will read this book.

House of Lords
May 1986

Acknowledgements

When one has received so much help and encouragement it is difficult to know who to thank, so will all those bomb disposal officers and men who told me their stories or gave me access to their records please accept this as my grateful acknowledgement and thanks. Some must, however, be given formal recognition and I can but do this in alphabetical order as all have helped in so many different ways. I therefore acknowledge with thanks:

The Council of the Institution of Mechanical Engineers for permission to use facts and diagrams reprinted from the Proceedings of the Institution (the Thirty-Third Thomas Hawksley Lecture given by H.J. Gough, CB, MBE, DSc, MIMechE, FRS, Vice President of the Institution and Chairman of the Unexploded Bomb Committee).

Mr Terry Gander, the well-known military author, whose idea it was that I should write this book and who throughout the work gave me encouragement, professional advice and guidance.

Wing Commander J.A. MacBean, MBE, RAF (Retd), for permission to use his unpublished historical notes and personal diaries relating to the history of RAF bomb disposal.

Herr Manfred Rauschert for visiting me and providing first-hand recollections of life as a member of the Luftwaffe bomb disposal organization during World War 2.

Mr C.E. Reeves and Mr W.D. Scott for permission to quote from their letters concerning their bomb disposal activities in Malta during the siege of 1940-43.

Lady Smyth for permission to use biographical material from *The Story of the George Cross* by her late husband Brigadier The Right Honourable Sir John Smyth, Bt, VC, MC.

Mr Philip Vella for permission to use facts taken from his book *Malta: Blitzed But Not Beaten* and for one short quotation.

Mrs Vanessa Wallis, a well-known local artist, for producing or reproducing most of the diagrams in the book.

Photographic acknowledgements are made to all those people and organizations who permitted their copyright photographs to be used in this book. Special acknowledgement is made to the following: Allied Newspapers Malta, Associated Newspapers plc, the Central Office of Information for permission to use the large numbers of Crown Copyright photographs, Major J.A.Craib, QGM, RE, Wing Commander J.A. MacBean, MBE, RAF(Retd), the National War Museum Association Malta, Herr Manfred Rauschert, Sergeant S.G. Wilkinson, BEM, RE and finally Squadron Leader D. Wilson, RAF.

Acknowledgement must also be made to the two ladies without whose help and support this book would never have been finished. First, my wife Eileen who, despite her many lonely evenings and weekends constantly encouraged me and provided an endless flow of coffee as I worked. Finally, my thanks to Mrs Shirley Jones who gave up so much of her spare time to type and proofread what I had written.

Harrietsham
July 1986

Introduction:
The bomb disposal operator

'I sometimes wonder if anything went wrong whether one would see a blinding flash or hear a bang or if one knows anything at all.'

So mused Major George Fletcher, MBE, GM, RE, an experienced bomb disposal officer, as he recalled his successful disposal of a large German parachute mine in Burghley Road, Camden, London, in October 1968. He, like most people involved in bomb disposal, will normally have such thoughts only in the small dark hours of the night when safely in bed. These thoughts are not morbid, they merely reflect an example of the scientific curiosity possessed by all bomb disposal personnel. When in the same small hours he is faced with a bomb, be it a sophisticated monster designed and built in a nation's ordnance factory or a device designed and built by a fanatic in a back kitchen, the bomb disposal operator has no time for thoughts other than those directly connected with the job in hand. Today he is well trained, he has a range of complex equipment at his disposal and in many cases he has been through a complex psychological assessment to determine his suitability for such work. Despite this, Explosive Ordnance Disposal (EOD) operators, as the bomb disposal personnel of today are called, still face danger and death when dealing with a bomb of whatever age, shape or nationality.

Historic bombs of both world wars, the details of which are fully known and understood, can still provide surprises and in some cases are more dangerous today than the day they were originally dropped. Similarly, more modern unexploded weapons are all, like their predecessors, designed to kill and will do so if not treated with the greatest of respect. This applies wherever they are found, from the Middle East to the Falklands, and includes the weapons produced by the modern terrorist.

What sort of men, or in recent years women, face these dangers as a matter of routine, to the extent that the stage is reached where some even claim that they enjoy it? There are many things that they are not. They are not unimaginative; a person lacking in imagination will not appreciate the dangers involved and may appear initially to be a hero or a fool. That fool or hero is likely to be a short-lived one. They are not impulsive. They always consider the risk to themselves and others before undertaking any sort of action. On the other hand they are not indecisive; when a decision has to be made it is based upon the best available information—the problem with new weapons is that the available information may range from very little to none at all. There is no room in the EOD organisation for the 'cowboy', the heroic impulsive personality who could be an excellent combat soldier in time of war but would be a potential hazard as an EOD operator. He must also be intelligent and able to work under stress, both alone and as a team leader. Not only is there the stress of the immediate situation, the anti-disturbance fuze, the ticking clock, the silent electronic timer, the general fear of the unknown weapon before him; there is also the stress imposed by external pressures. In war there is a risk from other bombs or enemy action. In peace there is the senior officer who wants the incident cleared as soon as possible or the civilian authorities who want to reopen the closed roads or railway lines. There may be pressures to allow evacuated families to return to their homes before nightfall or some other apparently important event, or demands from the Press who want an interview before their deadline. Yet despite these pressures the EOD operator must remain calm, work methodically, take no unnecessary risks and still maintain a degree of flexibility to cope with the unexpected.

So where do these supermen or superwomen come from? The answer, of course, is that they are not superpersons and in the United Kingdom they exist in adequate numbers in the Royal Navy, the Army, the Royal Air Force, the Civil Service and the Police Force. In other nations similar individuals exist in their Armed Forces and civilian organizations. They are disciplined people who are generally free from personal worries, in good physical and mental health, are methodical, courageous, decisive and free from group dependency and self-doubt. They are neither perfectionists nor slipshod in their approach to a problem. Finally, they must be dedicated to their work. This usually presents few problems, for once in the bomb disposal business one quickly becomes 'hooked' as it offers interest, excitement, personal satisfaction and an infinite variety of tasks.

So much for the person who actually deals with the bomb or explosive device but give a thought to the hundreds (at the peak of the Second World War, thousands) of often forgotten soldiers, sailors and airmen who spent hours, days and even years, digging, tunnelling and shafting to reach deeply buried bombs knowing that at any moment the monster they were seeking could explode beneath them with their death an almost certainty. These men, over 300 of whom were members of the Non-Combatant Corps (conscientious objectors), rarely gained medals, yet many died at the bottom of wet muddy holes as they dug and probed for bombs. The story of these brave men will be related later but let it never be forgotten that these are still the men without whom the bomb disposal officers and non-commissioned officers frequently could not operate.

1

The beginnings

Any weapon containing explosive which has been fired, dropped, placed or buried in the ground will eventually be found and present a problem to someone. By its nature bomb disposal must be as old as the use of bombs or indeed any projected explosive device. Missiles filled with black gunpowder and fired during the American Civil War are still, some 120 years later, causing casualties. It may be fashionable to have such a missile on your mantelshelf or in your den, particularly if you live near one of the Civil War battle sites, but it is foolhardy to paint it and then when you change the decor of the room take the paint off the missile with a blowlamp! Yes, that actually happened, but the decorator did it only once!

Unexploded projectiles have been a problem since the Chinese first fired their crude rockets but bombs dropped from the air must date only from man's first flights into the sky for warlike purposes. As early as 1849 Austrian forces besieging Venice released balloons to which were attached small charges of gunpowder fired by primitive slow match fuzes, but the first true aerial bomb was not dropped until after the advent of the aeroplane in 1903.

The attacks on Venice did little damage but the use of balloons to drop missiles was referred to in the Hague Convention of 1899 when the then major powers (not including the USA) agreed to render illegal the possible use of any poison gas, together with other forms of offensive warfare such as expanding bullets and the dropping of missiles from balloons. This just fifteen years before the start of World War 1! It is also interesting to note that during World War 2 the Japanese drifted balloons across the Pacific Ocean carrying explosive charges from Japan to the United States mainland.

The ban on the use of weapons dropped from balloons was paradoxically the signal for military and aeronautical engineers to investigate the possibilities opened up by the development of the aeroplane. At first, Spain, France, Italy and Germany clearly led the field. Italy had the dubious honour of being the first country to bomb fellow human beings from heavier-than-air machines. They bombed both Turks and Arabs in

North Africa in 1911, and were closely followed by the Spanish who bombed the Moors in northern Morocco in 1913. At this time the Spanish were using German-manufactured bombs. It is perhaps ironic that some 24 years later the German Luftwaffe was to use Spain as a proving ground for its latest bombs and bombing techniques.

By the start of the First World War high explosive bombs had been developed in both Germany and France. France tended initially to utilize artillery shells to which were fitted tail fins. The Germans had, however, developed the first true aerial bombs in 1913. These were developed by an army department known as the *APK—Artillerie Prufungs Kommission* (Artillery Test Commission)—and consisted of a cast iron spherical body with an internal fuze. They looked like large cannon balls and were made in a variety of weights. Many historians believe that these bombs quickly became obsolete, but in fact they were dropped extensively by German Army airships during World War 1. They were dropped on England, France, the Russian front and even on Salonika. One was recently (1983) recovered from the centre of Antwerp. They were used until the German Army Zeppelin (or more correctly Airship) Service was disbanded in August 1917.

Parallel with the development of the APK bomb or the *'Kugel Bombe'* the Carbonit Company of Schlebusch developed the range of Carbonit bombs. The Carbonit bombs had pear-shaped bodies and cylindrical tail fins (later to be known as drum tails), and to aid penetration the bombs were fitted with steel-tipped noses. They were equipped with fuzes which were armed as they fell, by a rotating propeller in the tail. Thus the bombs were intrinsically safe until well clear of the parent aircraft. These bombs were used by German Naval airships until 1917. The British Home Defence authorities used to be able to tell whether it was a Naval or Army airship which had raided the night before simply by the shape of any unexploded bombs recovered. In view of the speed of the airships, the shape of the bomb mattered little, though.

In 1917 the German Air Service developed into an independent arm and the Army-sponsored APK was replaced by the PuW *(Prüfanstalt und Werft der Fliegertruppen* (Test Establishment and Works for Aviation Troops). The PuW developed what can only be described as the modern bomb. It was streamlined, manufactured from steel rather than cast iron and had sound aerodynamic qualities. Its fins were such that they caused the bomb to spin in flight, thus stabilizing its fall, and the resultant centrifugal force was used to arm the internal fuze. These bombs were manufactured in weights up to 1,000 kg (2,200 lb).

In Britain the Royal Naval Air Service pioneered bomb dropping and indeed carried out the first British air raid of the war against Zeppelin sheds at Evere, north of Brussels, using 20 lb (9.09 kg) bombs. Even so Britain had a lot of catching up to do. The Royal Laboratory at Woolwich and the Royal Aircraft Factory at Farnborough started designing bombs as soon as the war started and a 1915 edition of

RANGE OF GERMAN CARBONIT BOMBS

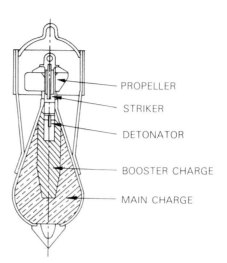

PROPELLER

STRIKER

DETONATOR

BOOSTER CHARGE

MAIN CHARGE

50 Kg	20 Kg	10 Kg	4.5 Kg
110 lbs	44 lbs	22 lbs	9.9 lbs

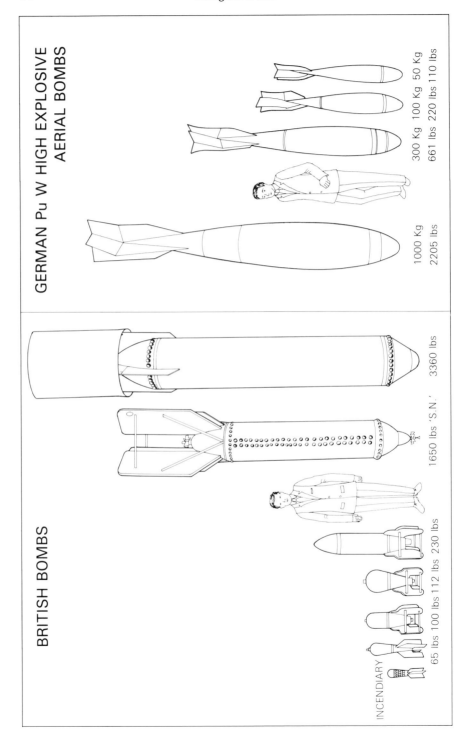

GERMAN Pu W HIGH EXPLOSIVE AERIAL BOMBS

50 Kg 110 lbs
100 Kg 220 lbs
300 Kg 661 lbs
1000 Kg 2205 lbs

BRITISH BOMBS

3360 lbs
1650 lbs 'S.N.'
230 lbs
112 lbs
100 lbs
65 lbs
INCENDIARY

the*Handbook of Aerial Bombs* lists high explosive bombs ranging in size from 10 lb to 336 lb (4.5 to 152.7 kg). By 1918 Germany's largest bomb weighed 1,000 kg (2,200 lb) and the British had one weighing 3,360 lb (1,527 kg). The British bomb was so large that only one aircraft, the Handley Page V/1500 of the Independent Air Force, could carry it and then only one bomb. (This load capability was repeated during World War 2 when Royal Air Force Lancasters were limited to carrying but one 22,000 lb (10,000 kg) Grand Slam.) Not all development was aimed at producing larger and larger bombs, however, for one bomb per aircraft leaves little room for error. Perhaps the most successful British bombs, used with great effect by the Royal Flying Corps by 1917, were the 230 lb (104.5 kg) bombs of the Royal Aircraft Factory and the 112 lb (50.9 kg) bombs of the Royal Laboratory.

Parallel to the development of high explosive bombs was the development of incendiary weapons. These ranged from large incendiary devices for dropping on cities (both Berlin and London suffered from this form of attack during World War 1), to small incendiary darts. The incendiary darts were designed for use against Zeppelins, tethered observation balloons, animal fodder and other 'warlike' stores. In most cases they were fitted with hooks to ensure that, having pierced a Zeppelin or balloon, they remained in position until the inflammable gas in the target had been ignited. One of the first of these darts was demonstrated by one Henri Guerre of Lyon in early 1914 when he dropped some of his darts from the first platform of the Eiffel Tower on to targets of straw and wood. His design, although effective in igniting the target, suffered from the fact that it had to be dropped by hand, a method with little appeal to pilots. A year later Lieutenant Commander F. Ranken, RN, of the Royal Naval Air Service perfected the Ranken Dart which had the advantage of being launched from a tube attached to an aircraft, although otherwise its method of operation was similar to that of the Guerre Dart.

Both the Guerre and Ranken Dart are now collectors' items but the larger German incendiary bombs are still, from time to time, discovered in old barns as they are stripped for conversion into desirable residences. This demonstrates once again that the bomb disposal operator must be constantly aware of, and able to identify, weapons devised many years before he was born.

During the First World War a total of 8,578 bombs were recorded as dropped on the British mainland, killing 1,414 and injuring a further 3,416 people. These bombs, by modern standards relatively unsophisticated, were fitted with simple mechanical impact fuzes and if they failed to detonate on impact it was due to malfunction rather than design. During the Second World War approximately twelve per cent of all bombs dropped on Britain failed to detonate on impact due either to malfunction or to the fitting of long-delay fuzes which produced the so-called time bomb. If it is assumed that fifty per cent of the unexploded bombs were fitted with deliberate delay mechanisms then some six per

FRENCH INCENDIARY DEVICE

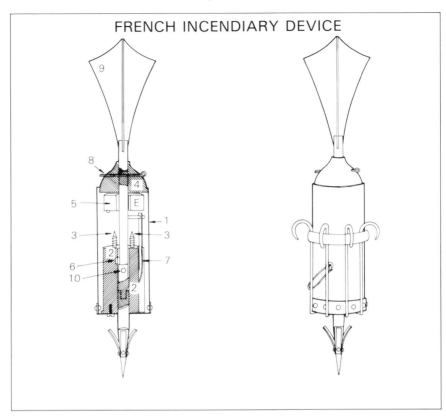

This device invented by M Henri Guerre consists of a steel cylinder (1) to which is secured a central block (2) fitted with two sharp spikes (3). A circular wood block (4) which is free to slide easily within the cylinder (1) closes the top of the cylinder and carries a small annular tank (5) containing an inflammable spirit. A central spindle passes through the device and is secured to the top block (4) by a split pin (8). A shoulder and key (6) prevents the block (2) from sliding down the spindle but leaves it and its attached cylinder (1) free to slide up the spindle. A rod (7) is attached to the spindle and rests in a slot on the side of block (2).

The method of operation is as follows:

The bomb, in falling through the air, is kept point downwards by the tail fin (9) attached to the end of the spindle. When the bomb strikes a balloon or airship the barbed point pierces the outer skin and passes through it, but the bottom of the cylinder is stopped by the fabric. This movement drives the annular tank (5) hard against the spikes (3) releasing the spirit onto the block (2). The same movement causes the rod (7) to slide in the slot in the block (2) striking a Vestas compound which ignites the spirit. A safety pin (10) passes through the cylinder and the spindle locking their relative movement and preventing a misfire. This safety pin is removed before dropping the bomb.

Should the bomb strike its target obliquely the hooks catch into the fabric thus stopping the movement of the cylinder and causing the bomb to function as previously described.

RANKEN EXPLOSIVE DART

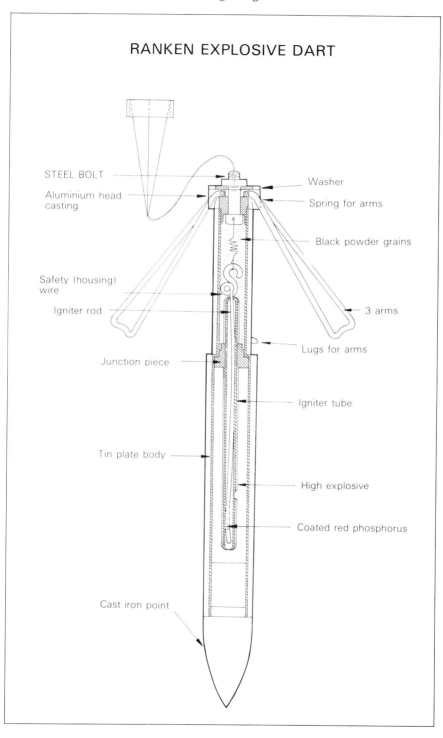

STEEL BOLT

Aluminium head casting

Washer

Spring for arms

Black powder grains

Safety (housing) wire

Igniter rod

3 arms

Lugs for arms

Junction piece

Igniter tube

Tin plate body

High explosive

Coated red phosphorus

Cast iron point

cent failed due to malfunction. Using this same figure on the 8,578 bombs dropped during the First World War there would appear to have been about 500 unexploded bombs in Britain during the period 1914-18. (The same number of unexploded bombs was reported in London in just two nights during the Second World War.) Of these 500 unexploded bombs many were so small that they could be safely detonated *in situ*. Due to their simple fuzes others presented no major problems and many of the incendiary bombs merely 'went out'. Thus, during the First World War only a very small bomb disposal problem existed in Britain. The bombs that were found were dealt with as a matter of routine by the trained personnel of the Royal Army Ordnance Corps who were responsible for the disposal of all military explosives. Thus, no specific bomb disposal organization existed, or indeed was needed.

After the horrors of the Great War there was a general military rundown and although most progressive military strategists accepted that air power was an essential factor in any future conflict, little other than lip service was paid to its development in those countries which had no aggressive territorial intentions. Although aircraft became more powerful, faster and more dependable, little progress was made in the development of aerial bombs and in the Royal Air Force their use was limited to colonial policing actions, using bombs little different from those of the First World War.

One major event in 1931 which passed practically unnoticed throughout Europe was the application for patent rights for a range of electro-mechanical devices described as 'Electric Time and Impact Fuzes for Projectiles and the Like' by the German organization RMW (*Reinische Metallwaren und Maschinenfabrik*). This patent application was made to most nations which had any form of inventors' protection and was granted a patent by the British Patent Office in July 1932. At this time it is worth remembering that Germany was in a state of economic chaos and the development of any aggressive weapon was contrary to her Versailles Treaty commitments. Clearly, someone was forward planning!

The year 1936 heralded the start of the Spanish Civil War and soon all Europe could have seen the effect of mass bombing on cities and the problems caused by unexploded bombs (UXB)—if only they had looked. The newly-developed Luftwaffe openly used the cities of Spain as a proving ground to assess the effects of bombs on built-up areas, the damage which could be caused to important installations and, above all as far as this story is concerned, the effect of UXB on the movement of both troops and civilian populations.

It has been claimed frequently that practically no one in Britain noted these effects or realized the problems which UXB in an industrial complex or busy city could cause. Yet someone in the Home Office had a glimmering of the problem because the Police War Instruction, Section 10, dated May 1936, stated:

'The War Office have undertaken general responsibility for the disposal of unexploded bombs through their Inspecting Ordnance Officers (IOO), unless a suitably experienced representative of the Navy or Air Force is available near at hand. This work may involve a special danger, having regard to the development of bombs fuzed to burst at any time up to twenty-four hours after having been dropped. The Police should not touch unexploded bombs until the arrival of the IOOs and should keep all persons at a safe distance. The IOOs, or other appointed Officers, will have to decide whether a bomb can safely be removed or whether it will be necessary to blow it up *in situ.*'

The time delay was understated by a minimum factor of three but at least the existence of a delay fuze was acknowledged, even if the general instructions for disposal were similar to those issued during the First World War.

Thus the start of a second world war drew nearer with no realization of the true UXB threat. The German air attacks on Poland provided some evidence of the disrupting effect of the UXB but by then British internal wrangling over who was responsible for bomb disposal was at its height. It continued until two days after the first German bomb fell on the British mainland near Canterbury on 9 May 1940. (The first German bomb to fall anywhere in Great Britain during the Second World War was at Hoy in the Orkneys on 17 October 1939.)

The cynics will no doubt consider that a bomb exploding just sixty miles from London concentrates the mind far more than any plea from a Ministry official.

2

Birth pains

The War Office, as early as September 1938, expressed the view that they were not satisfied with existing arrangements for dealing with unexploded bombs and projectiles and suggested that a conference be called, to include representatives of the Air Ministry, the Home Office, the Air Raid Precautions (ARP) Department and themselves, with the object of preparing a position paper on the subject. At that time confusion existed on all sides over the question of responsibility for the formation of an organization capable of dealing with unexploded bombs. On 5 November 1938, a War Office communication addressed to the Under Secretary of State at the Home Office stated:

'I am commanded by the Army Council to refer to the subject of the disposal of unexploded enemy bombs dropped in the UK in time of war and to say for the information of Secretary, Sir Samuel Hoare, that the Council have had this matter under consideration and after consultation with the Air Ministry are not satisfied that the existing arrangements in this respect are adequate. The present orders on this subject in the Police War Book are that the Police will report all cases of unexploded bombs to the nearest Military Authority, who will arrange for the disposal of them. The Military personnel finally responsible for this service are the Inspection Ordnance Officers, who are few in number and most of whom would accompany any land force which might be sent overseas.

I am to say that the Council consider that though these arrangements were adequate under the conditions of the last war, they would be totally inadequate to deal with the quantity of unexploded bombs which might be expected under present circumstances, and they further are of the opinion that this service could be undertaken by the Home Office, ARP Department.'

The Army Council justified their view that bomb disposal could be undertaken by the ARP Department on the grounds that the Army did not have personnel with a knowledge of 'air bombs' likely to be used by an enemy, that they 'understood' the Air Ministry would not be able to undertake the responsibility and that the Home Office could call on the services of persons trained in explosives who were normally well distributed over the country. In his turn, the Chief Inspector of Explosives for the Home Office totally disagreed that it should become a Home Office responsibility, mainly because he considered it to be a military responsibility and also because the Home Office had no persons trained in aircraft bombs.

In the early days of 1939 the question of responsibility constantly recurred. The main difficulties appeared to be the size and nature of the organization and the final disposal of the bomb after it had been located. The arguments as to whether the disposal organization should blow up the bombs where they were found or remove them to a safe place and then destroy them continued for many months. Everybody concerned agreed that it was immaterial who was finally responsible and the first consideration should be given (as always) to the formation of a committee, this time for the technical investigation into the best means of disposal. This proposal was of immense importance as at that time very little was known about the types of bombs which might be expected and, perhaps more importantly, the types of fuzes which might be expected in the bombs. The only modern German bomb in Britain was a 50 kg (110 lb) example which had been brought from Spain into the country by a journalist. There appears to be no record of whether the bomb contained explosive or even if it had a fuze. Perhaps a visit to HM Stationery Office and a look at that patent granted in 1932 might have provided the general specification of likely fuzes! However, this proposal for a technical committee was to lead to the formation of the Unexploded Bomb Committee which held its first meeting on 1 May 1940. This committee was to contain some of the best scientific brains in the country and, as will be seen later, also some extremely courageous men, all dedicated to defeating whatever device the enemy cared to drop from the skies.

On 15 March 1939 a conference was held at Horseferry House, London, and bucks were officially passed. The War Office once again expressed the view that disposal should be undertaken by one of the ARP services; the Air Ministry stated that they were unable to provide the requisite personnel, while the Home Office stated again that the matter was outside the scope of the ARP. It was, however, agreed that it would be necessary to set up a special service to deal with unexploded bombs, and that the department to be responsible was a matter for the ministries to decide. Further conferences and meetings were held and the view was taken that the Home Office would accept responsibility. In the meantime, the military would carry out the necessary training of the selected men.

It had originally been thought desirable to have a specially-recruited force under the Home Office, possibly obtained from the ranks of the British Legion. The War Office proposals led, however, to a new plan. Under their proposals, bombs not so deeply buried as to be inaccessible without excavation, or bombs buried in open spaces, would simply be exploded *in situ* after sandbagging. In more difficult cases the bombs would be sandbagged and application made to the Air Ministry for an Armament Officer to advise. They contemplated that squads of three men would be all that would be needed and advised that all the necessary training could be given in the course of one day! From this simple plan there did not appear to be a case for a specially recruited body of men, and it was thought to be more satisfactory to ask local authorities to provide reasonably intelligent men such as trained ARP instructors. It was thought that these men could carry on their normal training and deal with an unexploded bomb on the simple lines recommended by the War Office, in addition to their normal duties.

An arrangement was made finally that, until the Civil Defence organization was fully trained, the War Office would be responsible for bomb disposal and would assist in training the Civil Defence personnel. Here a major break from tradition occurred, for instead of unexploded bombs being the responsibility of the Royal Army Ordnance Corps (who traditionally, through the work of the IOOs, had been responsible for the destruction of explosives and ammunition), it was passed to the Royal Engineers. Traditionally they are trained in demolition and the construction of fortifications (including sandbagging) and the ability to excavate below ground level.

Thus, it was planned that small teams of Royal Engineers would be established near likely targets and spend their time training Civil Defence volunteers in the skills of bomb demolition, digging and the construction of sandbag walls. This scheme broke down due to the low number of civilian volunteers and in some cases the Home Office received letters from local authorities objecting most strongly to assuming any responsibility in connection with unexploded bombs. Consequently, on 12 October 1939, the War Office agreed to continue to hold themselves responsible for the demolition of unexploded bombs until such time as a new organization could be established. It should be noted that this was an agreement to demolish the bombs and not at this stage to dispose of them by either the removal of the fuze or picking them up and carrying them away, tasks that had variously been proposed at the many meetings held since 1938.

By November 1939, Bomb Disposal Parties RE were formed, the personnel being drawn from Field Companies RE. Each party consisted of one junior NCO and two Sappers (the junior rank of the Royal Engineers) equipped with: a vehicle (unspecified and often unavailable); 75 lb of explosives and explosive accessories; two shovels; two picks and 500 sandbags—and in some cases equipment for lifting bombs from a hole.

At this time, the only information available concerning bomb disposal techniques was an instruction giving details of how to build a sandbagged enclosure round the unexploded bomb of unspecified size, shape or characteristics, which it was apparently expected would be found either on or very near the ground surface. On such weak foundations were the first Bomb Disposal Parties RE trained and sent out to be attached to units in the vicinity of likely targets, there to await their fate. At about the same time, the Admiralty and the Air Ministry set up bomb disposal organizations to deal with possible bombs on their own property.

As a result of opposition from some local authorities to providing men to be trained in bomb demolition it was agreed that, until the problem of responsibilities had been resolved, civilian responsibilities would be limited to providing personnel and materials for sandbag wall construction.

During this month, November 1939, the first unexploded bomb was recovered by the Royal Air Force at Sullom Voe in the Shetland Islands and the fuze was sent to Woolwich Arsenal for evaluation.

During the next months the expected heavy air attacks did not develop—this was the period of the 'phoney war'—Belgium, the Netherlands and France apparently providing a barrier to the expected air armada. This apparent immunity to air attack produced a complacency in which the Bomb Disposal Parties RE tended to be forgotten. Abandoned by their parent Field Companies and used as fatigue men by the units to which they were attached, they gradually disappeared into oblivion. As will be seen later, this phoney war period was far from phoney for the officers and ratings of HMS *Vernon*, the Royal Navy's Torpedo and Mining School. During October and November alone they dealt with over 200 enemy mines, including the originally unknown menace of the magnetic mine.

On the civilian front between November 1939 and February 1940 all was far from quiet. The Regional Headquarters of the ARP Department kept up a constant stream of letters to the Ministry of Home Security, requesting information relating to future arrangements for dealing with unexploded bombs and asking the perpetual question relating to evacuation distances for various sized bombs. The Chief Constable of Leeds wrote to the Home Office requesting information about evacuation and elicited the following response:

'We have been in touch with the ARP Department on the question raised in your letter of 28 Nov 39, as to the possibility of giving instructions as to the area which should be cleared should an unexploded bomb fall in a thickly populated area. We understand, however, that at present it is not possible to give any instruction on this point.'

The excuse given at the time over the delay in issuing these instructions was that it was felt that if a new technique for rendering bombs safe could be evolved on the lines of experiments then proceeding, a much less exacting evacuation area could perhaps be specified. A word or two with anyone recently returned from the Civil War in Spain might also have provided a realistic evaluation of a safe evacuation area.

At the third meeting of the Technical Sub-Committee of the ARP Department held on 20 February 1940, the Secretary stated that he had been informed that the War Office would be responsible for dealing with unexploded bombs except possibly in premises owned either by the Admiralty or the Air Ministry. This was not, however, completely accurate, as at that time a vigorous correspondence was taking place between the War Office, the Admiralty and the Ministry of Home

Security over who was responsible for unexploded bombs on merchant ships arriving in British ports. The War Office, in trying to clarify their responsibilities, asked the Admiralty if they would extend the responsibility they already had for HM Ships to merchant ships in British ports. The Admiralty declined to accept this responsibility on the grounds that their only established bomb disposal organization was based at the five main Naval Bases at Scapa Flow in the Orkney Isles off the north coast of Scotland, Rosyth on the east coast of Scotland, The Nore on the River Thames estuary and the two bases at Portsmouth and the Plymouth on the English south coast. Furthermore, there were insufficient suitable technical Naval personnel then present in the commercial ports to permit an organization being established at each of them. The Admiralty further suggested that the nearest bomb disposal organization of any Service or the Civil Defence organization should be tasked. At this the Ministry of Home Security, who had been a copy addressee, jumped into the fray pointing out that the Civil Defence were not responsible for any form of bomb disposal, and so the correspondence continued until 11 May 1940, two days after the first enemy bomb dropped on mainland Britain. On this date the War Office agreed to accept, with some exceptions, all responsibility for dealing with unexploded bombs.

The Ministry of Home Security issued on 11 May 1940, *Home Security Circular No 88/40—Disposal of Unexploded Bombs*, which confirmed that the War Office was responsible for dealing with all unexploded bombs and ammunition except where they had fallen on Admiralty or Air Ministry property. (The full text of this circular is in Annex A.)

Thus, the battle lines were drawn and the embryo Bomb Disposal Organization was born and baptized, in many cases with fire. It reached manhood very quickly, or had manhood forced upon it. After 11 May 1940 the Royal Engineers quickly raised some 220 Bomb Disposal Sections (BDS). Details of this sudden expansion are given below, but it was none too soon. The Low Countries were invaded in May and the capitulation of France placed the enemy in occupation of the whole of Northern France as well as the Netherlands and Belgium, thus putting the whole of Britain within striking distance of the Luftwaffe. By the middle of August 1940 bombing had become general, the Battle of Britain raged, airfields were being heavily bombed and the War Office realised that bomb disposal was a field operation which could not be controlled from the War Office. Consequently, it was handed over lock, stock and barrel to GHQ Home Forces on 20 August 1940.

On 27 August 1940 a meeting at the Air Ministry, chaired by Major General C.J.S. King, Chief Engineer Home Forces, laid down not only the detailed inter-Service responsibilities for bomb disposal, but also details of its training, intelligence gathering and distribution methods and its technical support. The importance of this meeting and the long-term effects of its decisions cannot be over-emphasized and the full text of its minutes are also given in Annex A. These minutes were to become the

Joint Service Bomb Disposal Charter and many of its provisions are very similar to those existing today.

Two days later, on 29 August 1940, GHQ Home Forces set up a Bomb Disposal Directorate. The office of Director Bomb Disposal was assumed by the Inspector of Fortifications and Works, the combined appointment being known as IF and DBD. The first Director was Major General G.B.O. Taylor, CB, CBE, and by coincidence on the day of his appointment the London 'blitz' began.

Concurrent with the gestation and birth of the Bomb Disposal Organization and, indeed, a vital part of it, was the establishment of the Unexploded Bomb Committee referred to earlier in this chapter. By arrangement with the Secretary of State for War, the Ministry of Supply agreed to take over financial and other responsibilities for all research, technical development and production involved in the methods for dealing with unexploded bombs as from 1 April 1940. The Minister of Supply placed the responsibility for consideration of, and advice on associated problems, on a specially formed Committee of the Scientific Advisory Council. This, the Unexploded Bomb Committee, besides its scientific members, included representatives of the Army (Engineer-in-Chief, War Office and GHQ Home Forces), the Admiralty, the Air Ministry, the Home Office and Ministry of Home Security, since the research, development and production involved were carried out on behalf of all these Services and departments. The Director General of Scientific Research and Development, Dr H.J. Gough, MBE, DSc, PhD, MI MechE, FRS, was the chairman of the committee throughout the war. This committee held its first meeting on 1 May 1940 at Savoy Hill House, London, and its terms of reference were: '1. To consider the general problem of the unexploded enemy bomb and advise on methods of dealing with the problem. 2. To report to the Council [The Scientific Advisory Council].'

When the Ministry of Supply took over from the Ministry of Home Security, little information was available concerning German aircraft bombs and fuzes, but some simple tools had been designed to facilitate removal of the fuzes. Certain experimental work was also in progress on methods of opening bomb casings and emptying the explosive filling.

Within a very few weeks the large-scale aerial attack on England had begun and the technical problems to be solved had increased greatly in nature and in scope. New fuzes were introduced by the enemy including delayed-action and anti-handling devices. Larger and more complex bombs and parachute mines were employed. Unexploded bombs, after penetrating to considerable depths and following devious and unknown courses underground, became lodged within or close to factories, power-houses and other vital buildings, on airfields and in dockyards. At the same time roads and railways had to be closed, and people evacuated from their homes. The sound of the 'All Clear' and the retirement of enemy aircraft no longer meant that danger had ceased, for explosions could continue for the next three or four days, each taking its toll of life and property. There was also the effect on the morale of the people who had to see and hear, long after a raid, bombs exploding—bringing home the fact that there was no respite for anyone in modern war. The most urgent problems were, therefore, to provide means of locating unexploded bombs and for making them safe for removal. In the words of the Prime Minister: 'The rapid disposal of unexploded bombs is of the highest importance. Any failure to grapple with this problem may have serious results on the production of aircraft and other vital war material. The work of the Bomb Disposal Squads must be facilitated by the provision of every kind of up-to-date equipment.'

In order to facilitate rapid consideration of new problems, a Research and Development Sub-Committee of the Unexploded Bomb Committee was formed in October 1940. This was a purely scientific body composed of those working in the unexploded bomb field, meeting at frequent intervals to review and discuss the details of all the researches in progress, to suggest new methods, and to report successful methods to the parent committee. The main committee was able to consider long-term problems at its monthly meetings and to advise the Services on the application of methods recommended by the sub-committee. After a very fruitful existence the sub-committee went into abeyance in June 1942 and its functions were assumed by the main committee.

The day-to-day progressing and co-ordinating of the many researches in progress, the evaluation of disposal techniques satisfactory to the Services, and the production of the necessary apparatus for all three Services, was the responsibility of a special group of scientists and engineers at Ministry of Supply Headquarters in London. Members of this branch were always available to advise on the spot when new or difficult problems were encountered. They frequently assisted regular bomb disposal units in the handling of new apparatus and in the recovery of new types of bombs, fuzes and explosives. The award to members of this branch of two George Crosses (one posthumously), one George Medal and two posthumous Commendations for Bravery, is testimony to the hazards of their work.

Many well known figures served on the Unexploded Bomb Committee. Its Chairman, Dr H.J. Gough, was no boardroom figure or laboratory warrior. The committee first met in May 1940 and by June 1940 had designed a device known as a steam sterilizer to cut a hole in the case of a bomb and then emulsify the explosive and force it out of the bomb without the need to touch the fuze. This was first used on a live bomb on 12 September 1940 when a Captain Kennedy, RE, of the Bomb Disposal Directorate Staff, Dr Gough and Dr Merriman of the Directorate of Scientific Research (another member of the Unexploded Bomb Committee), attempted to use the new equipment on a 250 kg (550 lb) bomb lying in Regent Street, London. The bomb contained two clockwork time fuzes, at least one of which was ticking so the bomb could explode at any moment. Work started at about 14:00 hours and the equipment clearly had teething problems. After frequent approaches and work on the bomb it was not until 17:55 hours that the apparatus was working reasonably efficiently and an explosive/hot water mixture was flowing from the bomb. The team was watching the operation from behind sandbags when, at exactly 18:00 hours, the bomb blew up. It had been a tense afternoon's work and indeed a lucky one, but much useful information had been gained and it demonstrated that bomb disposal equipment could only be properly evaluated on live bombs.

The original Army representative on the committee was Major General K.M. Loch, MC, Director of Anti-Aircraft and Coast Defence, but he was replaced by Major General G.B.O. Taylor, CB, CBE, Director of Bomb Disposal, upon the formation of the Directorate in August 1940. He, in turn, was replaced in early 1942 by Brigadier H.H. Bateman, DSO, OBE, MC, as the new DBD.

The Air Ministry was represented throughout the war by Wing Commander J.C. Stevens, OBE, of Technical Armaments 4 (T.ARM.4), later to be known as Operations 10 (Bomb Disposal) (O.10(BD)). He was head of RAF bomb disposal and was personally responsible for the development of a number of bomb disposal equipments, perhaps the best known being the 'Stevens Stopper'. A version of this, known as the 'S Set', was still in service with Royal Air Force and Royal Engineer EOD teams in 1987. It is interesting to note that his son, Warrant Officer J.T.S. Stevens, RAF, was also 'in the game'. He was awarded the George Medal in 1944 for his bomb disposal work.

Early meetings were also attended by Flying Officer J.S. Rowlands, RAF (who in later years was to become Air Marshal Sir John Rowlands, GC, KBE), and Flight Lieutenant (later Squadron Leader) E.L. Moxey, RAF, who invented several early versions of automatic fuze extractors and fuze dischargers. He, like many of the early pioneers, was killed later in 1940 when engaged in bomb disposal. He was awarded the George Cross (posthumously) for his work.

Dr A.D. Merriman, MA, MEd, DSc, initially Joint Secretary of the Unexploded Bomb Committee, was forever out and about wherever new bombs or fuzes were to be found or there was new equipment to be tested. At the fifth meeting of the Unexploded Bomb Committee, held on 12 December 1940, it can be noted that the chairman expressed the congratulations of the committee to Dr Merriman on the award of the George Cross for his work in connection with unexploded bombs. Throughout the war Dr Merriman was associated with the Unexploded Bomb Committee, although he tended to leave the country from time to time. As a Lieutenant Colonel Royal Engineers he did sterling work on the recovery of Italian unexploded bombs and fuzes from the Middle East. Wherever he travelled he returned with valuable information for the Unexploded Bomb Committee and when away corresponded regularly with Dr Gough. Some of his work in North Africa is described later in the

Early fuze extractor invented by Flight Lieutenant E. L. Moxey, GC, RAF.

book when the whole problem of unexploded bombs during that campaign is considered.

The Admiralty were fully represented on the committee and one of the most regular attenders was Captain L.E.H. Llewellyn, RN, Director Unexploded Bomb Department (DUBD). At an average meeting some twenty people sat down to consider problems or hear answers relating to enemy bombs and it would be invidious to list them all for fear of missing out someone. Apart from a small nucleus of regular attenders, many scientists, Service chiefs or junior (in rank but not in experience) bomb disposal officers were present whenever their particular expertise or experience was needed by the committee.

Advice, equipments, procedures and safety measures were made available to end users in the shortest possible time by the Unexploded Bomb Committee. It should not be forgotten that the committee was supported by its Research Sub-Committee, various groups of scientists, engineers and selected bomb disposal personnel. The support personnel came as individuals or from the various Service Ministries and Head-quarter Staffs. They were not all concerned with the *status quo* either—they also looked ahead to anticipate problems and generally make provisions for the future.

We have seen the speed with which the steam sterilizer was designed, but in 1943 the enemy dropped bombs fitted with a type of fuze designed deliberately and solely as a booby trap to harass and kill bomb disposal personnel. This fuze was an extremely sensitive anti-handling device, which could not be made safe by any methods then in use. Yet such were the measures taken by the Unexploded Bomb Committee that just a week after the first anti-handling fuze was recovered (a story in itself and told later in the book) a render-safe procedure and the specialist equipment to carry it out were in the hands of bomb disposal personnel. In this instance the 'render-safe procedure' (the procedure necessary before a bomb can be safely removed from wherever it has lodged) was relatively simple—once the thought had occurred to someone. It consisted of freezing the fuze so that its electric batteries could no longer function. This procedure was a temporary measure since, once the batteries were allowed to return to normal temperature, they regained the ability to activate the firing circuits. Not one recorded example exists of this fuze ever operating as designed and thus the whole of the enemy's effort on this particular project was wasted.

Altogether the Unexploded Bomb Committee met formally 48 times, the last meeting being in Shellmex House, The Strand, on 23 October 1945, five and a half years after the first meeting. A more detailed study of its work and the fuzes and bombs with which it had to cope is given in Annex B.

While the birth pains of the basic organization were being suffered, sections and individuals of the single-Service bomb disposal unit were going through their own troubled times. During the period 1939-40, much was learnt of the dangers which were to face them and others for the duration of the war and an indefinite period (which has still not ended) afterwards. These lessons were learnt at the cost of death, mutilation and after countless acts of bravery, as totally new devices were found and methods of dealing with them discovered. For the sake of clarity the early development of each of the three armed services bomb disposal organizations will be considered in turn. Also considered will be the development and organization of that frequently forgotten force—the Auxiliary Bomb Disposal Squads of the Home Guard. These squads rarely receive a mention in any accounts of either bomb disposal activities or the activities of the various Home Front organizations. Consequently, many of their exploits, and even their existence, are forgotten and their ex-members rarely get included in reunions or old comrades' gatherings.

The Royal Navy will be considered first, not only as they are the Senior Service, but also because they were the first Service to come face to face with the enemy's unexploded devices. One of the Navy's problems was that not only were they responsible for unexploded bombs, they were also responsible for mines found at sea, on the foreshore or in the centre of an industrial complex or a large city such as Coventry or London. Consideration of the Navy's minesweeping activities on the high seas, the estuaries and harbour approaches is outside the scope of this book. The story of their land activities, however, must be recounted whether dealing with the magnetic mine which had landed by accident on the foreshore, the so-called land mine dropped by parachute on to cities or the many conventional bombs dropped upon Admiralty property.

3

More birth pains—the Services

The Royal Navy

By its very nature mine warfare at sea is a clandestine activity, but once new types of mine are recovered they lose their mystery and merely present yet more dangerous technical problems to those responsible for investigating their secrets and devising countermeasures. During the early part of the war the Royal Navy had three separate, although closely linked, groups of officers and ratings dealing with explosive objects dropped from the air by the enemy.

There were those dealing with sea mines who, to aid their sweeping techniques and other countermeasures, were naturally keen to discover the inner workings of such weapons. Consequently, they were responsible for any which came ashore or had been dropped accidentally on a foreshore or in shallow estuaries. There were those responsible for mines which were deliberately dropped on cities to harass, kill and destroy. Finally, there were the Naval bomb disposal teams responsible for dealing with unexploded enemy bombs on Naval property and other areas for which they were responsible.

The 'credit' for first inventing the magnetic mine and using it operationally falls to the British, who laid 472 of them off the Belgian coast during August and September 1918. They were not a great success as many of them detonated shortly after being laid. Britain then undertook little further activity relating to magnetic mines until forced to take a very personal interest in those laid by the German Navy and Air Force from September 1939 onwards.

The German Navy first started work on the design of a magnetic mine as early as 1932 (the year the first electro-mechanical bomb fuzes were patented), but their design presented a complex problem and the first really satisfactory model was not available until 1936. It was planned to lay these mines from both surface craft and U-boats (submarines) and for this reason two versions were designed using the same firing unit. On completion of a satisfactory design in 1936, the German Air Force raised the question of laying magnetic mines by aircraft. This idea was not liked by the German Navy. They objected on the grounds that such methods would increase the risk of revealing the mine's secrets by accidental drops on dry land or from the shooting down of a loaded aircraft over land. However, the Air Force argued that they could lay mines in river estuaries and other areas inaccessible to the Navy and revisit existing minefields to 'top them up' until their case was accepted by the German Supreme Command. This resulted in the designing of magnetic mines specifically for laying by aircraft, which were basically the same as those for the Navy with the addition of a parachute to limit the force of impact upon the water and so protect the mine mechanism. Some were also equipped with a bomb fuze which would explode the mine a given period after impact if by that time the fuze was not subjected to an increase in pressure indicating that it was covered by at least 4 m (13 ft) of water. This was incorporated to prevent any risk of exploitation by the British should a mine fall into shallow water or on dry land.

The German Air Force did not like the parachute as it made accurate mine-laying difficult and so they designed a 'bomb' mine of their own. This did not have a parachute but used a plastic tail and magnetic firing device similar to that used by the German Navy. This design was not, however, ready for use until 1941.

Directly hostilities started on 3 September 1939, the German Navy started laying moored mines from their destroyers. These were laid by night in the approaches to the British east coast ports and in the Thames estuary as close inshore as the Tongue Sand area approximately 10 km (6.2 miles) off the north Kent coast. This was made much easier for them as the British had taken a policy decision to keep their lighthouses operating normally. While this was going on U-boats laid the first magnetic ground mines, ie, those which remained on the sea bed. These were laid in relatively small numbers, 65 being laid during the first week of the war. The number was limited as the German Navy were keen to assess their effects before committing themselves to a major campaign. There was always the fear that, as the British had used a magnetic mine during the First World War, they now had a countermeasure to its mode of action. In fact, no countermeasure existed at that time and from the German point of view the mines were a huge success.

The German Air Force, seeing how successful the new mines were proving, became anxious to begin laying their own and by 17 November 1939 had started to drop parachute magnetic mines. This was much against the German Navy's wish for they knew their success was due to surprise rather than to the technical properties of the mine. Furthermore, they were aware that allowing a single mine to fall into British hands would compromise years of development work and enable a countermeasure to be developed before a really heavy attack on British shipping could take place.

By 23 November 1939 their worst fears were realized and the first magnetic mine was safely recovered from the mud flats near Shoeburyness. The Germans quickly learnt their lesson and, as will be seen, subsequent designs were booby-trapped to prevent easy acquisition of their mysteries even if the mines were recovered intact.

In September 1939 the Admiralty were aware that Germany possessed a magnetic mine but that was the extent of their knowledge. Consequently, as shipping was being sunk by explosions which were clearly not caused by contact mines, the Admiralty directed that the new mine's secrets had to be discovered as soon as possible. The responsibility fell upon the newly appointed Rear Admiral Mine Layers (RAML) Rear Admiral W.F. Wake-Walker, OBE, RN. He in turn directed that he be informed immediately of any reports of a known or suspected unexploded magnetic mine being discovered so that an officer from the RAML staff or HMS *Vernon* (the Royal Navy Torpedo and Mining School at Portsmouth) could be sent to recover it.

By November 1939 approximately 200 German mines had been recovered and 'rendered safe', much of the work being undertaken by Lieutenant J. Glenny, RN, Lieutenant R.S. Armitage, RNVR, and their assistants. These mines were all buoyant moored mines which had either broken free from their moorings or been swept free by minesweepers, and no magnetic mines had been recovered. However, on the night of 21/22 November 1939 there was a dramatic change of events. Reports were received that German aircraft had been spotted laying mines in the Humber and off Harwich and Southend. HMS *Gypsy* (a destroyer) had been sunk and shipping in the three rivers was held up. The mines concerned were described as 'long cylindrical objects rather like large kit bags attached to parachutes'.

Officers from HMS *Vernon* and RAML staff were alerted and Lieutenant Commander R.C. Lewis, RN, left for Southend at 03:00 hours on 22 November. Other officers went to the Humber and Harwich. Lieutenant Commander Lewis, after interviewing eye-witnesses, was able to determine the general area into which the mines had fallen but unable to trace an actual example. He therefore returned to the Admiralty where Lieutenant Commander J.G.D. Ouvry, RN, one of the staff of the Mines Department of HMS *Vernon*, was also on standby.

Just before midnight on the same day, both were alerted and told that a parachute mine had been dropped that evening off Shoeburyness on the north coast of the Thames estuary, and was expected to be uncovered at low water at about 04:00 hours. Both Ouvry and Lewis were driven post-haste to Southend, arriving at 03:30 hours on 23 November 1939, their orders being to examine and recover the mine at all costs. Meanwhile, a special mine recovery party from HMS *Vernon* had been alerted to take non-magnetic tools direct to Shoeburyness. The two officers were joined at Southend by Commander Bowles, RN, on the staff of Naval Officer in Charge, Southend, and a photographer. They carried on to Shoeburyness where Commander Maton, RN, Commander of Shoeburyness Experimental Department, was to provide guides and other facilities as required.

'. . . and a hollow tail containing a massive phosphor bronze spring' — the first Type A mine recovered.

Lieutenant Commander Ouvry described the first few minutes at Shoeburyness as follows: 'A private soldier led the cavalcade, splashing through the pools of water left by the receding tide, until the light of our torches showed us a dark menacing looking object lying partially embedded in the sand. It was cylindrical in shape, made of some aluminium alloy, had tubular horns on the nose and a hollow tail containing a massive phosphor bronze spring. There were two unpleasant-looking fittings near the fore end and these looked like being our Public Enemies Numbers One and Two.'

The two officers, having divested themselves of all metal items likely to influence the mechanism of the mine, then approached it, leaving the remainder of the party in the rear. Examination showed the external fittings of the cylinder were secured by screw rings requiring a special type of pin spanner to remove them. Lieutenant Commander Lewis took a rubbing of the ring and later gave it to Commander Maton, who undertook to have a brass (non-magnetic) spanner made in his workshop by noon next day. There was little else that could be done at that stage and so photographs were taken and the mine was securely lashed down ready for an attack at the next low tide. On the way back from the mine a parachute was recovered from the mud confirming that they had actually found what they were looking for.

Whilst they were having an early breakfast it was reported that another mine had been sighted about 300 m (382 yd) from the first, but when they arrived at the foreshore the tide was such that it could not be found.

By 13:00 hours Lieutenant Commanders Lewis and Ouvry were able to see both mines and while more photographs of the first mine were being taken they looked at the second one which appeared to be of the same design as the first. Meantime, the recovery party from HMS *Vernon* had arrived, consisting of Chief Petty Officer Baldwin and Able Seaman Vearncombe, both of whom had worked with Lieutenant Commander Ouvry on previous mine 'render-safe' operations.

It was decided that Lieutenant Commander Ouvry and Chief Petty Officer Baldwin should endeavour to remove the vital components of the first mine. Lieutenant Commander Lewis and Able Seaman Vearncombe would watch from a safe distance, recording exactly what was being done, the first pair having agreed a definite sequence of events. This record would form a useful reference in case of an accident as there was always the possibility that the mine had unknown devices other than the magnetic one. If there was an explosion the notes taken by the watchers would be available to those who would have to deal with the second mine.

Lieutenant Commander Ouvry and Chief Petty Officer Baldwin, in accordance with the agreed plan, first started on the aluminium fitting on the upper part of the mine. The top of this showed a small plate jointed with tallow. Using the special four-pin spanner made in the local workshop to the specifications obtained the night before, the keep ring was easily unscrewed and the fitting lifted free. 'Lifted free' sounds so easy but at the time the fitting was thought to contain either a detonator or some sort of magnetic device, the movement of which could detonate the mine. Hence, this lifting free was done with the greatest care and with considerable trepidation. Once out of the mine the fitting was quickly seen to contain what was thought to be a detonator. Still in the mine small booster charges designed to detonate the main charge were visible. These were fished for but could not be removed and the pair, believing that the principal danger had been removed, called forward Lieutenant Commander Lewis and Able Seaman Vearncombe to help roll the mine over. This would enable the booster charge to drop out and the remaining fittings then buried in the sand could be reached. The first fitting subsequently proved to be a delayed-action bomb fuze and the so-called detonator the fuze gaine (charge) with a detonator behind it (see bomb fuzes in Annex B). It is appropriate at this stage to explain that the main charge of a bomb or mine is detonated in a way analogous to the lighting of a coal fire. First, a match is struck which lights the paper. This in turn sets fire to the wood which generates sufficient heat to set the coal alight. The coal continues to burn giving out large amounts of energy until it is completely consumed. In the case of the bomb or mine the fuze, by a variety of means, causes a detonator to fire or detonate. This has sufficient energy to cause an initiating charge, or gaine, usually attached to the fuze, to detonate with the greater energy necessary to cause a secondary or booster charge to detonate. This in turn initiates the main

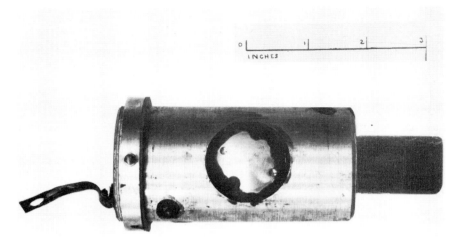

Bomb fuze as fitted to the Shoeburyness Mine.

high explosive filling of the weapon which, like the coal, gives out a large quantity of energy. Unlike the coal the high explosive gives out all its energy over a very short period of time and this is the explosion.

Meanwhile, Dr Wood, the Chief Scientist of the Mine Design Department of HMS *Vernon*, arrived and from a distance watched the remainder of the work. Aided by Lieutenant Commander Lewis and Able Seaman Vearncombe, the mine was rolled over and work commenced to remove a plate flush with the mine case. Underneath were a number of wires, a further plate and the classic situation 'which wire do I cut?'. In the end all the wires were cut and the second plate was removed. This caused a little surprise as it was found to be another detonator carrier fitted with an electric detonator similar to that used in German horned mines. A number of other fittings were removed, some requiring a certain amount of force. The last extraction produced a heavy cylindrical object with an unmistakable hydrostatic valve at one end and five electric leads connecting it to some invisible object inside the mine. Lieutenant Commander Ouvry commented, 'We cut these leads after noting that each was marked'. A simple statement but yet again covering five separate occasions when, as far as they knew, a single cut could kill them all.

When all the external fittings had been removed the mine was hoisted on to a vehicle and stored under cover for the night. The tide was rising, the light was failing and so no attempt was made to recover the second mine that day. At 17:00 hours on 23 November 1939 a report was made to the Admiralty that the first magnetic mine had been recovered and was intact.

Lieutenant Commander Lewis then travelled to London to attend a Board of Admiralty conference starting at 23:15 hours. He had been told that a number of senior officers would be interested in hearing about the day's work but when he was ushered in he found he was to sit between the First Lord of the Admiralty (Winston Churchill) and Admiral Sir Dudley Pound. Also present were some sixty very senior officers. He was later heard to comment that it was the most frightening part of the past 24 hours!

At the conclusion of the meeting the chairman, the First Lord of the Admiralty, said, 'We cannot carry on any further at the moment. We have got our prize, as good a ship as ever sailed the seas, and we owe a great deal to the public spirit of Lieutenant Commander Lewis and his colleague Lieutenant Commander Ouvry who have been up against it today. They have given us a lot of most valuable particulars which the science of *Vernon* and the Admiralty will employ to the full.'

The next day, 24 November 1939, the body of the mine and its components were sent to HMS *Vernon* and work started on determining all its secrets. This task was undertaken by Dr A.B. Wood and his two assistants, Mr W.F.B. Shaw and Mr H.W.K. Kelly, assisted by Chief Petty Officer Baldwin and Commander G.B. Sayer, RN (Commander Mines HMS *Vernon*). These experts worked on into the night until the mine had nothing left to reveal. In the light of later events it is frightening to think what might have happened if the Germans had fitted these particular mines with booby traps to prevent them being stripped.

On Saturday 25 November 1939, the second Shoeburyness mine, left until the method of dealing with the first had proved satisfactory, was given to Lieutenant Glenny assisted by Chief Petty Officer Baldwin and Able Seaman Vearncombe to 'render safe'. They arrived on site late in the afternoon and found the mine in the gathering gloom some 350 m (382 yd) below the high-water mark. Although work started that evening it was suddenly abandoned when a sharp click was heard in the mine. Glenny and Baldwin ran for their lives, but nothing further happened and it was decided to leave things until dawn next day. The next morning the job was completed with the assistance of Lieutenant Commander Lewis, and the second mine was delivered to HMS *Vernon*. These two identical mines became known as Type A mines.

On 7 December 1939 a larger version known as Type B was rendered safe and brought to HMS *Vernon* by Lieutenant Glenny, assisted by Lieutenant Armitage. The Types A and B were similar mines, both being 660 mm (26 in) in diameter, but the smaller Type A was only 1,727 mm (68 in) long and contained 305 kg (671 lb) of explosive, while the Type B was 2,640 mm (104 in) long and contained 699 kg (1,535 lb) of explosive. To the man on the spot, the weight of explosive was purely academic!

Early in 1940 a second Type B mine was rendered safe and recovered by Lieutenant C.A. Hodges, RNVR, assisted by Chief Petty Officer Ellingworth and Able Seaman Hurlstone. This one fell in the middle of the Whitstable oyster beds but, due to bad weather, sticking fuzes and the positioning of the mine, it took some four weeks to clear.

Between 23 November 1939 and 9 September 1940, fifteen magnetic mines were found, the majority of which were safely stripped and investigated. All the mines between November 1939 and May 1940 had been Type A or B but in May a Type C was recovered at Clacton and a few days later a second one was recovered from Maplin Sands. In July 1940, the little brother to the Type C was found and called the Type D. This mine was recovered under very trying circumstances by Lieutenant Glenny on the mud flats of Liverpool Bay. It was now clear that Types A and B had been replaced by Types D and C respectively. They were very similar to their predecessors except that the magnetic mechanism worked on the opposite polarity. They were still fitted with a dangerous bomb fuze invented by the German Air Force, as mentioned earlier. In simple terms it was a self-destruct fuze designed to detonate the mine should it fall on land or in water less than 4 m (13 ft) deep, thus preventing recovery and the discovery of its workings. On release from an aircraft a safety pin was withdrawn from the face of the fuze which allowed the clockwork mechanism to run for approximately five seconds to arm the fuze. On impact the clock restarted and if not interrupted ran for a further seventeen seconds. It then detonated the mine. Should the mine fall into water over 4 m (13 ft) deep the clock started to run as before but the sequence was interrupted as the water pressure forced down a rubber seal. A spring loaded plunger then stopped the clock and prevented the fuze from operating and detonating the mine.

The clockwork mechanism within the bomb fuze of an unexploded mine might fail to start for some reason, or might even start and then stop. In either event the mechanism was in a highly sensitive state and the slightest jolt, or even vibration from nearby traffic, could set the clock ticking. There was then a maximum of seventeen seconds before the fuze detonated the mine. Initially, as we have seen, these fuzes had their locking rings unscrewed and the fuze lifted gently out of the mine by hand with the small attached explosive charge (the gaine) being unscrewed from the fuze. There are a number of recorded cases where, the gaine having been removed, the fuze fired its small detonator as it was being carried away from the mine, thus demonstrating it was still capable of functioning. It was probably that the clock had started ticking as a result of the fuze being removed from the mine or having its gaine unscrewed.

The danger of this type of fuze was quickly realized and initially, after removing the locking ring, the fuze was pulled from the mine remotely using a long length of cord. However, a device known as the Safety Horn was quickly developed. This was designed to apply pressure to the fuze head and so cause the fuze to react as if under water. This would either stop the clock from starting or stop it if it had already started. This equipment consisted of a rubber motor horn bulb attached to lengths of brass tubing threaded at one end and containing a tap. The mine disposal officer opened the tap and, using a bicycle pump, pumped up the bulb and closed the tap. He then attached the apparatus to the fuze, opened the tap and the air pressure forced down the rubber seal and plunger to 'gag' the bomb fuze. With the gag in place it was then possible to unscrew the locking ring and remove the fuze with little fear of that particular hazard detonating the mine. All the other hazards associated with a magnetic mine remained, of course, and had to be dealt with accordingly.

As with all aspects of bomb or mine disposal a measure is followed by a countermeasure and then by a counter-countermeasure. In the case of the bomb fuze the enemy counter-countermeasure was to drill a hole in the side of the fuze case. This prevented any pressure building up in the fuze case unless the whole mine was subjected to pressure, ie, by immersion in water to the full depth. Thus, the Safety Horn could no longer gag the fuze, but this was countered by the Navy with the design of a purely mechanical gag which, after minimal removal of components, could be fitted to the fuze head and jam the mechanism. This was yet to come at the end of 1940.

By the end of July 1940, not only were ships adequately protected, but new sweeping gear had been designed and a fairly stable routine had been established for rendering the mines safe, including the use of the Safety Horn. Then disaster struck. On Monday, 5 August 1940, Lieutenant Hodges, RNVR, had, after some difficulty and with the assistance of Lieutenant West from the Chatham Torpedo School, recovered a Type C mine from a field near Birchington, Kent. Having rendered it safe by the usual procedure he sent it back to HMS *Vernon* for evaluation, where it arrived at about 20:00 hours. By the next morning the dismantling was well underway in *Vernon*'s mining shed. Lieutenant Hodges visited the shed and, noting that the removal of the rear door of the mine was well in hand, left on an errand to Priddy's Hard across the harbour.

Shortly afterwards there was a violent explosion and the roof of the

Type A mine.

Above *Type C mine.*

Below *Type D mine.*

mining shed was seen by Lieutenant Hodges to disintegrate. Commander G. Thistleton-Smith, RN, who had taken over the Mining Department from Commander Sayer in January, rushed to what was left of the shed and found it a shambles, although clearly the full explosive charge of the mine had not detonated. A damaged Type C mine had been thrown against the office, the roof was gaping, there was glass and blood everywhere. A blackened man had been flung into a corner, and a sailor was collecting the blood-soaked and charred remains of another man and putting them on a trolley. One other man was clearly dying, a Petty Officer had been blown to pieces and several others, including Lieutenant Glenny, were taken to the sick bay. For all concerned it was a sickening tragedy.

It later transpired that at the time of the explosion Petty Officer Fletcher had been lifting off the rear door of the mine with Lieutenant Glenny standing a few feet behind him. There was a whirring sound followed by a blinding flash and a deafening roar. Three men died at once and three more died in hospital, but it was not a total waste as the subsequent reconstruction demonstrated. The mine had been fitted with an electrically-fired charge of just 1 kg (2.2 lb) of explosive, the circuit of which was completed by the withdrawal of a stud attached to the mine's rear door. It was obviously a booby-trap designed to kill the mine 'render-safe' team and protect some aspect of the mine, but surprisingly it was not designed to fire the main charge. Had this occurred the greater part of HMS *Vernon* would have been destroyed with much greater loss of life.

The *Vernon* team determined to defeat the enemy's plans and were quickly put to the test. Within a few days two special mines were recovered which had clearly been designed and constructed with the sole purpose of killing more mine experts and dissuading others from ever trying to strip a mine again. The first mine was found on 17 August 1940 at North Boarhurst, Hampshire, some 11 km (7 miles) from Portsmouth Dockyard, and later the same day a similar mine was reported to be at Piddlehinton, Dorset, just inland from Portland Harbour. These two weapons, although looking like Type D mines, had no bomb fuzes or any place for them to be fitted and were clearly designed to arouse curiosity. The Piddlehinton mine was X-rayed repeatedly and the Naval trepanner developed by the National Physical Laboratory to drill holes in mines was used for the first time. Unlike the machine developed for dealing with bombs (see later), this machine was not driven by steam but by compressed air. It drilled holes large enough to enable components to be removed from a mine without having to use existing hatches or doors, thus avoiding obvious sites for booby traps.

After several days' hard and, at all times, courageous work, most of the booby-traps were revealed. As a climax and following an attempt to enter the rear door using explosives, the mine detonated. All those working on the mine were unhurt as they were in positions of cover. Neither device was designed to function as a mine but solely as a deterrent to anyone attempting to open up a similar-shaped mine.

With hindsight we now know that these two booby-trapped mines were the harbingers of the acoustic mine, the first of which was recovered on 28 October 1940. However, before that was to happen the dramatic use of magnetic mines as pure blast bombs on the nation's capital was to occupy the minds of all at *Vernon* and lead to the formation of the second group of Naval personnel responsible for dealing with explosive objects dropped from the air. These were the Rendering Mines Safe (RMS) Section of the Department of Torpedoes and Mining (DTM), later in August 1941 to be renamed the Land Incident Section. It is believed that this was the only operational Naval unit ever to be established and based within the walls of the Admiralty in Whitehall.

On the night of 16/17 September 1940, reports were made to the Admiralty that the Germans were dropping parachute 'bombs' on London. From the descriptions given it soon became clear that these 'bombs' were in fact parachute-delivered magnetic mines. On that first night at least 25 were dropped, of which seventeen failed to explode. The use of mines on a large scale to destroy built-up areas had not been envisaged, but upon reflection a large container of some 698 kg (1,535 lb) of explosive detonated at roof-top or ground level is a most effective use of explosive when the main objective is to create blast damage. As a result of this unexpected development a new organization had to be created rapidly, but until this could be done HMS *Vernon* was expected to fill the gap.

The presence of a number of unexploded mines in a large city presented a problem without precedent. Firstly, as has been shown, any vibration which might occur in the area of the mine was quite capable of starting the fuze clock and causing the mine to explode. It is still extremely difficult to limit vibration when rescue work is continuing in the same area and when heavy emergency vehicles such as fire engines are passing. Secondly, the evacuation area for a single mine was huge. The accepted safety distance was a radius of 350 m (380 yd) from an unexploded mine or a total area in excess of 385,000 sq m (over 92 acres). The problems of evacuation in a densely populated district were con-siderable and if disruption was to be kept to a minimum the mines had to be cleared with the greatest possible speed. The responsibilities at this stage lay solely with the Royal Navy. To avoid undue loss of life an urgent signal was sent to all other Services indicating the high sensitivity of the mines, the large danger area if one exploded and above all a warning that no 'render-safe' operation should be attempted by anyone other than Naval personnel.

On the night of 16/17 September 1940 a call was made to HMS *Vernon* requesting assistance. Altogether there were thirteen officers available from *Vernon*, nine from the Enemy Mining Section and four from the Mine Sweeping Branch. There were also four officers from DTM at the

Admiralty with some knowledge of the methods of rendering mines safe. Two further officers (Commander Obbard and Lieutenant Ryan) came to London from the Torpedo School at Chatham.

This small group of men, courageously supported by ratings, continued to deal with this first mine onslaught on London for the next several days. Initially, because of the shortage of equipment they had to work without the benefit of the Safety Horn. Work immediately started at *Vernon* to produce more equipment, but the disorganization caused in London by the mines was so great that work to 'render safe' the mines had to start at once. The bomb fuzes had to be removed by unscrewing the keep ring and then pulling out the fuze using a long line. If the clock started to tick whilst an officer was working on a mine, he ran. In some instances the mine detonated before the officer could find cover and he died. In other instances officers had miraculous escapes and in many more the fuze was safely pulled clear of the mine before it fired. By 19 September equipment began to arrive but the pressure on this small group of men continued and it was realized that the men dealing with these incidents could not be spared indefinitely from their normal duties. It was, therefore, decided by the Admiralty to form a separate section of the DTM to take over the responsibility for dealing with unexploded mines on land—unexploded mines which fell in water or unknown mines wherever they fell would remain the responsibility of HMS *Vernon*. Twelve volunteer officers (all RNVR or Commonwealth equivalent of RNVR) from HMS *King Alfred* (the RNVR Officers Training School near Brighton) were given a short course at *Vernon*. Together with fourteen ratings trained in RMS duties they formed the nucleus of the RMS Section of DTM which was formally established on 26 September 1940 under Captain C.N.E. Currey, RN.

The story of the RMS Section is told later in the book as are some of the detailed incidents of the small volunteer band who cleared the first mines from London. These London pioneers were honoured for their courageous work by HM the King with the award of three George Crosses (one posthumously to Lieutenant Commander Ryan, RN) and four George Medals.

Finally, before leaving the story of the early days of HMS *Vernon*, we should remember again the initial work carried out on the very first magnetic mines when nothing at all was known about them. This work was undertaken by a few men who risked, and in some instances lost, their lives to obtain information which was later to save many others both at sea and on land. Their bravery was recognized by the award of three DSOs, two DSCs and two DSMs to ranks ranging from Commander to Able Seaman. It should perhaps be noted that when these awards were made the George Cross had not been created. This was done on 23 September 1940 when HM King George VI announced in a broadcast to the nation the creation of a new and very high decoration for gallantry which was to be called the George Cross. Members of the bomb and mine disposal teams of all three Services were to feature regularly in subsequent awards of this Cross.

In addition to the two Naval organizations already mentioned, there was a third, which was truly bomb disposal in that it was responsible for dealing with enemy unexploded bombs which fell on Royal Navy property or property for which the Navy had a particular responsibility. The scope of Naval responsibility for the disposal of unexploded bombs grew rapidly during 1940 as various situations were shown to affect the efficiency of Naval operations. As was mentioned in Chapter Two, in February 1940 the Admiralty was declining to accept responsibility for enemy bombs lodged in merchant ships either in or entering British ports, on the grounds that their only bomb disposal organizations were based at the five main Naval bases at Scapa Flow, Rosyth, The Nore, Portsmouth and Plymouth.

By August 1940, Captain L.E.H. Llewellyn, RN, had been appointed Director of the Naval Unexploded Bomb Department (DUBD) of the Admiralty and as such attended the second meeting of the Unexploded Bomb Committee held on 12 August 1940. He was to be a regular attender at subsequent meetings up to and including the forty-first held on 22 August 1944. After that the DUBD was absorbed into the Department of the Director of Torpedo and Mining. In August 1940, the minutes of a meeting held on the 27th recorded that eighteen bomb disposal teams existed at Naval shore establishments and proposals for increases were under consideration. By 20 September 1940 there were Naval teams at 27 shore establishments and on 3 October 1940 the DUBD issued formal instructions to all Naval authorities in Great Britain detailing the organization and working of the Naval Bomb Disposal Organization. By this stage the Naval responsibility for bomb disposal (as opposed to mine disposal) had grown and was by then defined as all unexploded bombs which fell on Admiralty property, on board HM and other ships, on harbour works, docks both wet and dry, wharves and the approaches thereto where the presence of an unexploded bomb might affect or endanger the working or safety of any vessel. These responsibilities were later to be further extended to include certain shipyards, armament firms and other factories producing material of vital importance to Naval requirements. In these instances, the responsibilities were met by establishing a Naval bomb disposal team at each location. Where a Naval representative was established within the installation he worked very closely with the military organization within whose area the installation was based.

The instruction of 3 October 1940 made it quite clear that the officers appointed for bomb safety and disposal duties, termed Bomb Safety Officers (BSO), were part of the staff of the DUBD Admiralty and that it was the DUBD to whom they reported and from whom they would receive their technical instructions and control. In all other respects they would be under the command of the Senior Naval Officer of the port, station or district in which they were based and to whom they would copy all reports written to DUBD. These BSOs were all Sub Lieutenants, RNVR, or the Commonwealth equivalent of the RNVR, who were trained in bomb disposal. Some, but not all, had additionally received training in the handling and making safe of enemy mines but they were not permitted to be employed on such duty except under the supervision and control of an officer from HMS *Vernon* or the Department of DTM.

Thus, wherever there was an important Naval interest there would also be a BSO. Their personal stories are related later in chronological sequence but when one remembers that there were BSOs in Cardiff, Glasgow, Hull, Liverpool, London, Malta, Plymouth, and Sheffield, to name but a few locations, it can clearly be seen that they had an eventful and dangerous part to play in the story of bomb disposal. The BSO organization also provided a useful training facility for overseas officers, perhaps the most notable example being that of Sub Lieutenant D.L. Kauffman, an American. He graduated from the US Naval Academy in 1933 but retired to civilian life because of weak eyesight. In 1939 he joined the French Ambulance Service and was later captured when the Germans overran the Low Countries. Upon his release as a citizen of a neutral country, he joined the Royal Navy as a Sub Lieutenant, RNVR, and was appointed a BSO. For the next fourteen months he was engaged in mine and bomb disposal until October 1941, when following an accident, he returned on leave to Washington. Whilst in Washington he was approached by the US Bureau of Ordnance and asked to establish a US Bomb Disposal School to run parallel to the already established Mine Disposal School. Thus, Lieutenant Kauffman, RNVR, became Lieutenant D.L. Kauffman, USNR, and officer in charge of the US Bomb Disposal School. He was subsequently awarded the Navy Cross for bomb disposal work at Pearl Harbor and finally retired from the US Navy with the rank of Admiral! The Royal Navy will always claim that this was due to the period he spent as a BSO!

The Army

What of the other Services, how were they faring during those early days? Considering the Army in the form of the Royal Engineers first, we have seen that in November 1939 the first Bomb Disposal Parties, RE, were established. Their role was to build sandbag enclosures around bombs found on the surface and then to detonate the bombs where they were. We have also seen that, with the failure of the heavy enemy air attacks to materialize during the so-called 'phoney war', these men tended to be forgotten and were absorbed into their host units.

In February 1940, following the War Office's acceptance of responsibility for all unexploded enemy bombs except those on Admiralty and Air Ministry property, some effort was made to prepare for enemy air attack and its resultant unexploded bombs. In May 1940 the War Office issued an instruction to the Commandant of the School of Military

Engineering at Chatham and the Commanding Officers of the four RE Training Battalions (at Shorncliffe, Newark, Chester and Colchester) stating it had been decided to form 109 Bomb Disposal Sections, RE, for dealing with unexploded enemy bombs. Furthermore, the first contingent of 25 Bomb Disposal Sections were to be formed immediately by the addressees. The instruction showed in an Annex the names of sixteen officers who were to be the first section commanders. Of these sixteen it is perhaps interesting to note that five were to be awarded the George Cross, three the George Medal and one the MBE and a number were to die as a result of their bomb disposal work. Not all were young men either. A number were professionally qualified engineers or architects and at least two were over fifty years of age when they started their new duties.

By the middle of June 1940 the full complement of 109 sections had been formed, each consisting of one officer and fifteen men. By July the number of sections had increased to 220. At this stage the War Office realized that bomb disposal was a field operation which could not possibly be controlled from the War Office and, as was seen in Chapter 2, responsibility was handed over to GHQ Home Forces on 20 August 1940. On 29 August GHQ established a Bomb Disposal Directorate under the command of Major General G.B.O. Taylor.

Simultaneously, an urgent demand was put in for the immediate doubling in strength of all sections, to be followed as soon as possible by the doubling of the total number of sections—this was approved on 12 September 1940. Thus, in the space of three weeks the strength of the RE Bomb Disposal organization had quadrupled—or rather had been quadrupled on paper. Owing to the urgent necessity of converting this paper strength into men on the ground (or more frequently in the hole), the temporary expedient was adopted of converting other Engineer units into bomb disposal units. Consequently, seven General Construction Companies (Nos 718, 719, 720, 724, 725, 726 and 727) and four Quarrying Companies (Nos 125, 851, 853 and 854) were converted to Bomb Disposal Companies by the addition of extra officers and specialist equipment. By 14 October 1940 the converted companies had been trained and equipped to start their new role with enthusiasm, courage and success.

In the meantime, new units were being formed and trained as rapidly as possible. It is noteworthy that when the newly-formed units were ready to replace the Construction and Quarrying Companies in January 1941, many of the latter begged to be permanently converted into bomb disposal units. This was not then possible as they had a specialist role of their own to play.

In November 1940, General Taylor was offered conscientious objectors as a labour force and he accepted them. Three hundred and seventy-five members of the Non-Combatant Corps (NCC) volunteered for bomb disposal work and, despite the misgivings of some section officers, they were successfully employed. Whatever one's religious beliefs there must be a certain commonality of disquiet when digging for several days towards a bomb which may at any moment explode!

With the introduction of the extra eleven companies in October 1940 the RE Bomb Disposal organization was at its peak strength of over 10,000 all ranks. The enemy had not been idle during this period and the number of unexploded bombs waiting to be dealt with rose steadily. On 20 September 1940 there was a peak of 3,759.

Concurrent with the expansion the DBD realised that sections must be commanded through a proper chain of command. One was accordingly established and functioning by September. The new bomb disposal unit was a company designed to control twelve or more sections and the whole organization was one of 25 companies and four area groups. The majority of the companies were commanded by Group Headquarters situated in the south and south-east of England, East Anglia and London. The companies outside these areas were independent. Operationally the Group Headquarters was static, the Company Headquarters semi-mobile and the sections were completely mobile and interchangeable between companies.

Since the London blitz had started on 29 August 1940, just as the initial sections were completing their training, their birth could not have been more timely. Their courage, the difficulties they faced, their determination and personal stories are related in later chapters.

The Royal Air Force

Like the Royal Navy, the Royal Air Force was also in close contact with enemy unexploded weapons well before the general public were aware of them. Indeed, the first unexploded enemy bomb in Great Britain was recovered by an RAF armourer NCO at Sullom Voe in the Shetland Islands during November 1939, following raids at the seaplane base, and on Lerwick Harbour. The very first action of the war for which a George Cross was awarded was carried out by Flight Lieutenant J.N. Dowland, RAF, and a civilian armament instructor, Mr L.H. Harrison. They dealt with a bomb on the steamship *Kildare* at Immingham Dock near Grimsby on the Humber estuary in February 1940. (For the pedantic these were not the first GCs to be gazetted as there was a gap of nearly eleven months between the action and the publication of the awards in the *London Gazette*. A number of awards for later actions were gazetted within a month of their relevant action and so appeared in the *London Gazette* well before Dowland and Harrison.) Squadron Leader J.N. Dowland, GC, RAF, was later to be killed in action. Mr 'Len' Harrison was to become Wing Commander L.H. Harrison, GC, RAF, often referred to as the father of RAF bomb disposal.

The RAF was well aware that aerial bombs could on occasion fail to explode and the responsibility for dealing with them on their own bombing ranges fell to the Warrant Officers and senior NCO armourers.

These men underwent long and comprehensive technical training in all aspects of explosives and air weaponry including guns, together with bombs and their related fuzes. Consequently, when it was realized that a threat existed from enemy bombs it was accepted quite naturally that the Warrant Officer and senior NCO armourers would deal with them, assisted by untrained airmen or occasionally soldiers to dig for bombs that might be buried.

Initially, until the term 'bomb disposal' was coined, these teams—consisting of an armament NCO and a small labour force—were known as Demolition Squads. Their role was essentially to destroy the unexploded bomb *in situ* or drag or carry it to a location where it could be safely demolished. As equipment was developed and became available it was possible to render safe simple impact fuzes and remove them from bombs. However, by the end of August 1940 bombs were being found with long-delay and anti-withdrawal fuzes. No one who has not confronted an unexploded bomb, with the fuze ticking or otherwise, can ever appreciate the dedication and courage displayed by these Demolition Squads who, with little experience and only primitive tools, made a significant contribution to the victory achieved by the RAF during the Battle of Britain.

Up to and including the last weeks of September 1940 there were 188 bomb disposal qualified armament NCOs, ie, those who had completed a five-day bomb disposal course at the RAF Armament School at Manby. These NCOs were located at eighty of the more important RAF stations nominated as 'X' stations. In addition, there were a number of mobile squads with a roving commission to support those X stations that were being most hard-pushed. An indication of the pressure under which the squads worked can be seen from the returns for the last week of August 1940 indicating the number of unexploded bombs not yet dealt with on RAF stations: Detling—15, St Athan—16, Thorney Island—18, Debden—18, Wattisham—20, South Cerney—21, Kenley—26, Manston—27, St Eval—30, Biggin Hill—62.

Throughout this hectic period squads working under the command of the bomb disposal trained armament NCOs received all their technical control direct from the Air Ministry, and this method of control was to continue until April 1943.

However, by May 1941 some RAF officers had been put in charge of the Bomb Disposal Squads for it had by then been accepted by Station Commanders that bomb disposal could be a full-time job! Initially, the officers' task was to administer the squads' activities while the senior armament NCOs undertook the technical task of bomb disposal. The only RAF officers carrying out bomb disposal at this stage were specialists based at the Air Ministry. This caused some discontent among the administrative officers who, having completed a bomb disposal course, felt themselves well qualified to do the job. Indeed, they were equally qualified in respect of enemy bomb disposal as any of the officers carrying out the same task in the Navy or Army, although the latter two Services had a wealth of experience gained during the hard months of 1940 and early 1941 which the RAF officers lacked.

In time, despite Air Ministry orders to the contrary, many of the administrative officers became experienced bomb disposal officers. From the 188 armament NCOs in bomb disposal at the end of September 1940 the numbers had by May 1941 risen to: 38 administrative officers, 411 armament NCOs for technical duties, 244 aircraftsmen for non-technical duties (ie, digging), 3 technical officers at the Air Ministry (TArm 4) and 92 drivers, motor transport.

Between the beginning of the war and the end of October 1940 the RAF bomb disposal organization dealt with 535 enemy bombs. During the next seven months up to 21 May 1941 they dealt with a further 977 and the three specialist Air Ministry officers dealt with another 114. These totals do not include bombs found and dealt with on crashed enemy aircraft.

Thus was the RAF bomb disposal organization well and truly born, tried and proven, but it was not until 21 April 1943 that a regular chain of command existed. On that date a formal organization was established consisting of a Wing Headquarters commanding six Bomb Disposal Squadrons, RAF. Each had between four and six Bomb Disposal Flights, making a total of 29 Flights.

It should perhaps be remembered that RAF bomb disposal personnel were then, as now, responsible for all enemy bombs which fell on RAF property, all bombs on crashed aircraft of whatever nationality and all allied bombs. This latter aspect imposed a very high load when it is considered that bombers frequently had to jettison their loads after an abortive attack or return to base with bombs 'hung up' (technically dropped but still in the bomb racks) and often in a hazardous condition. It is sometimes forgotten that our bomb fuzes were just as treacherous as those employed by the enemy, if not more so. Throughout the war by far the largest number of unexploded bombs dealt with by Royal Air Force bomb disposal units in Great Britain were of British or American origin.

The Home Guard

The proposal to form Auxiliary Bomb Disposal Squads, which were later to play such an important part in the organization for dealing with enemy bombs, came from the Ministry of Aircraft Production who, on 20 August 1940, addressed a letter to the War Office calling attention to the then existing arrangements for dealing with unexploded bombs in factories under the control of the Ministry. These were that an Army Bomb Disposal Section would visit the factory and estimate the damage which would be caused if or when the bomb exploded. The detachment could also arrange for the immediate detonation of the bomb should the responsible factory management so desire. Not surprisingly the writer expressed his dissatisfaction with this extremely limited function and asked that the procedures should include the steps necessary to render the bomb safe.

The War Office replied in what can only be described as a holding letter. It agreed that the present limitation of function was unsatisfactory and that the problem was one of considerable difficulty in view of the depth to which bombs penetrated and of the period of time over which the delay-action fuze was operative. They also said that earnest consideration was being given to the problem and that in the very near future the operational control of Army Bomb Disposal Sections was to be vested in the Commander-in-Chief Home Forces. Actually, as was recounted earlier, this change of command took place on 29 August 1940.

On receipt of this letter the Factory Defence Section of the Ministry of Aircraft Production wrote to GHQ Home Forces asking for approval in raising volunteer squads which would be competent to take preliminary action on unexploded bombs and so prepare the way for the arrival of the Army bomb disposal parties. At this stage little knowledge of unexploded bombs was available and the only duties proposed for the volunteer squads were those of excavation and general clearance so that the bomb was made more accessible.

GHQ Home Forces, or to be more exact the IF and DBD, in one of his first actions after accepting responsibility for Royal Engineer bomb disposal, replied to the effect that this suggestion was agreed and that instructions would be issued to ensure that the necessary assistance from the Royal Engineers for training these volunteers would be available.

On 16 September 1940 a meeting was held between representatives of the IF and DBD and the Factory Defence Section of the Ministry of Aircraft Production to agree formally to the formation of Volunteer or Auxiliary Bomb Disposal Squads in those factories under the control of the Ministry of Aircraft Production. The agreement was welcomed and it was further agreed that factory squad leaders should be trained at the Bomb Disposal School then situated at RAF Melksham in Wiltshire, and that local arrangements would be made for attaching subordinate squad leaders to Bomb Disposal Companies, RE, for training on bomb location, recognition and recovery. No time was lost and in early October 1940 the Ministry of Aircraft Production had circularized all their factories defining the role of the Auxiliary Bomb Disposal Units as: reconnaissance and identification; reporting of unexploded bombs; establishing safety distances; institution of safety precautions and pre-liminary access to the bomb. It was also specified that the Auxiliary Units should be a component of the factory's Home Guard and that the unit should consist of one or more squads, the ideal being three working on a shift system. Each squad should consist of one trained man and five assistants.

Before the end of the month (October 1940) applications from civilian firms for vacancies on the bomb disposal courses were flooding in. The first course which civilians attended was No 26 Course at RAF Melksham starting on 19 November 1940. At this stage it appeared to Major General Taylor, IF and DBD, that the scheme was developing well and could usefully be extended to other factories committed to work of national importance. On 27 December 1940 a meeting was held at the offices of the Home Defence Executive at which the scheme was expounded to all the other ministries concerned. In view of the large number of factories involved it was agreed that the scheme should be confined to those employing 1,000 men or more. Even with that criterion the number of factories involved was estimated at over 1,200. However, general agreement was given to the principle of forming squads in all important factories subject to certain conditions, of which only four were in any way contentious. The first of these conditions was that compensation in the case of death of injury should be put on a clear and definite basis. This created no difficulty and the position was rapidly clarified by the Ministry of Pensions. Secondly, the Trade Union Congress should record its agreement. General Taylor visited the Council of the TUC who gave their cordial support to the proposals. Thirdly, the Army should guarantee to train the necessary squad leaders and to inspect and supervise the training of the squads. Fourthly, the roles of the squads should be defined in detail. These last two conditions caused some problems.

The third condition relating to training presented considerable difficulties which should perhaps have been foreseen. However, once they occurred they were quickly rectified. RAF Melksham was a major Royal Air Force training centre and, like most other technical training centres, was expanding rapidly. The bomb disposal courses were putting an added burden on the already stretched facilities in respect of messing and accommodation. It was obvious that existing facilities would be totally inadequate for training the large numbers of civilian officials contemplated and in addition for continuing to train the increasing numbers of Army and Royal Air Force personnel joining the bomb disposal organizations. On 4 January 1941 proposals were submitted for the formation of two Army bomb disposal schools, one in the north of England and one in London. This was later reduced to one large school and the search was on for a suitable set of buildings which could rapidly be converted into a school. Finally, Donington Hall in Lincolnshire was selected and its first bomb disposal course started on 21 July 1941 attended, among others, by thirty factory officials. It was fortunate that the school could be opened so quickly as on 18 June 1941 RAF Melksham had given notice that, owing to the shortage of accommodation, they could take no more civilian students on their bomb disposal courses after 5 July 1941. (It is worth noting that between 19 November 1940 and 21 July 1941, thanks largely to the perseverance and energy of Captain Paterson of the Factory Defence Section of the Ministry of Aircraft Production and his liaison with RAF Melksham, no fewer than 132

Factory Squads had been formed and 143 officials had been trained at Melksham. In the first three months after the Army school was opened a further 210 civilians from factories (other than those engaged in aircraft production) were trained.

In respect of the fourth condition, in April 1941 a GHQ Home Forces letter was issued by the Home Guard Directorate saying that, although there was no objection to members of the Home Guard joining Auxiliary Bomb Disposal Units, their primary role was as Home Guardsmen and bomb disposal was not a function of the Home Guard. At this time the War Office had notified the IF and DBD that, owing to the shortage of manpower, bomb disposal units for Expeditionary Forces or overseas tours of any kind would have to be found from home units and that replacements would not be available.

It was obvious that Auxiliary Squads in factories provided a very large potential reserve for bomb disposal work at home — if they could be organized and put on a proper footing. Consequently, the Commander-in-Chief Home Forces was approached with a proposal that, under certain conditions, bomb disposal should be accepted as a Home Guard liability and that factory squads should be established in two categories. They were: 'A' squads trained for and accepting liability to fully dispose of bombs both in and outside their factories; and 'B' squads trained in diagnosis and safety precautions and measures.

'A' squads were to be of Home Guardsmen volunteering for the job, working in uniform and under military discipline, and to be called out on the authority of the Regional Commissioner. 'B' squads were to be volunteers for the job, but with no insistence on their being Home Guardsmen, although it was preferable.

The Commander-in-Chief concurred and the ban on bomb disposal imposed by the Home Guard Directorate was lifted. The scheme was also explained to all ministries concerned, who also concurred. The final hurdle was cleared when the TUC and the Employers Confederation reached a complex agreement over the money to be paid to volunteers whilst engaged upon bomb disposal in their employer's time but officially working for the Home Guard. With this final agreement the Home Guard Bomb Disposal Organization formally came into being. They formed a fourth uniformed and professionally trained bomb disposal organization which rarely receives a mention in official records but whose members carried out some remarkable feats of bravery to enable their respective factories to continue with their production of war materials.

Throughout this period, both before and after the auxiliary squads were recognised as full bomb disposal units, a very close liaison was established between Bomb Disposal Companies, RE, and the factory squads within their areas. Similarly, as will be seen in Chapter 4, when the Royal Navy had representatives in selected factories they too established a close liaison with the auxiliary squads.

Although initially the auxiliary squads were raised for work within the confines of their respective factories, it was often found that after a heavy blitz the general disorganization in a town or city and the presence of unexploded bombs prevented a factory from working. In many cases the workmen themselves and their families, or those of their friends, were either bombed out of their homes, or had to evacuate them because of the presence of unexploded bombs. Thus there was a real desire on the part of the members of the auxiliary squads to do something which would help in restoring normal life to the community. One instance of this was during the Birmingham blitz of April 1941 at about the same time that the Home Guard Directorate was saying that bomb disposal was not a function of the Home Guard. During this blitz the Austin Aero Company Auxiliary Bomb Disposal Squad, under the leadership of Mr W. Lovell, left the factory and dealt with 23 unexploded bombs in a period of under 24 hours.

One of the first members of the Home Guard to be awarded a decoration for work in bomb disposal was Platoon Officer R.E. Cooke, a member of an auxiliary bomb disposal squad of Messrs Burman Ltd, Leebank Works, Highland Road, Birmingham. On 26 October 1940 a 250 kg (550 lb) bomb fell on the machine shop of Messrs Burman and failed to explode. The factory at that time was engaged on vital aircraft production work and so the bomb was given a high priority for clearance and a Royal Engineer detachment from 9 Bomb Disposal Company, RE, under the command of Second Lieutenant R.H. Lee, was detailed to clear it. Despite the combined efforts of the Army and the auxiliary squad the bomb was not exposed until 28 October 1940, some 45 hours after it had fallen. Upon inspection it was found to have a clockwork long-delay fuze which was still ticking. In view of the time which had elapsed since the bomb had fallen its detonation was probable at any moment. Second Lieutenant Lee cleared his men and the members of the auxiliary Squad from the area and attempted unsuccessfully to remove the fuze. After fifteen minutes' determined work he had to admit defeat and withdrew to consider the next move. In view of the importance of the factory it was decided to attack the fuze a second time but with less finesse and more brute force. (The fuze would be prized out with a crow-bar!) This could not be done by one person alone and Mr Cooke volunteered to assist. At this attempt they managed to break off the top of the fuze but the dangerous clockwork mechanism was still ticking and the bomb's detonation was imminent. It was then decided to flood the hole in which the bomb was lying in an endeavour to stop the clock. Second Lieutenant Lee and Mr Cooke completed this task together and to their relief the clock stopped and the bomb was safely removed. Both Second Lieutenant Lee and Platoon Officer Cooke were subsequently awarded George Medals.

To conclude on a lighter note, many of the auxiliary bomb disposal squads attended courses of lectures given by the Royal Engineer Bomb

Disposal Company working in their area. After one such course they were asked, 'What do you consider to be the ideal qualifications and character of a member of a bomb disposal unit?' Most replies stressed the importance of common sense and keeping quiet about what had been taught. A few emphasized the need for courage and tenacity of purpose but some of the choicest answers were, 'He should be strong, unmarried and a fast runner', 'He should not be indispensable', 'He should have an excellent character and be fully prepared for the after life'.

One may smile at these answers but it does indicate that these men, already doing a job of national importance, were prepared to volunteer for additional work which they clearly considered to be dangerous.

4

The onslaught 1940-1942

On 8 August 1940 the Battle of Britain began over the sea and coastal areas of southern England. By 12 August, German attacks on Royal Air Force airfields in southern England had started in earnest. The onslaught continued until 18 September by which time it had been largely replaced by air attacks against the civilian population of London. At first these attacks were by day, but later they were by night due to the enemy's heavy losses. These attacks against London started on 29 August 1940 and were to continue for many months. The heaviest raid against London occurred on the night of 16/17 April 1941 when some 446 tonnes of bombs were dropped, producing 237 unexploded bombs. On the night of 16/17 September 1940 the first parachute magnetic mines were dropped on London. There followed attacks on Coventry, Birmingham, Liverpool and many other towns and cities throughout the land.

This was the period when the men of the bomb disposal teams of all three Services earned the respect of all for their courage, devotion to duty and downright persistence in freeing the towns, cities and essential installations of the menace and fear created by unexploded weapons. To attempt to describe the many acts of courage carried out would be impossible. There were far too many recorded in the *London Gazette* and the memorial stones of the churches, garrisons and villages throughout the country. There were, too, an equal number of acts of bravery which never reached a unit history or a record of medals awarded. They were undertaken by the large number of soldiers, sailors and airmen who did not defuze the bombs or carry them away on heroic shoulders but instead dug for them, often while raids were still in progress. They knew that any sudden vibration or the stopping of a clock, ticking silently beneath them, could mean instant death.

To appreciate what the officers and men had to face, it is necessary to understand a little about the range of German bombs and the working of their fuzes as used during this period. Full details are given in Annex B but a brief description is given here. The high explosive bombs themselves ranged in weight from 50 to 1,800 kg (110 to 3,960 lb). Their length without their tail fins was from 725 to 2,630 mm (2 ft 4½ in to 8 ft 7½ in) and their diameters from 200 to 660 mm (8 to 26 in). Their powers of destruction naturally varied with the weight of explosive, and also decide whether they were on or near the surface, or deeply buried in the ground. To the bomb disposal team, however, the size of the bomb was not of prime importance other than to determine the area to be evacuated or decide whether it was safe to detonate the bomb where it had fallen. The main interest was in the fuze for should the bomb 'go off' when they were working on it the size of the explosion was of little importance. There would be problems finding their remains whether it was a 50 kg or a 1,800 kg device.

Unlike British and American bombs which were fuzed in the nose or tail (or both), German bombs had a transverse fuze. This meant the fuze was let into the side of the bomb leaving visible only the circular disc of the fuze head. The 250 and 500 kg bombs had either one or two fuze pockets, others only one. All aircraft high explosive bomb fuzes have at least two primary functions, the first being that they must cause the bomb to detonate at the correct time. The correct time can vary from the moment of impact or slightly later (to allow the bomb to bury itself or penetrate several stories of a building before exploding), to the true long delay of up to several days after impact. The correct time could also be at any time the bomb is disturbed after its initial impact. The second function of all fuzes is to ensure that the bombs to which they are fitted are safe to handle whilst being stored, loaded and carried on an aircraft.

The principle of most German bomb fuzes was similar to those patented by Rheinmetall in 1932 but with some variations on the theme. Each fuze head had two spring-loaded plungers and carried markings to enable the German armourer (and, incidentally, the bomb disposal man) to identify the fuze. When the bomb was in the aircraft bomb racks a battery in the aircraft was attached to the fuze head via two sockets. When the bomb was released and fell from the bomb rack the aircraft battery automatically charged a capacitor in the fuze as the plug was jerked from the fuze head. Thus, no bomb still attached to an aircraft could have a charged fuze.

As the bomb descended the charge on the first capacitor leaked through a high resistance into a firing capacitor, thus arming the bomb. The time gap between the charging of the first capacitor and its charging of the firing capacitor enabled the aircraft to reach a safe distance from the bomb before there was any risk of an explosion. In the firing circuit was an igniter and an impact switch; thus, after the firing capacitor was charged the impact of the bomb hitting the ground closed the impact switch and the igniter caused the bomb to explode. All electrically armed fuzes as just described required a minimum fall of about 20 m (65 ft) before the firing capacitor was fully charged. Thus, an impact after a fall of less than 20 m would produce an insufficient electrical charge to fire the igniter and the bomb would not function — but it would remain dangerous. After impact the voltage in the firing capacitor would continue to increase to full charge and then any sudden movement simulating the shock of impact could detonate the bomb. There were other causes of malfunction, but the bomb disposal operator had no way of knowing where the failure lay and in every case had to assume he had a bomb about to detonate.

In the early part of 1940 the most common German fuze was the No 15 which was a direct impact fuze as just described and as recovered from the incidents at Sullom Voe and Immingham Docks, but with the extra ability to be used as a short-delay device. (The details of how this was achieved are given in Annex B.) The No 15 fuze could be made safe merely by depressing the plungers and then earthing them for long enough to allow both capacitors to discharge. A simple tool for this purpose was quickly produced in April 1940 and issued to all bomb disposal teams — this was the Two-Pin Plug Discharger.

In August 1940 the first No 17 long-delay fuze was recovered. This had a top part as described for the direct impact fuze except that when the small electric igniter fired, it freed by various means the balance wheel of a clockwork mechanism rather than causing the bomb to explode. This clock was able to run for a preset period between 1½ and 72 hours, after which the bomb would detonate. The clockwork mechanism at the lower end of the fuze pocket was completely separated from the enclosed electrical section. It was, therefore, no use trying to do anything with this upper electrical section since it had served its purpose when the bomb impacted and the clockwork mechanism had been freed.

Thus, from August 1940 onwards, any bomb buried out of sight could have a No 17 fuze which might or might not be ticking away. If ticking it would run its preset period and then detonate the bomb. If not ticking, all it would require was a slight jolt to start it up. This jolt or shock, as was seen with the bomb fuze in the magnetic mines, could be produced by digging, the explosion of a nearby bomb, or even the passing of a heavy vehicle.

The immediate bomb disposal response to this fuze was to destroy the bomb where it was, if possible. If the bomb was in a critical position the only thing to do was hurry in and remove the fuze before its clockwork mechanism reached the end of its run. This was a most hazardous operation but one successfully completed a number of times. If the bomb was in a less critical position it was left for at least 84 hours and then, if it had not exploded, the fuze was removed. This was also a hazardous operation since many clocks stopped with only seconds left to run and any attempt to remove the fuze could cause an explosion. The No 17, as with all others, was eventually defeated, as will be seen later.

In the following month, September 1940, the first No 50 fuze was recovered. This was usually found in a two-fuze bomb in conjunction with a No 17 fuze and was designed to act as a booby trap and anti-handling device. Again it was similar to the direct-impact fuze except that it took minutes rather than seconds to arm. Thus, it was several minutes after the bomb had come to rest before it became armed and extremely dangerous. Instead of a simple impact switch, the firing circuit had two very sensitive switches, either of which could be closed by the slightest movement of the bomb, causing it to detonate. Also, if the charging plungers were depressed the firing capacitor was connected direct to the igniter, also detonating the bomb. Thus, the use of the Two-Pin Plug Discharger on this fuze would be fatal. Similarly, the practice of rolling a bomb over to better read the fuze heads would also prove fatal, as would any movement of the bomb. The problem of this fuze was overcome as well.

The early days were therefore full of danger for the bomb disposal men of all three Services, and unfortunately this was reflected in the casualties. On reflection it has always been thus; whether new weapons of war are deployed in the 1940s or the 1980s, their secrets can only be discovered by the cool heads, steady hands and courage of dedicated men. The Royal Engineers, being responsible for bomb disposal throughout the country, except for those areas which were the responsibility of the Admiralty and the Air Ministry, bore the brunt of the 1940-41 onslaught.

Initially, bombs were fitted with straightforward impact fuzes which could be discharged with the Two-Pin Plug Discharger and then removed from the bomb. At that time it was considered that the capacitors in a bomb fuze could not be expected to hold their electrical charge for more than two or three days at the most. Hence, a No 15 fuze uncovered after a period longer than this could reasonably be expected to be safe, but there are always exceptions. During this early period there were a number of instances of bombs exploding for no apparent reason several days after they had been dropped. The fear that the enemy would use delayed action bombs was realized.

'Danger UXB' — a common sight during the war years.

The first No 17 fuze, the clockwork time fuze described earlier, was discovered and recovered on 13 August 1940. The bomb, a 250 kg (550 lb), fell at 07:30 hours on 13 August and was uncovered at 11:30 hours the same day by 95/96 Bomb Disposal Section, RE, under the command of Captain H. Mitchell, RE. Captain Mitchell, recognizing the fuze as a new type, decided to remove it from the bomb rather than destroy the bomb where it was. He was fully aware that a new fuze could contain any number of horrors including a possible booby trap. He therefore cleared the area and at great personal risk removed the fuze. He saw that it was different in both length and design from fuzes he had previously seen but that it appeared to have a standard gaine attached. He unscrewed the gaine from the base of the fuze and informed the War Office of his find. At 02:00 hours the next day he handed the fuze to the Research Establishment at Woolwich for investigation. It later transpired that the clockwork mechanism had been ticking throughout the operation and eventually functioned at 22:15 hours on 14 August, thus giving a delay time on this occasion of 38¾ hours. A second No 17 fuze was recovered by Lieutenant C. R. Wood, RE, of 50/51 Bomb Disposal Section, RE, from a 500 kg (1,100 lb) bomb which had fallen on to an Electricity Depot at Lyndhurst, Hampshire, on 14 August 1940. On arrival Lieutenant Wood, assisted by Sapper J. Williams, excavated to the bomb and, like Captain Mitchell, recognized that the fuze was marked differently from the more familiar No 15. Between them they removed it from the bomb. Both Lieutenant Wood and Sapper Williams were well aware of the risks they were taking but their prompt and decisive action not only gained an extra fuze for research but also prevented the very serious damage to the Electricity Depot that would have resulted had the bomb been allowed to explode. When this fuze reached Woolwich it was not ticking, but once started in the laboratory it ran for a period of seven hours before activating the striker. Less than a month later Lieutenant Wood and Sapper Williams were injured dealing with a bomb at Wanbourne, Lymington, Hampshire, but both recovered and were later to receive George Medals for their work.

During August and September 1940 many more No 17 fuzes were recovered and in most cases the personnel concerned were fully aware of the risks they were taking. For example, Second Lieutenant H. A. Manser, RE, and Sergeant W. A. Jones, RE, of 97 Bomb Disposal Section were called on 18 August to deal with a 250 kg (550 lb) bomb deeply embedded in the concrete floor of a factory. The fuze was heard to be ticking and yet they both spent a considerable time chipping at the concrete in an attempt to free the bomb and fuze. They were eventually ordered to leave the bomb which exploded some hours later. Lieutenant Manser later successfully removed a No 17 fuze on 2 September but his luck was running out. He was killed with Lance Corporal E. R. Wood, RE, at Godalming, Surrey, on 30 September 1940.

During this period people were taking risks almost as a matter of course but as the secrets of the fuzes became known instructions were issued and new equipment designed which tended to reduce the risks being taken. Frequently it seemed to be pure luck as to who lived or died. A classic example of this is perhaps Second Lieutenant A. F. Campbell, RE, the officer in charge of 68 Bomb Disposal Section, RE. He and his section were engaged in the recovery of a 250 kg bomb from the Triumph Engineering Company's works at Coventry, located in the city centre. The bomb had penetrated over 8 m (26 ft) through the floor of the factory, rupturing gas pipes as it passed through. The presence of the bomb had halted war production in two factories, involving some 1,000 workers, and forced the evacuation of residents from nearby houses. For these reasons Lieutenant Campbell, assisted by Lance Sergeant J. H. Hinton, RE, and the remainder of his section, worked practically without rest for nearly 48 hours in the most difficult and hazardous conditions until the bomb was finally exposed. Throughout this time the entire section working near the bomb were fully aware that it probably was fitted with a long-delay fuze and could explode at any moment.

When the bomb was finally exposed Lieutenant Campbell's worst fears were confirmed. The bomb was indeed fitted with a delayed-action fuze which was impossible to remove. A slight consolation was that the clock was not ticking, but any movement of the bomb could cause it to start and there was no way of telling for how long it might run before detonating the bomb. Lieutenant Campbell, well aware of the need for the factories to resume production, decided to remove the complete bomb with its fuze to a safe place for destruction. Recognizing the extreme danger involved, he and Sergeant Hinton moved the bomb by lorry for a distance of just over a mile, Lieutenant Campbell lying beside the bomb listening in case the clockwork mechanism should start. One wonders what he could have done had the clock started, other than to continue with the bomb to a safe area. However, the clock did not start and the bomb was removed from the vehicle and safely destroyed. The next day Campbell's luck ran out and the vagaries of the German electric fuzes were tragically demonstrated. He was called to Chapel Street in Coventry to deal with a 250 kg bomb which had fallen 81½ hours previously and had finally been uncovered. The bomb was seen to have a simple impact fuze, but it was too damaged to be removed from the bomb. This fuze, according to the teaching of the time, should have been inert since the capacitors were thought incapable of holding a charge for more than three days. However, Lieutenant Campbell, despite his actions of the previous three days, was a careful man and applied the discharger to the fuze head. On two counts, therefore, he could reasonably believe the bomb to be totally inert. He loaded the bomb on to a vehicle and together with his section drove it to an area outside the city where it could be safely destroyed. The journey was uneventful but during the unloading the bomb exploded killing Lieutenant Campbell and all six soldiers with him. For three days he had taken a series of calculated risks to enable war production to recommence as soon as possible and yet on the fourth day, doing what must be considered a routine task, he and six soldiers died. Second Lieutenant A. F. Campbell, RE, was later to be awarded a posthumous George Cross for his bomb disposal work. Lance Sergeant J. H. Hinton, RE, was awarded the George Medal. Sapper H. W. Carman, another member of 68 Bomb Disposal Section, received a BEM. All three medals were awarded for their unhesitating willingness to work without rest in the extremely hazardous conditions pertaining in the factory.

The bravery of the soldiers who spent long hours digging for or working in the vicinity of those delayed action bombs must always be recognized, as all too often later reports tended to forget them. A typical example was that of Sapper S. Chesher of 96 Bomb Disposal Section, RE, whose citation for the George Medal reads:

'The conduct of Sapper Chesher, under conditions of extraordinary difficulty and danger, has been especially meritorious. He has never allowed considerations for his personal safety to interfere with his work and no situation, however perilous, has been able to affect his nerve. He has shown himself to be as ready to face hard work as he is to meet risk and it has been found more difficult to persuade him to come out of a bomb hole than to get him to enter one. On 18 August 1940 he worked for nine hours, stripped and up to his waist in water, in order to reach a large High Explosive delayed-action bomb which had fallen in a pond.'

Clearly at the time his worth was recognized but later histories tend only to recall the person who finally dealt with the bomb.

Many actions, whether carried out by officers or more junior ranks, do not reach official histories and many others are merely a statistic which provides no indication of the drama, human interest or even the funny side of an incident. One apocryphal story concerns a Corporal and his section who, when ordered to deliver a large but fuzeless and perfectly safe bomb to a demolition area, decided quite illegally to stop en route for a drink. They parked their vehicle outside a pub, entered and ordered their drinks. After ten minutes or so the publican noticed that a number of his regulars had walked up to the door, paused then hurried away without stopping for a drink. Being curious he walked outside and quickly summed up the situation. Outside his front door was a vehicle marked 'Bomb Disposal' with a large bomb plainly visible on the back. Returning to the bar he suggested it might be a good time for the corporal and his men to move on. It is to the Corporal's credit that he did not profit from the situation and, one is led to believe, did not in the future use what was clearly an easy way of being offered a free farewell drink.

Anyone working on a bomb in an area evacuated of its population is by necessity lonely and on occasions afraid. Yet on the successful completion of a task he may be handed a folder of thank you letters written by members of a junior form of the local school from within the evacuated area. The cynic will say the teacher was occupying the children while they waited in a nearby hall, but the phraseology and feelings expressed in the letters are the children's own and this folder can mean more than any mention in an official history. An instance where the thank you was perhaps more materialistic was the case of Lieutenant W. G. Parker, RE, serving with his section in Manchester as part of 10 Bomb Disposal Company, RE. On 27 August 1940 he was ordered to Birmingham to assist with the disposal of a number of unexploded bombs still remaining after heavy air attacks against the city earlier in the month. On 28 August Lieutenant Parker and his men started digging for four bombs and by 30 August all four were uncovered and found to be 250 kg weapons. Once again a simple sentence, yet the Sappers of Lieutenant Parker's section had just spent two days digging out four bombs any of which might have exploded at any instant. In fact, when the bombs were inspected three of them were found to contain No 17 long-delay fuzes which might have started ticking at any time following a knock or vibration. All the bombs were near or on major routes through Birmingham and their presence caused considerable disruption to a city still recovering from a major attack. There was clearly a degree of urgency and Lieutenant Parker, using normal hand tools, removed all the fuzes to enable the bombs to be safely transported to an area where they could be destroyed.

One of the areas which had been at risk should the bombs have exploded was the local cinema owned by Odeon Cinemas Ltd. Grateful for the safe removal of the bombs without damage to their property, and once again being able to open to the public, they presented to Lieutenant Parker a rectangular medallion which read on one side, 'To Commemorate the Bravery of Lt Parker in helping to save Perry Barr Odeon from dangerous time bomb, Sep 1940'. It was signed 'Oscar Deutsch, Managing Director'. On the obverse was, 'Freedom of Odeon, Admit Bearer, Lt Parker, to any Odeon Theatre — Anywhere — Any Time — For All Time'. Since Lieutenant Parker remained in bomb disposal throughout the war, being awarded a MBE in 1944 and a George Medal in 1945, it is to be hoped that

Below left *Free Pass to all Odeon Theatres — as presented to Lieutenant W. G. Parker, RE (later Colonel W. G. Parker, MBE, GM, ERD).* **Below right** *Reverse side of Lieutenant Parker's Odeon Pass.*

he made good use of his Odeon award. After the war he could not give up bomb disposal and commanded a Territorial Army Bomb Disposal Squadron, RE, for a while. From 1955 to 1958 he was the Commanding Officer of 144 Bomb Disposal Regiment, RE (Army Emergency Reserve) and was appointed a Brevet Colonel in 1958. He died on 1 August 1986.

Returning to 1940, the day after the Birmingham incident Lieutenant Parker received an instruction stating that an anti-withdrawal device had been recovered from under a No 17 fuze and that in future all No 17 fuzes were to be removed by remote control and precautions taken in case of the possible detonation of the bomb. This instruction was issued as the result of a most incredible piece of luck and the heroism of Lieutenant B. S. T. Archer, RE, on 29 August, the day before Lieutenant Parker removed the No 17 fuzes from the bombs in Birmingham. Lieutenant Archer was one of the original bomb disposal section commanders and in August 1940 commanded an independent section based in Cardiff. By that time he was already an experienced bomb disposal man and a subsequent citation referred to his actions in dealing with four bombs at RAF St Athan in July 1940, a booby-trapped bomb at Moulton on 17 August and other bombs at Port Talbot Docks on 27 August. However, on 29 August he was ordered to take his section, consisting of Sergeant F. Adams, RE, and fourteen Sappers to Swansea where, on the previous night, a heavy raid had taken place at the oil refineries just outside the town. Unexploded bombs were seriously hindering the work of the fire services in their efforts to control the fires which were burning in an oil storage area.

Arriving mid-morning his team was confronted by an installation, from which clouds of black smoke and leaping flames could be seen, suggesting that any work—or, indeed, survival within the area—was out of the question. Their guide took them to a tank farm (a storage area consisting of rows of large fuel tanks the shape of gasometers), where many oil tanks were ablaze and those not on fire were becoming dangerously hot. In this area were four unexploded bombs, one directly under a non-burning tank. The bomb had pierced the concrete plinth and had been deflected under the tank. Another bomb was about 140 m (153 yd) away between two rows of tanks and another two were far enough away not to pose an immediate threat to the oil store. To prevent a further fire and loss of oil, Lieutenant Archer decided to deal first with the bomb under the tank. The immediate surroundings were far from ideal for any type of work and for bomb disposal they were hazardous in the extreme. Two tanks were blazing furiously, one only 45 m (50 yd) away and the other slightly more. At least one other unexploded bomb was within killing distance.

Working to enlarge the bomb's entry hole through the concrete plinth on which the tank stood would have been hard work under any circumstances, but the conditions of intense heat with flames leaping high into the air from a tank only a short distance away made work impossible, other than in very short shifts. The men dug in relays but excavated as quickly as possible as it was a race to reach the bomb before it exploded.

At noon the other nearby bomb exploded and, although no one was hurt and no additional fires were started, it concentrated everyone's mind on the possibility of their bomb exploding at any moment (assuming the thought had ever left their minds). By 14:00 hours they reached the bomb when there was a second explosion and one of the farthest away pair of bombs exploded—time was running out fast! The bomb under the tank was identified as a 250 kg with its case so cracked that the powdered explosive filling was visible. The fuze head had been ripped off, exposing the electric components of the fuze and leaving wires hanging from it. As the other bombs had exploded without being touched it was assumed that they were all fitted with No 17 clockwork long-delay fuzes, in which case the damage to the electrical part would have no effect upon the lower clockwork section.

Lieutenant Archer decided the only way to deal with the bomb was to remove the base plate through which the bomb had been filled and carry out the reverse process, namely scoop out the main filling. After some difficulty in the cramped and desperately hot situation the base plate was removed. Lieutenant Archer then could see that the fuze pocket normally fixed at both ends had broken free from the bomb case at the end farthest from the fuze head. He therefore grabbed the fuze pocket and wrenched it free from the bomb. The bomb was now comparatively safe and he left it to his men to empty the explosive out of the bomb and take away the empty case. It was then just before 15:00 hours and they had been working for nearly five hours in surroundings which would have done credit to Dante's version of Hell. Not only were they all expecting to be blown up at any moment by their bomb, there was the added hazard of the possible explosion of any of the surrounding oil tanks covering the area with burning oil. There was also the ever constant discomfort of heat, fumes and smoke.

Lieutenant Archer, having removed the fuze pocket, knew that it was still a time bomb capable of killing him and anyone near him, so with a pair of pliers he pulled the fuze by its wires from the fuze pocket. It was a normal No 17 fuze so he unscrewed the gaine and put the fuze into his pocket. Looking into the fuze pocket, expecting to see the usual booster charge of explosive to be shaken out, he saw instead another mechanism. He shook the pocket and the mechanism slid out attached to another gaine. He quickly unscrewed the second gaine and, as he separated it from the mechanism, there was a crack and a flash from the mechanism but by now the gaine was too far away to be affected. Another second and the story of Lieutenant Archer would have ended there and then. He sent the No 17 fuze and the new device found under it for technical examination. The device was in fact an anti-withdrawal fuze known as the ZUS 40. Its operation was quite simple. The gaine of the upper fuze, in this case the No 17, held back a striker in the ZUS 40 and as the top fuze and its gaine were withdrawn the movement allowed the ZUS 40 striker to fire a cap which detonated the second gaine and so explode the bomb.

FUZE POCKET FITTED WITH No [17] FUZE AND ZUS 40

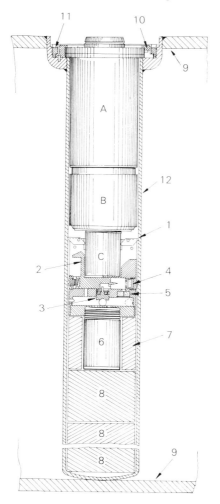

A Electrical portion of No [17] fuze
B Clock of No [17] fuze
C Gaine of No [17] fuze

1 Knife-edge
2 Spring-loaded trigger member with needle striker
3 Spring-loaded locking detent with retaining ball
4 Detonator (ignitory)
5 Booster pellet
6 Gaine

} Zus 40

7 Picric ring
8 Picric pellets
9 Bomb casing
10 Fuze locating ring
11 Fuze locking ring
12 Fuze pocket casing

No 17 fuze with a ZUS 40 anti-withdrawal device. The calipers indicate the amount of withdrawal required to activate the device.

There is no question of the courage shown that day by the whole section but luck also played a major part in the recovery of the latest device in the enemy's constant battle with the bomb disposal men. Firstly, the bomb for which they were digging was clearly timed to detonate several hours after the other two which had detonated at 12:00 hours and 14:00 hours. In fact the No 17 fuze from Lieutenant Archer's bomb finally fired at 18:05 hours that same evening. Secondly, having removed the fuze pocket from the bomb, the No 17 fuze was removed from the fuze pocket containing the ZUS 40, an action designed to detonate the gaine of the ZUS 40, yet in this case it did not. There is no doubt Lieutenant Archer was the first man to do this and survive to tell the tale. He had then shaken out the ZUS 40 fuze, an action which in an undamaged fuze pocket would have been impossible since the ZUS 40 was designed to jam in the pocket, allowing the top fuze to be separated from it when any attempt was made to withdraw the top fuze. Finally, for some unaccountable reason the ZUS 40 fired several seconds after the withdrawal of the No 17 fuze, allowing time for it to be shaken out and its gaine unscrewed.

For this exploit and others already referred to, Lieutenant B. S. T. Archer, RE, was awarded the George Cross in September 1941, thirteen months after the event. In his citation the Inspector of Fortifications and Director of Bomb Disposal said, 'The fact that Lieutenant Archer has enjoyed such remarkable immunity from death in no way detracts from his record of deliberate and sustained courage coupled with devotion to duty of the highest order'.

In fact, Lieutenant Archer served in bomb disposal throughout the war and was demobilized with the rank of Major in January 1946. Like so many of his contemporaries, bomb disposal was in his blood and he served with distinction in the Reserve Army, finally commanding 142 Bomb Disposal Regiment, RE (Army Emergency Reserve) from 1955 to 1961 when he finally retired as a Brevet Colonel. He was then appointed an Officer of the Order of the British Empire. The author had the honour to be present in March 1985 when Colonel B. S. T. Archer, GC, OBE, was presented to His Royal Highness The Prince of Wales on the occasion of His Royal Highness's visit to 33 Engineer Regiment (Explosive Ordnance Disposal). This unit is now the direct and only descendent of the many bomb disposal companies and independent sections of 1940-41.

Soon after August 1940 instructions were issued in respect of the threat posed by the ZUS 40, and details were released of the No 50 fuze described earlier in the chapter. This was a deliberate and dangerous anti-handling device. Used in conjunction with a No 17 fuze, with or without a ZUS 40 under it, it presented a major threat to the bomb disposal teams, especially in vital areas where the detonation of the bomb had to be avoided at all costs. In the past a No 17 fuze could have been removed and the only threat would have been from the clockwork mechanism. Now there was always the added risk that the removal of a fuze, whether carried out by hand or remotely, could cause an explosion. When one then considers that the second fuze pocket frequently contained a No 50 fuze, which upon the slightest movement would detonate the bomb and which could not be discharged with the Two-Pin Plug Discharger, the problem can be appreciated.

As will be seen later these problems were solved mainly by the efforts of the Unexploded Bomb Committee and the technical officers within the bomb disposal organization. They were helped by the grass roots workers who provided a steady supply of fuzes for experimentation, despite the risks involved. Indeed, following the recovery of the first No 17 fuzes in mid-August, detailed technical reports on them were published on 7 and 30 September 1940. In forwarding the second report to the Ordnance Board the following request was made:

'It would be appreciated if a few unfired specimens of the clockwork mechanism could be forwarded to this department to enable a more precise value of the minimum time setting to be established'.

This request was made a month after the first ZUS 40 anti-withdrawal device had been recovered! So knowing the new risks involved in attempting to remove unfired No 17 fuzes, the Unexploded Bomb Committee were still asking that attempts be made to recover them.

While this initial onslaught was being faced by the Royal Engineers, two other battles were raging. One was the Battle of Britain, both in the air and on the airfields, and the other was the Naval battle against mines which were deliberately being dropped on the town and cities of the United Kingdom.

As seen in Chapter 3, the first magnetic mines were dropped on London

No 61 Bomb Disposal Section, RE, removing a German 250 kg bomb 'somewhere in England', 1940/41.

during the night of 16/17 September 1940, of which some seventeen failed to explode. The clearance of these mines was solely the responsibility of the Royal Navy and an *ad hoc* team of officers, petty officers and junior ratings from HMS *Vernon* were quickly deployed to the London area. At the same time the War Office was requested to warn all Army authorities of the high sensitivity of the mines and the grave and widespread damage which would occur should one explode. Similarly, Army bomb disposal staff were warned of the extreme inadvisability of attempting any 'render-safe' operation other than under the guidance of Naval personnel.

Mines continued to fall each night and, as related earlier, the RMS Section of the DTM was formally established on 26 September 1940 using volunteers from HMS *King Alfred*. By 4 October 1940 the original officers and ratings from HMS *Vernon* and the Torpedo School at Chatham, less those who died, had returned to their units. At this time the United Kingdom was free from land-based unexploded mines: 183 had been dealt with, 137 rendered safe, 37 destroyed *in situ* and nine exploded whilst being rendered safe. Each of these 183 mines represents a story of bravery and dedication by men working with the most primitive tools and equipment and, for the initial few days, with virtually no specialist equipment of any kind.

Some of the names which spring to mind whenever those days of late September 1940 are thought of in respect of mine disposal are (in alphabetical order): Armitage, Beadle, Danckwerts, Ellingworth, Hodges, Obbard, Ryan, Speirs, Thistleton-Smith and Wadsley. No list of this sort is ever complete because as always there are those whose actions went without notice or those who died with no one to tell of their passing; but what of those we do know about? We know that on that first night, 16/17 September, HMS *Vernon* was alerted that mines had been dropped on London and the Commander Mines, Commander G. Thistleton-Smith, RN, together with Lieutenant G. A. Hodges, RNVR, set out for London from HMS *Vernon* at about 08:00 hours on Tuesday 17 September 1940. On arrival they found that in the area of Edmonton and Walthamstow over 2,000 people had been evacuated and that three magnetic mines awaited disposal; one was on a tennis court and two among the crowded terraced houses of the area. The latter produced a scene familiar to all who have been involved in bomb or mine disposal. There is the weapon embedded in the front room or the outhouse or the garden. The house is deserted showing all the signs of hasty evacuation. A half eaten meal may still be on the table but whatever the state of the house it represents a frozen tableau of what was happening when the bomb or mine made its appearance; all that is missing are the actors. In this case the 2,000 actors were all keen to return to their respective stages. By 17:00 hours the mines had been cleared and the people returned gratefully to their homes.

The following day Lieutenant D. W. Speirs, RNVR, and Sub Lieutenant H. E. Wadsley, RNVR, joined the HMS *Vernon* teams in London, as did Lieutenant Commander R. Ryan, RN, and Commander E. O.

Obbard, RN, who had arrived from the Torpedo School at Chatham. These early pioneers had some remarkable escapes from death and yet, when recording their accounts of what happened, they refrain from anything other than passing references to their escapes and maintain a casual but factual report of events. Indeed, more emotions appear to be aroused by the thanks of the people allowed to return safely to their homes than any threat of, or near escape from, death. For example, Commander Thistleton-Smith, recording the first day's work in London, states, 'All went smoothly and the explosion of the bomb fuze shortly after its withdrawal did not bother us'. At this stage no bomb fuze gags or motor horns (as described earlier) were available, so the bomb fuze locking ring was unscrewed by hand and the fuze withdrawn using a long length of line. Any delay or jamming of the fuze could have caused the mine to explode yet this eventuality appeared not to bother them. Indeed, in Lieutenant Hodges' report of the above incident he states, 'the fuze fired on withdrawal', not mentioning they were within a second of the mine exploding. The report by Commander Thistleton-Smith relating to the same incident ends with the words, 'At the end of the street we got a great ovation. It made us feel that we had done something really worthwhile; I thought happily of all those people going back to their homes in safety.'

The next day Lieutenant Armitage calmly reported to the Admiralty that he and Sub Lieutenant Wadsley were working on a Type D mine when it exploded but that they had got clear and were both ready to continue work. In fact, Lieutenant Armitage was actually at the mine when the bomb fuze started to tick and, knowing that he had only seconds to spare, he took to his heels. He covered thirty yards before the mine exploded. He was blown through the air and, although badly shaken and severely bruised, he reported for duty the following day.

Lieutenant Hodges was not quite so lucky, but even so escaped death when, in similar circumstances, many others did not. He is describing his actions in dealing with a Type D which had fallen on a Metropolitan Line railway bridge in Clifford Avenue, south-west London.

'The mine lay in the gutter with the bomb fuze underneath. Speirs and I stuffed the parachute round the mine to prevent it rolling over on to us and then tackled the bomb fuze keep ring. It was stiff and I began to tap it round with a punch, heard the fuze whizzing and we ran for it. Speirs ran about twice as far as I did and the mine fired [exploded] as he touched down. I lay 35 yards from the mine and so got shaken up by the hot blast. Speirs arranged for me to go to Richmond Hospital suffering from shock, a discharge from the ears and feeling bruised.'

In fact, Lieutenant Hodges was to remain in hospital for several weeks.

Lieutenant Commander R. Ryan, RN, was one of the earliest pioneers in the rendering safe of magnetic mines and was the first person to render safe a Type C mine. He was fully aware, therefore, of the risks involved when he volunteered to join Commander Obbard and travel to London from Chatham. In those first early days of the London attack he dealt

Type C mine with parachute.

personally with six mines, one of which was at Hornchurch. Here, working with Chief Petty Officer R. V. Ellingworth, RN, he rendered safe a mine which was threatening both the nearby airfield and an explosives factory. Chief Petty Officer Ellingworth was an extremely experienced man and had, in January 1940, assisted Lieutenant Hodges in the Whitstable oyster beds incident (his first mine). After the Hornchurch incident they both went on to Dagenham where another mine was hanging by its parachute inside a warehouse. As they entered the warehouse to investigate, the mine exploded killing both men.

Throughout this period another name kept appearing in other officers' reports, namely that of Sub Lieutenant P. V. Danckwerts, RNVR. On several occasions officers detailed to deal with a mine, found on arrival that the mine had already been rendered safe by a certain Sub Lieutenant Danckwerts. This happened to Lieutenants Hodges and Speirs and later to Lieutenants Armitage and Wadsley. Although agreeing that they were in luck, Lieutenant Armitage requested the Admiralty to get in touch with Sub Lieutenant Danckwerts lest his keenness should bring him to grief. Sub Lieutenant Danckwerts was an ex-pupil of Lieutenant Hodges and at this time he had fewer than six weeks' service in the Navy; without orders and with incomplete equipment with which to deal with unexploded mines, he set out to clear the mines in his district of London. Assisted by Chief Petty Officer J. E. T. Beadle, RN, he worked almost without rest for 48 hours and dealt successfully with sixteen mines. There were air raids in the area throughout much of this time. Sub Lieutenant

'Gently does it' (Lieutenant Sturge RNVR working on a Type C Mine).

Danckwerts was reproved for his actions and also awarded a George Cross for showing courage of the highest order. Chief Petty Officer Beadle was awarded the George Medal for those same incidents.

Sub Lieutenant Danckwerts, contrary to early expectations, survived the war and studied at the Massachusetts Institute of Technology and at Cambridge University. He was Professor of Chemical Engineering at Imperial College, London, from 1956 to 1959, and from 1959 to 1977 was Shell Professor of Chemical Engineering at Cambridge and a Fellow of Pembroke College. He was elected a Fellow of the Royal Society in 1969 and died in 1984 aged 68.

In addition to the awards to Sub Lieutenant Danckwerts and Chief Petty Officer Beadle, Lieutenant Armitage was awarded the George Cross for his work during those early and dangerous days in London. This was followed in 1944 by the George Medal, also for mine clearance, while Lieutenant Commander Ryan and Chief Petty Officer Ellingworth were awarded posthumous George Crosses. Commander Obbard and Lieutenants Hodges and Speirs were each awarded the George Medal as was Sub Lieutenant Wadsley who gained a Bar to it in 1942.

Another officer to be awarded the George Medal for work during this period was Commander Thistleton-Smith for his work on the two booby-trapped mines at Soarhunt and Piddlehinton referred to earlier. He too survived the war and when he finally retired from the Royal Navy in 1960 he was Vice Admiral Sir Geoffrey Thistleton-Smith, KBE, CB, GM, RN. He later became a West Sussex county councillor and a Deputy Lord Lieutenant. He died aged 81 in November 1986.

On 7 October 1940 there began a short lull in RMS activities. By this time all unexploded enemy mines on land had been cleared, the RMS Section had been formally established and the early pioneers had returned to their units. Within the Admiralty discussions began as to what should be done with these eager Sub Lieutenants and seamen all trained in RMS duties. These discussions quickly became academic as the second attack upon London commenced on the night of 15/16 October 1940. During the same night mines as well as bombs were dropped in Birmingham. Many other towns and cities including Liverpool, Coventry, Cardiff and Sheffield were to be attacked during the next six months to the extent that the RMS Section and BSO organization were to be stretched to their limit.

To record all the events and actions of the RMS Section during the months following its formation in September 1940 would require more space than is available in this book. An outline of its development and examples of the bravery, initiative and determination of those involved will have to suffice.

The second major air attack upon London between 15 and 23 October 1940 was followed by an attack upon Coventry during the night of 14/15 November. To combat the unexploded mine problem resulting from this attack (at least ten unexploded parachute mines had been reported) the Admiralty despatched to Coventry a special RMS 'blitz' team. This consisted of eight RMS officers, two staff officers and seven RMS ratings. They travelled in ten small cars, each with its own driver, making a total team strength of 27 all ranks.

On arrival in Coventry slow progress was made along the few remaining roads which were not completely impassable due to bomb craters and fallen buildings. The cars crossed countless fire hoses, skirted bomb craters and deep pools of water and passed masses of debris and smouldering ruins. Eventually it was only possible to proceed on foot and by this means the team made its way to the main police station. This was the only administration building still habitable in the city centre. Here, despite the difficulties under which they were working, the authorities were able to provide details of where the unexploded mines were located and provide a map of the city area.

The first difficulty for the team was to find the mines in localities which were totally unknown to the officers, ratings and drivers, and in many cases barely recognizable to the local inhabitants. The second was to find suitable accommodation for the team. This problem was delegated to the staff officers who, with the assistance of the police, managed to 'persuade' local residents to accept unexpected guests. By now it was late evening and it was decided that work would start at dawn the next day, Saturday 16 November 1940.

That Saturday conditions were even more difficult than on the previous afternoon. The Royal Engineers were in the process of demolishing many of the more dangerous buildings and had cordoned off large areas of the city centre. However, the teams quickly started their hazardous work. An unpleasant feature of their working conditions was the presence through-out the city of unexploded bombs. These were gradually being dealt with by the Royal Engineers. The sound of demolition charges being fired, the crash of falling masonry and the occasional explosion of a bomb did not make for a relaxing atmosphere. As one RMS officer commented 'To render safe a parachute mine amidst such provocative surroundings called for considerable sang-froid'.

The provision of food and drink in the city centre was also a problem, solved mainly by the untiring efforts of the Womens' Voluntary Service and its mobile canteens. These seemed to turn up in the most inaccessible and hostile locations but were welcomed gratefully by those in need. Another benefactor was the City Coroner who had a supply of bottled beer which he dispensed from the womens' cells of the police station. The team eventually left Coventry and returned to London on Monday 18 November 1940 having rendered safe sixteen unexploded mines, one of which exploded during the course of the operation. Fortunately this caused no casualties but did add to the great damage already sustained by the city.

Much was learnt from this first deployment of a RMS 'blitz' team away from London. Clearly such teams needed, if possible, to be self-supporting and have some local knowledge. The avoidance of a long car journey through wartime Britain prior to undertaking a stressful task would also be an advantage. The initial response to these problems was for the Admiralty to approach the London Midland and Scottish Railway Company and try to arrange for the provision of a special train to be ready to move at two hours' notice. This was agreed by the railway company who provided a train consisting of two sleeping cars and a saloon coach. Arrangements were made for the installation of a telephone in the saloon coach which could be connected to any available railway or Post Office line whenever the train was stationary. A supply of food and drink was also placed in the train immediately before departure. In this way it was hoped that RMS teams travelling in the train would be independent of the difficulties arising when accommodation was sought in a blitzed area. They would also arrive fed and refreshed after a journey hopefully free of stress. This train was, in fact, used only twice throughout the war, in both cases when Glasgow was attacked. The Air Ministry was also asked to hold a suitable aircraft in readiness to transport teams to areas of need. This arrangement was designed to cater for possible air attacks in Scotland or Northern Ireland. This aircraft was used on only three occasions, twice to Belfast and once to Sunderland in north-east England.

In addition to these VIP-type arrangements, it was decided to base a small RMS team consisting of an RMS officer and rating plus a car and driver at strategic points throughout the country. The points selected were Birmingham, Leeds, Edinburgh, Cardiff and Newcastle-upon-Tyne. In this way each important Civil Defence Centre had an RMS team upon which to call for help and advice. Also, the teams acquired a degree of local knowledge and geography. In addition to these small groups permanently detached from London, the Admiralty continued to deploy their 'blitz' teams.

During the early months of 1941 an appreciation was made of the vast amount of damage, confusion and general havoc which could be created by the large-scale dropping of parachute mines on built-up areas and lines of communication. During those same months it was still considered to be both possible and likely that Germany would invade Great Britain. These two factors indicated that a situation could exist where members of the RMS Section would be unable to deal unaided with an excess of unexploded mines. Consequently, a selected number of commissioned and non-commissioned officers in both the Royal Engineers and the Royal Air Force were given instructions on the 'gagging' of land dropped mines. It was not intended that they should carry out the full operation of rendering the mines safe. The intention was that they should only carry out the procedures necessary to render the mines comparatively safe until such time as the full operation could be completed by Naval personnel.

In May 1941 a new type of magnetic mine was recovered at Dumbarton, Scotland. It was a Type 'G' or 'George Mine'. This was the Luftwaffe-designed BM 1000 which intelligence sources had long warned the Navy to expect. The Dumbarton mine had a pointed nose like a bomb and a domed tail from which bakelite fins had broken off on impact. It was painted pale blue and was 1,930 mm (76 in) in length and 660 mm (26 in) in diameter. Stencilled on it was 'BM 1000'. It did not take much imagination or linguistic ability to guess that this probably stood for Bombe Mine (Mine Bomb) and that its weight was approximately 1,000 kg (2,200 lb). This mine not only had a complex fuzing system which incorporated an anti-recovery device (from the water) but also a bomb fuze and an anti-stripping device. The latter was such that when the tail dome was removed (a necessary action to get at the working parts) two small circular windows in the mine case were exposed, behind which were two photo-electric cells. These were highly sensitive to light and were wired directly to the detonator of the main high explosive charge. Thus, the unwary, on removing the dome in any condition other than near total darkness, could cause the mine to explode. How then was the mine at Dumbarton recovered? The ingenious anti-stripping arrangement failed to work due to a simple fault in the wiring of the electrical circuit. A moment's lack of attention in assembly, or a friendly gesture from someone working under duress? We will never know, but whatever the cause, that mistake saved many British lives. The recovery of the Dumbarton G mine meant that the until-then strictly adhered-to rule, stating that no mines were to be dealt with during the night hours, was res-cinded. The new procedure was to remove the dome in darkness, black out the windows to the photo-electric cell and continue with the work in daylight or under artificial light. The other problem with the G mine was that, since it had no parachute and fell like a bomb, it buried itself like a bomb, often to depths in excess of 10 m (32.8 ft). Thus, those digging for

BM 1000 (German G Mine) fitted with nose and tail.

a bomb could be surprised to discover they had a very nasty and unexpected customer with which to deal. The only indication that a G mine had fallen rather than a conventional bommb was the possibility of finding fragments of the bakelite tail on or near the surface.

The introduction of this new mine necessitated the design and manu-facture of an entirely new range of non-magnetic tools. It also introduced the Royal Navy to the joys of shafting, ie, the digging of timber-lined shafts to reach deeply buried bombs or mines. This was normally the prerogative of the Royal Engineers and, to a lesser extent, the Royal Air Force. Until Naval equipment was available it was usual at this time (early to mid-1941) for the Royal Engineers to dig shafts down to the point when the mine was located. Naval personnel then took over to render the mine safe. (Later the Navy developed their own concrete-lined ring shaft.)

G Mine showing one of the two windows behind which were fitted the photo-electric cells.

An example of this co-operation occurred during the same month in which the first G mine was recovered. On 22 May 1941 a G mine was reported as having fallen at Nuneaton, just north of Coventry. Two RMS officers, Lieutenant F. R. B. Fortt, GM, RNVR, and Lieutenant D. J. P. O'Hagan, GM, RCNVR (Royal Canadian Naval Volunteer Reserve), were sent to deal with it. Both were experienced RMS officers with over sixty mines to their joint credit but this was their first G mine, as it would have been for almost anyone else. On arrival at Nuneaton it was agreed that the Royal Engineers under Lieutenant R. A. McClune, RE, would undertake the initial excavation. This they did and the mine was located at a depth of just over 6.7 m (22 ft). Lieutenants Fortt and O'Hagan then continued with the excavation until sufficient space had been made for both of them to work on the mine. (Another problem with the G mine was that components such as the dome and the magnetic unit, both of which had to be removed, were too heavy for one person to lift unaided. Accordingly two officers were sent.) Working in the dark the two successfully completed the initial operation. After further excavation they removed the bomb fuze and so rendered the mine safe for removal.

At this stage the full details of the G mine were still unknown. The Admiralty therefore recommended that when carrying out the initial dome removal, even though it be at night, a canvas cover should be erected over the mine to avoid moonlight or other extraneous light falling on it. During the early summer of 1941 Lieutenants Mould and Syme, both Royal Australian Naval Volunteer Reserve officers, were dealing with a G mine which had fallen near Pembroke Dock in South Wales. The mine was on the surface, the night was totally dark with full cloud cover and no sign of light or life was visible from the nearby town. The two officers, therefore, decided to dispense with the canvas cover and proceeded to remove the nuts securing the mine dome in place. As the dome was lifted carefully clear of the mine there was a blinding flash of lightning and a clap of thunder, followed by a succession of flashes as a summer storm broke. The storm ended as suddenly as it started and the two Australians returned and completed the render-safe procedure. Later, at HMS *Vernon*, scientists discovered that the photo-electric cells required light lasting only a fraction of a second longer than a normal flash of lightning to activate the firing circuit. The Australian luck was indeed running true to form.

Lieutenants Mould and Syme were part of a band of Australian Naval officers who were engaged in mine disposal and related occupations throughout World War 2. Their record of courage, daring and (in some cases) luck, is very difficult for any other group to equal. Seven of them were awarded a total of three George Crosses, ten George Medals and one Distinguished Service Cross. One of them, Lieutenant J. H. H. Kessack, GM, RANVR, was unfortunately killed whilst rendering a mine safe.

Lieutenant Kessack was typical of many of the Naval officers working for the RMS Section during late 1940 and early 1941. Considering the risks taken and the pressures under which they were required to work it is surprising that more did not lose their lives. Lieutenant Kessack, assisted by Seaman J. McFetridge, RNR, dealt with his first mine in Birmingham on 14 December 1940. Later the same month he was in Romford, Essex, dealing with two more mines. Each of these was found to contain a new type of magnetic unit which he recovered and sent for technical evaluation. A few days later, on 4 January 1941, accompanied by Able Seaman D. Mountford, RN, he was in south Wales working in the basement of a house in Ninian Park, Cardiff. Here, because the bomb fuze was damaged to the extent that it could not be removed remotely, he was forced to remove the fuze by hand. This was an action known to be hazardous. His two assistants, McFetridge and Mountford, were subsequently awarded George Medals for their help and support of RMS officers. Three months later, at the time of his death on 28 April 1941, Kessack had dealt with a total of 27 mines. The following extract from *Report on Mines Laid on Land, 9 January 1941 to 30 November 1941*, signed by Admiral H. Phillips, Director of Mines and Torpedoes, on 18 December 1941 and addressed to the Third Sea Lord says it all:

'It is regretted to report that on 28 April 1941 Lieutenant J. H. N. Kessack, GM, lost his life while attempting to render a mine safe. Kessack was an experienced officer who had already dealt with 27 mines and had been recommended for high awards. The mine that killed him was "lying pretty" and was apparently a normal one. His death emphasises that, in spite of improved techniques, the act of rendering a mine safe is still extremely dangerous as any mine may blow up on being approached or in the course of operations.'

Whenever a RMS team attempted a mine render-safe operation they were advised to find or dig a funk-hole, ie, a place into or behind which they could throw themselves within seconds of the clockwork mechanism of the bomb fuze starting to tick. Making these preparations ensured that they did not run blindly from the mine but moved deliberately to a carefully considered place of relative safety. Some paced themselves to determine just how far they could run in seventeen seconds. In a muddy field it is a depressingly short distance! One officer commented, 'My colleagues used to think my funk-holes were too close to the job, but I reckoned they were better too close than just out of reach'. Despite this teaching, officers and ratings were frequently forced to deal with mines from which there was no possible way in which they could get clear within the time limit. Examples were when working up to their knees in sticky mud or at the bottom of a 10 m (32.8 ft) deep shaft. Some specific examples of this sort of situation and ones where a mad dash for cover saved a life are given below.

On 17 April 1941 an unexploded parachute mine was reported to have fallen in the churchyard of St Paul's Cathedral in London. Lieutenant R. J. Smith, RNVR, was sent to the cathedral and saw that the mine was covered by its parachute. Despite strenuous efforts to remove the parachute it proved impossible to free the tangled mess of cords and fabric within which the mine lay. Lieutenant Smith decided to crawl under the parachute and with difficulty wriggled into the mess and found the bomb fuze. From this dark and very restricted position he started to remove the small cover plate on the head of the fuze prior to fitting the fuze gag. He knew that if he moved the mine the fuze could start to tick and there would be no possible way in which he could scramble free from his cocoon within the time available. As he removed the cover plate, a large fire engine drove past, approximately 10 m (32.8 ft) from the mine, and the vibration so caused started the fuze ticking. There was no escape for Lieutenant Smith so he carried on with the fitting of the gag and completed the operation safely before the clock had finished its countdown. It is on such occasions that the advice of the 'old hands' to carry a spare gag, preferably between your teeth, makes sense. The sense of utter frustration at having dropped the gag and having to search desperately for it while the clock ticks away must be unbearable, although likely to be short-lived. Happily in this incident the mine was rendered safe and the almost certain destruction of the cathedral was averted. It was the second occasion that St Paul's Cathedral had been saved by the efforts of mine or bomb disposal personnel. The first was when a party of Royal Engineers from 5 Bomb Disposal Company, RE, removed a 1,000 kg (2,200 lb) bomb which had fallen and buried itself deep under Deans Yard next to the cathedral on 12 September 1940.

Another example of an impossible escape situation was that in which Lieutenant B. H. W. Fenwick, GM, RNVR, and Able Seaman D. Mountford, RN, found themselves whilst dealing with a mine which had fallen in Liverpool on 13 March 1941. The mine had come to rest somewhere in a high office building adjacent to the main telephone exchange. The telephone exchange had been evacuated and there was an obvious need to dispose of the mine as quickly as possible. The building containing the mine consisted of a number of small offices, storerooms and winding staircases, all of which had been badly damaged during a previous air raid. It took Lieutenant Fenwick and Able Seaman Mountford some considerable time to find the room in which the mine lay. When it was eventually discovered, it was in a third-floor office full of rubble, timber and damaged furniture making it quite impossible to open the door wide enough to enter.

A long ladder was obtained and Lieutenant Fenwick entered the third-floor room via the window. He crawled through the tangle of debris and under a heavy desk until he reached the mine. He then rendered the mine safe. A simple sentence but again covering the full gamut of hazards faced each time a mine of this sort had its teeth drawn. Had the clock started at any time whilst he was in the room there would have been no safe means of escape.

Finally, there was the sort of situation which will always cause a smile but was not a joking matter at the time. A mine had penetrated a roof of an outside lavatory in Old Nichol Street, Bethnal Green, London. Owing to the damage caused by its fall, the mine was completely jammed with most of the available space filled with rubble. The only means of access was by crawling through the hole in the roof. This Lieutenant G. E. Stubbs, RNVR, accordingly did, knowing that once in there was no easy or fast way out. Nothing daunted he entered and successfully rendered the mine safe.

During the last three situations related the RMS personnel had no-where to run to and luckily on only one occasion was there a need to leave in a hurry. In each of the following instances there was very much a need to race to safety, but complete safety was not always found.

On 11 May 1941 an unexploded parachute mine had fallen through the roof of the Palladium Theatre, London. Sub Lieutenant C. M. Wright, RNVR, and Able Seaman W. H. Bevan, GM, RN, were sent to the incident and after a prolonged search over the rooftops located the mine jammed in the roof girders immediately above the stage. Clearly the mine had to be approached from below. Sub Lieutenant Wright, using a very unsteady ladder, managed to climb to within 2.5 m (8 ft) of the mine. Using the light from his torch he was able to see that access to the bomb fuze was masked by a piece of timber 230 mm by 76 mm (9 in × 3 in) which had broken under the weight of the mine. Sub Lieutenant Wright lashed himself into position beside this bulk of timber, utilizing one of the many ropes normally used for hoisting stage scenery. Able Seaman Bevan stood on the ladder holding the torch. Then with a small saw, which was all that the cramped and difficult conditions would allow, Sub Lieutenant Wright cut through the rafter and so exposed the bomb fuze. He then carried out the normal procedures and fitted the gag into position.

The next task was to unscrew the fuze locking ring but as soon as this was touched the fuze began to tick. Both men made every effort to get clear. Sub Lieutenant Wright succeeded in freeing himself and slid down one of the handy ropes. Able Seaman Bevan slid down the ladder, falling free for the last 3 m (10 ft) and both rushed from the stage. Fortunately the gag worked perfectly and the mine did not explode. They returned to the mine not knowing the condition of the fuze but decided to continue with its extraction. This was safely accomplished. To remove the remaining hazardous components from the mine it was necessary for the Sub Lieutenant to actually lie on the mine whilst Able Seaman Bevan held his feet. The mine was eventually rendered fully safe and lowered on to the stage. The London Palladium has seen many great stars but most would find it difficult to follow the act which was played out above the stage in May 1941. Within a year Sub Lieutenant Wright was reported missing, presumed killed, whilst travelling by sea to Gibraltar.

Another instance of a desperate dash from a mine is that of a Type C mine which fell in Hoxton in the East End of London on 17 October 1940. The mine was found in a ground-floor room suspended through a hole in the ceiling by its parachute and with its nose approximately 150 mm (6 in) from the floor. It was the usual incongruous setting referred to before, namely a small family home with treasured ornaments, family photographs and all the signs of a rapid exit as this huge and definitely unwanted guest arrived through the roof.

Sub Lieutenant J. M. C. Easton, RNVR, accompanied by Able Seaman B. Southwell, RN, was called to deal with the mine. Sub Lieutenant Easton decided to render the mine safe where it hung. He would carry out the actual render-safe procedures but Able Seaman Southwell would stand in the doorway to the hall and pass him the necessary tools and equipment and assist as required. After about a minute's work the mine slipped and jerked to a halt again. There was a crash of falling brickwork as the parachute above regained its hold on the mine. Immediately the clockwork mechanism in the fuze started to whirr and after a shouted warning both men dashed from the house. Able Seaman Southwell was out of the house first and turned to race down the street. Sub Lieutenant Easton realized that he had even less time than Southwell to get clear. He ran across the road and dived behind a brick and concrete surface air raid shelter so that the shelter was between him and the house containing the mine.

The mine exploded destroying six complete streets. Sub Lieutenant Easton was buried deep beneath a mass of bricks and mortar. He was eventually dug out unconscious and with a broken back. Able Seaman Southwell was less lucky for he was killed by the blast and it was some six weeks before his body was recovered from beneath the rubble. Of that incident Sub Lieutenant Easton said, 'I heard no explosion. It has since been explained to me that if you are near enough to an explosion of such tremendous force unconsciousness is upon you before the sound reaches you, which is a very merciful thing. I was blinded by the flash that comes split seconds before the explosion, but that was all I experienced.' This may help to answer the question posed by Major Fletcher in the opening paragraph of this book! Sub Lieutenant Easton spent a year in plaster but eventually recovered and spent the rest of the war years as the Commanding Officer of a mine sweeper. Both he and Able Seaman Southwell were later awarded the George Cross, which in the case of Able Seaman Southwell was received on his behalf by his widow.

Whenever the exploits of the RMS Section of the early 1940s are discussed amongst mine or bomb disposal officers there is always one name which comes into the conversation sooner or later. It is that of Lieutenant Commander H. R. Newgass, GC, RNVR. Many of the Lieutenants in the RMS Section were young men, but Lieutenant Newgass, as he then was, was 41 years old when he volunteered for mine disposal work. Within two months of volunteering, he was to have the whole mine and bomb disposal fraternity waiting for news as he dealt with a parachute mine in one of the most difficult and dangerous situations that can be imagined.

On the night of 28/29 November 1940, a magnetic parachute mine fell on to Garston Gas Works, Liverpool, rupturing a large gasometer but failing to explode. The presence of this mine paralysed industry over a large

G mine recovered in Belfast on 11 May 1941.

area of Liverpool. Six thousand people were evacuated. Railways and dock sidings were closed and the whole of the gas supply to east and south Liverpool was threatened. The mine had pierced the top of the gasometer and continued downwards until stopped by its parachute which caught on the jagged edges of the hole. This hole allowed some of the gas to escape. As this happened the top half of the gasometer sank downwards until the mine rested on the floor in an almost vertical position leaning against one of the internal pillars. To add to these problems the mine was completely covered by 2 m (6.5 ft) of foul smelling, oily water which lay in the bottom of the gasometer.

This was the situation when Lieutenant H. R. Newgass, RNVR, arrived to deal with the mine. The Chief Engineer of the gas works had opened an entry hole into the tank well above the water level through which Lieutenant Newgass was able to assess the situation. He asked the Chief Engineer to pump out the water, some 1,250,000 gallons (5,682,500 litres). This was eventually completed but there was still left in the tank several inches of black tar and sludge. The atmosphere in the tank was a highly inflammable (if not explosive) mixture of air and gas, within which it was impossible to breathe without some form of breathing apparatus. Lieutenant Newgass, having assessed the problems and dangers, decided that he would undertake the task entirely on his own. The work would clearly take a number of hours and so a supply of oxygen was arranged from the local Fire Brigade. This consisted of a set of breathing apparatus and a number of gas cylinders, each of which contained sufficient oxygen to support life for a period of half an hour. Thus, work could only be undertaken during a number of relatively short visits to the mine.

Lieutenant Newgass was therefore required to work alone, inside a dark steel tank, the floor of which was covered with a black sticky sludge and inside which the atmosphere was inflammable and unable to support life. In one's worst dreams a more frightening 'no escape' situation would be difficult to imagine. However, Lieutenant Newgass entered that environment not once but six times, each time leaving only when his gas cylinder was almost empty. His first visit was to carry out a thorough inspection and make a plan. During his second he took down his tools and a ladder to enable him to reach the top of the mine and to get in and out of the tank more easily. On his third visit he stabilized the mine by building sandbags round its nose and lashing its other end to the pillar against which the mine rested. On the fourth visit he turned the mine sufficiently to enable him to render safe and remove the bomb fuze. This was a hazardous operation under the best conditions. In those circumstances it required not only courage but determination of the highest order. On his fifth and sixth visits to the mine he removed the other hazardous components and so completed the full render-safe procedure. The mine was subsequently removed by a Naval working party.

Although Lieutenant Newgass had been in the RMS Section for only two months it was just as well that he was not superstitious as the mine in the Garston Gas Works was his thirteenth! In recognition of his bravery in saving not only the gas works and the industrial complex around it, but also a very large section of Liverpool, the gas company presented him with a gold cigarette case. Their employees gave him a set of gold cuff links. Many of the evacuated 6,000 whose homes had been saved by his action also gave him presents. His Sovereign approved the immediate award of a George Cross.

Lieutenant Newgass continued in the Navy for a further four years after which he was discharged on medical grounds. He died aged 85 in November 1984, when much of the above story was published in the obituary columns of the national Press. The obituary notice acted as a timely reminder to the current generation of what had gone on in the past. By coincidence, at the time of his death news was also being published of Royal Navy clearance divers rendering safe an unknown mine recovered from the Red Sea. A different location, era and political background but it demonstrates that the modern equivalents of the RMS Section live on and display the same degree of courage and determination as their predecessors.

When one thinks of bomb disposal (as opposed to mine disposal) in conjunction with such cities as Liverpool, Plymouth, Portsmouth or Glasgow, the tendency is to think of the Royal Engineers. This is quite correct since the majority of the bomb disposal work in the actual cities was carried out by the Royal Engineers. However, all the places referred to above and over twenty others, have within their boundaries dockyards, ports or Naval installations. Within these areas, as we have seen earlier in the book, the responsibility for bomb disposal lay firmly upon the shoulders of the Naval Bomb Safety Officers (BSO) working under the technical direction of the Director Unexploded Bomb Department (DUBD) in the Admiralty.

Their story, although they dealt with the same enemy devices as the Army, is different in that the BSO worked alone with perhaps one or two permanently-attached ratings. When a major digging task was needed, the BSO was expected either to do it himself or make do with volunteers from the local Naval installations. Indeed, one BSO complained bitterly of this situation since, unless there was a ship in port, many of the available hands were of low medical category and quite incapable of digging for a full day. He was told firmly to make do with what he had, as was every other BSO. Thus the BSO tended to be a solitary worker. He dealt directly with DUBD to whom he sent his reports and from whom he received technical advice. He was well supported by DUBD receiving the most up-to-date information on all enemy devices so far recovered. He was also well provided with the most recently-developed equipment with which to deal with those devices. On occasions he even received cryptic comments upon his report writing or failure to use correct service procedures.

One classic example of this was when a young officer, having carried out a most creditable render-safe procedure and written a detailed report complete with sketches and diagrams of the bomb, signed the report with just his initials. He received a curt note from the Admiralty which pointed out that he should in future sign his name in full, as the only persons entitled to use initials in official correspondence were members of the Board of Admiralty. The officer concerned wrote 'noted', initialled the letter and returned it to the Admiralty where it was filed without comment. Thus are Naval traditions fostered.

One report prepared by a BSO dealt with a 250 kg (550 lb) unexploded bomb which had fallen through the wardroom floor of the Royal Naval Base Devonport and into the cellar below. As the result of its passage through the building the bomb had split open and some of its explosive content was spread across the cellar floor. The bomb was still very much 'alive' and capable of destroying the wardroom should it explode. The BSO in his report, notes that 'the stewards had swept up the loose explosive before the bomb was reported'!

Whatever one's views on report writing, there is no doubt that the BSO organization represented some of the very best Naval traditions of bravery and determination in the face of danger. Such an example occurred on 17 May 1941. During the night of 15/16 May 1941 a 250 kg bomb fell into the sluice valve chamber between two graving docks at Falmouth and failed to explode. (A graving dock is one from which the water can be pumped out to allow work to be carried out on a ship's hull; the sluice valve chamber is a deep chamber, one side of which is open permanently to the sea and with two sides open to the adjoining docks via sluice gates.)

At low tide on 16 May 1941, the bomb was spotted for the first time and the seriousness of its position appreciated. Should the bomb explode the two dry docks would become flooded and unusable until repairs to the sluice gates and valves could be completed. The BSO was alerted and at the following daylight low tide he climbed down into the valve chamber. He climbed using various cross girders until he reached the water level some 10.5 m (34.5 ft) below the top of the dock. The bomb lay at the bottom of the chamber still covered by 2 m (6.5 ft) of water. The fuze was visible but it was impossible to recognize any identifiable features through 2 m of murky sea water. The BSO just managed to fit a rope round the base of the bomb, the tail fin having been smashed off. He intended raising the bomb out of the water and lowering it on to a strop with which he could finally remove it from the chamber. (At this stage pause for a moment and consider the situation. The BSO was at the bottom of a 10.5 m (34.5 ft) shaft standing on a cross girder. Below him was 2 m (6.5 ft) of sea water at the bottom of which was a bomb. Yet he managed somehow to fix a rope round the base of the bomb and intended to lift it clear of the water with its, as yet, unidentified fuze.) Having fixed the line the bomb was slowly raised but before it was clear of the water it slipped and fell again to the bottom of the shaft. As the water cleared, and presumably as the BSO's heartbeat returned to near normal, it was seen that the bomb had turned so that the fuze was now pointing vertically downwards. Furthermore, it could be seen that there was a hole in the bomb case where the furthest end of the fuze pocket had been wrenched from the case.

The BSO then had a rope lashed to a boat hook and managed to get the hook into the hole, knowing that directly below the hole was the end of the fuze pocket. By lifting on the boat hook the bomb was raised until it was clear of the water. It was then possible, with difficulty, to identify the fuze and determine that it was not a No 17 long-delay fuze as feared but instead the relatively simple No 38. This was a fuze used in anti-ship bombs which was very similar to the No 15 fuze described earlier. The only difference was that it had a short delay of either 0.05 seconds or 0.2 seconds— sufficient to enable the bomb to pierce the deck or side of a ship and enter well into the hull before exploding. On occasions this fuze could have a delay as long as five seconds but this was only used when dropped in an anti-submarine role. The fuze could be rendered safe using the same method as for the No 15 fuze. Reassured, the BSO unscrewed the rear filling plate and passed a strop through the filling hole and the hole in the side of the bomb and so was able to lift the bomb without fear of a further slip. The placing of this strop was only possible because the high explosive filling was in a powdered form rather than a solid cast block. The bomb was then raised by crane with the BSO steadying it at every stage. There was only about 25.4 mm (1 in) to spare between the wall of the shaft, the girders and the bomb. The bomb was subsequently emptied of its main high explosive filling and the case and fuze pocket were later dumped at sea.

The BSO was Lieutenant J. Bridge, GM, RNVR, who, as a result of this and a number of other incidents, was to receive a Bar to his first George Medal awarded for BSO duties during 1940. Lieutenant Bridge was later to be awarded the George Cross for his work in clearing charges from Messina Harbour, Sicily, in 1943. Before the war this much-decorated officer had been a schoolmaster teaching physics. After the war he eventually became the Chief Education Officer for Sunderland and at the time of writing is enjoying his retirement.

Lieutenant Bridge's decorations may not have been typical of all BSOs, but his dedication and ability to work in strange, cramped and dangerous situations were attributes shared by them all. For example, Lieutenant D. Law, RNVR, was called to a ship from which it had been reported that an unexploded bomb of unknown size was in its bunkers (the parts of a ship which contain its fuel, in this case coal). This was to be his 39th bomb since becoming a BSO. Once on board, Lieutenant Law discovered that the location of the bomb within the coal was only very roughly known. With the aid of stokers he dug into the coal until he located the bomb. This necessitated going 3.5 m (11 ft) down and 5 m (16.5 ft) horizontally into the coal. Apart from the risk of the bomb exploding there was also the very real risk of being buried alive should the ship change its angle of list. Having found the bomb he located the fuze and rendered it safe. The bomb was removed and the flooded engine room was pumped out—revealing a second bomb. This bomb was lying so that its fuze was on the underside and, therefore, inaccessible. Lieutenant Law, working alone and using wedges and crow-bars, managed to turn the bomb very carefully and so get at the fuze. This he also managed to render safe with no problems.

It should be remembered that the majority of these BSOs, prior to joining the RNVR, had no connection with the sea other than perhaps as amateur yachtsmen. Consequently, the hold or engine room of a ship or the mechanical workings of a dockyard were initially as strange to them as they would be to a member of the Army or Royal Air Force. However, a tour of duty as a BSO quickly made them familiar with things Naval and the odd locations in which bombs may come to rest. In April 1941 Lieutenant S. W. Lowe, RNVR, for example, dealt with two 1,400 kg (3,085 lb) unexploded bombs within a few days of each other. The first was in the Submarine Dock at Barrow-in-Furness on the north-west coast of England and the second in a hole 6.7 m (22 ft) below the Vickers Armstrong Gun Shop. Indeed, during eight nights' work he dealt with eight parachute mines and seven bombs, all in the Barrow-in-Furness area. Similarly, Lieutenant H. V. Cronyn, RNVR, was in equally strange surroundings when a tanker reported that a 500 kg (1,100 lb) unexploded bomb had come to rest in one of her tanks, then full of petrol. Clearly nothing could be done while the tank was full, so it was emptied of petrol but was then full of an explosive petrol vapour/air mixture. Nothing daunted, Lieutenant Cronyn entered the dark tank, located the bomb and using a block and tackle turned it to expose the two fuzes. One was damaged and unidentifiable but the other was identified and rendered safe. Despite not knowing the state of the damaged fuze the bomb was hoisted on deck and finally disposed of. The important point is not the render-safe procedure but the strange hazardous surroundings from which the bomb was recovered.

There are many hundreds of other stories of courage and fortitude taking place in locations ranging from chemical works whilst still under air attack to a manure dump very close to the home of the First Sea Lord.

In addition to the BSOs deployed in Great Britain there were also BSOs in a number of overseas commands. One example, Malta, is looked at in Chapter 5.

When the average person thinks of the summer of 1940 and the Battle of Britain, visions of fighter aircraft of the Royal Air Force bravely flying to meet the might of the Luftwaffe spring to mind. Indeed, it is the well documented story of 'The Few' which is the essence of the Battle of Britain. Unfortunately, very little is ever thought, written or recorded of the work of the Royal Air Force bomb disposal teams of that period. (They were then known as Bomb Demolition Teams.) While the spectacular battle ebbed and flowed overhead a less spectacular, but in its own way no less important, battle was taking place on the ground at many Royal Air Force stations. The urgency to clear the airfields of unexploded bombs and thus enable the aircraft to be serviced and rearmed in relative safety was just as important as filling the bomb craters to enable the aircraft to land and take off.

During the Battle of Britain the responsibility for the clearance of unexploded bombs on Royal Air Force stations rested with the armament personnel of nominated first line or 'X' stations. A number of mobile squads were also available to support any of those 'X' stations under temporary pressure. As was shown earlier these teams received all their technical control direct from the Air Ministry. During the hectic times of the Battle of Britain when most eyes were turned upwards it is understandable that the contribution made by the Bomb Demolition Teams was perhaps not fully appreciated or recorded. Nevertheless, but for their efforts there is little doubt the flying at a number of important stations would have been seriously curtailed if not brought to a standstill.

The main battle, as far as the Royal Air Force was concerned, was being fought in the skies over southern England. The Bomb Demolition Teams were controlled from the Air Ministry and, consequently, very few records were kept, or have survived, to record the day-to-day activities of these teams. No record of the number of bombs dealt with by the teams could be established by the author. Neither could the number of bombs cleared by armament personnel from the British Expeditionary Force airfields in France during May 1940 be established.

Unfortunately, during these two hectic months of August and September 1940, the Royal Air Force Bomb Demolition Teams were often badly placed for official recognition compared with the bomb disposal teams of the other two Services. They were small teams working on their own using *ad hoc* channels of communication and were not considered by the Air Ministry to be operationally employed. Indeed, some station commanders even looked upon them as a nuisance until the bombs began to fall— then their sudden popularity was often startling.

At the beginning these Royal Air Force teams, although commanded by armourers well versed in the complexities of British bombs and fuzes, were all inexperienced in respect of German bombs and fuzes. However, they, like their counterparts in the other Services, very speedily gained their experience. It would be hard to do otherwise under the conditions prevailing in 1940. Some diary notes of an eye-witness at Royal Air Force Manston, in Kent, show the activities on the airfield during a period of twelve days in August 1940. Under those circumstances one became experienced or dead very quickly.

12 August 1940—About fifteen Me 110s attacked. Resulted in over one hundred bomb craters on the airfield and seventeen unexploded bombs. Some Spitfires were able to operate on flagged runways. (Unexploded bombs not yet dealt with were marked by red flags.)

15 August 1940—Nine Me 110s attacked. Four hangars damaged and seven more unexploded bombs, mostly 50 kg (110 lb).

16 August 1940—Eight Me 109s attacked the airfield. Some aircraft damaged.

18 August 1940—A number of He 111s raked the airfield with gunfire. Some Spitfires destroyed and some personnel killed.

20/22 August 1940—Minor attacks only.

24 August 1940—Twenty bombers with heavy fighter escort attacked. Nine men killed. There were craters and unexploded bombs everywhere. Communications were cut and the airfield isolated. Service and civilian firemen fought fires in hangars, stores and ammunition buildings for about two days afterwards. This was followed by three more raids on the same day and people not directly involved took to the woods for safety for at least a week afterwards. Even by 28 August 1940 the airfield surfaces or supporting facilities were barely useable. Between forty and fifty unexploded bombs were reported and clearance work was going on continuously from 12 August under very adverse and dangerous conditions. The middle of an airfield was no place to be with air raids always in the offing.

By the end of the Battle of Britain nobody in Royal Air Force bomb disposal needed reminding that it was a hazardous occupation. Despite the majority of the warrant officers and senior non-commissioned officers being qualified and experienced armourers, a number were killed. Some were killed whilst carrying out a particularly hazardous operation, some by chance and some for no apparent reason. Among those killed was Squadron Leader E. L. Moxey, RAFVR (Royal Air Force Volunteer Reserve), a member of the Unexploded Bomb Committee referred to in Chapter 2. He went to Biggin Hill airfield on 27 August 1940 as it was reported that two unexploded delay-action bombs had been found embedded in the airfield. One of them was fitted with a device to prevent interference, possibly a ZUS 40. The fuzes were required for technical evaluation and Squadron Leader Moxey, a technical intelligence officer at the Air Ministry, volunteered to go to the site and recover the fuzes. By the nature of his work he was fully aware of the risks he would be taking. On arrival at Biggin Hill he was met and assisted by Warrant Officer E. G. Hunt, RAF, who had been busy dealing with unexploded enemy bombs dropped on the airfield during six previous bombing attacks. Squadron Leader Moxey succeeded in removing safely one of the fuzes and was attempting to remove the second when the bomb exploded. He was killed instantly but Warrant Officer Hunt by some miracle of fate was blown

20 m (22 yd) from the scene and, although injured, survived the blast. The warrant officer returned to duty to assist in the clearance of the airfield and, to quote from his George Medal citation: '. . . he continued to show a complete disregard for his own safety and his gallant actions have been instrumental in keeping the aerodrome operationally serviceable'.

Squadron Leader Moxey was awarded a posthumous George Cross.

Another incident when a bomb caused fatal casualties to bomb disposal personnel occurred on 11 October 1940 at Royal Air Force Eastchurch in Kent. The particular bomb involved, a 250 kg (550 lb) probably fitted with a No 17 clockwork long delay fuze, was dropped on the station on 2 September 1940 and penetrated to a depth of 7 m (23 ft) about 50 m (55 yd) from the Sheppey Light Railway. When ultimately the bomb was reached, the fuze or fuzes were hidden and the bomb nose was pointing upwards. The recovery operation was a joint Royal Air Force/Royal Engineer project. The intention was that the Royal Engineers, who were not bomb disposal trained, would excavate down to the bomb and a Royal Air Force senior non-commissioned officer from the mobile team based at Royal Air Force Detling would deal with the fuze or fuzes.

Just after the bomb had been exposed it exploded. Later, at the enquiry Sergeant Blackwood, RAF, of Eastchurch, who had just left the excavation, said that two Royal Engineers were working at the bottom of the shaft. One Sapper was standing on a platform a third of the way up and Flight Sergeant Bishop of Eastchurch and Sergeant Roper, RE, were on another platform near the top of the hole supervising operations. When the bomb exploded Flight Sergeant Bishop and three Royal Engineers were killed and one other member of the team was most seriously injured.

At least thirty unexploded bombs had been successfully dealt with at Eastchurch during the previous three weeks. This particular bomb had been in the ground for over a month and so it must be assumed that vibration from the digging had set the clock in motion and time continued to run out until it exploded. It is just possible that the bomb was fitted with one of the earliest No 50 anti-disturbance fuzes and one of the Sappers disturbed the bomb. We shall never know now. A few months later in a similar situation an electric stethoscope would have been put on the bomb as soon as any part of it was uncovered to provide a warning if the fuze was ticking. Even this, however, would not necessarily have prevented a similar tragedy from occurring.

During the three vital months of July, August and September 1940 heroic actions were the norm. Without them the Battle of Britain would have been lost and all were aware of the enemy poised on the other side of the English Channel. However, even among the gladiators of the air, certain members of the ground-based bomb disposal teams stood out amid their peers. At that time even fliers were heard to remark 'rather you than me', and they meant it!

One such example was Warrant Officer W. H. Charlton, RAF, who, during August and September 1940, was responsible for bomb disposal on Royal Air Force stations in Gloucestershire and Wiltshire. During those two months he dealt with over 200 unexploded bombs, many of which were unfamiliar to him and were fitted with No 17 long delay fuzes. The report on his activities states that his work called for personal courage of an exceptional order. In January 1941 he was awarded a George Cross and is next recorded as a Flight Lieutenant in the Far East. By means which are not clear he travelled to the interior of China and returned to Singapore with the first detailed information on Japanese bombs and fuzes. In 1942 he was captured by the Japanese and spent the next three years as a prisoner-of-war in Java.

Another group of men worthy of comment was the Bomb Demolition Team based at Royal Air Force Upper Heyford, just north of Oxford. They were Sergeant K. Lythgoe, Aircraftsman R. Nicholson and Aircraftsman A. Simpson. They did exactly what a demolition team was supposed to do. They dug for the bombs and when they were found (if it was acceptable) destroyed them *in situ*. When this was not acceptable they removed the fuzes or carried the bombs to more suitable spots and there destroyed them. With the fuzes then known to be in existence any one of these actions was potentially dangerous. Yet the three of them, being fully aware of the risks, continued with this work until their station had been

An RAF bomb disposal team digging for a bomb.

cleared of unexploded bombs. On one occasion they had to dig for eight days to a depth of 12 m (39 ft), to expose a bomb which they then demolished *in situ*. On another occasion they dug to a depth of 2 m (6.5 ft) to an unexploded bomb which lay close to a building. Having found the bomb they pulled it out using a vehicle driven by Sergeant Lythgoe. On inspection they discovered the bomb was fitted with a No 17 fuze which they had been instructed not to remove. They had no means of knowing if the fuze was ticking—the rough handling it received when the bomb was dragged from the hole would suggest that it probably was. The bomb could not be transported to the demolition site in the vehicle as the ground was too rough. Aircraftsmen Nicholson and Simpson therefore carried the bomb approximately 500 m (547 yd) to a suitable place for demolition. Throughout these operations the three airmen faced constant danger with the utmost contempt.

Finally, two contemporaries of Warrant Officer Hunt were Warrant Officer E. G. Alford, based at Royal Air Force Kenley, a few miles from Biggin Hill, and Warrant Officer J. V. Saunders, based at Royal Air Force North Weald, Kent. Both these warrant officers led parties on their respective stations to deal with large numbers of unexploded bombs. Both displayed qualities of leadership, skill and gallantry. The two warrant officers and the three men of the Upper Heyford Bomb Demolition Team were all awarded George Medals.

Of those Royal Air Force personnel involved in bomb disposal during the Battle of Britain, it is possible only to select a small cross-section to demonstrate their work. It was, however, this band of poorly-equipped but enthusiastic pioneers who were to develop into the highly skilled and well equipped Royal Air Force Bomb Disposal Organization, the same organization which was to deal with 83,700 weapons in the United Kingdom and over 92,000 in the European theatre of operations during the war.

5

Malta — the battle for survival

Much has been written of Malta, 'The George Cross Island', but in this story we are only concerned with the problems of bomb disposal. It would, therefore, be inappropriate to discuss the strategic importance of Malta and the fabulous bravery and sacrifice of its population, or to relate the daring exploits of the Servicemen based there. They not only fought off the enemy from the ground but also went forth to do battle with the enemy in aircraft, submarine and surface craft.

However, to appreciate the bomb disposal problem it is important to understand the intensity of the air attacks upon Malta. Malta is an island only 27 km (17 miles) long and 14.5 km (9 miles) broad. In 1940 it had a population of nearly 250,000 plus over 15,000 troops. It is situated 96.5 km (60 miles) south of Sicily and 290 km (180 miles) from the north African coast. This small island endured almost constant air attack for three years. During April 1942 a greater weight of bombs fell on Malta than fell on London during the worst three months of the blitz.

It is, therefore, appropriate before dealing with the detailed work and experiences of the bomb disposal personnel, to consider exactly what happened during those three years of almost daily air attacks.

At midnight on 10 June 1940 Italy declared war on Great Britain and France. At the same time Malta was thus formally at war with both Italy and Germany. Within seven hours, at 06:55 hours on 11 June 1940 to be exact, the first Italian bombers attacked Malta. Their initial target was the airfield at Hal Far. That same day there were a total of seven bombing attacks against nominally military targets, but because of the compactness of the island, civilian targets were also hit. A total of eleven civilians and seven members of the Royal Malta Artillery were killed. On that day the first unexploded bomb was dealt with by a combined Royal Engineer/Royal Army Ordnance Corps team.

For the next eight days air raids by the Regia Aeronautica (Italian Air Force) continued without a break. On 19 and 20 June 1940 there was a lull but this was abruptly ended by the first night attack on the night of 21/22 June. Attacks continued intermittently until December 1940 but, from the German point of view, with little success (although on 5 September successful dive bombing attacks were made against the three airfields at Luqa, Hal Far and Ta'Qali). So in December Luftwaffe units moved into Sicily to solve the 'Malta Problem'.

On 10 January 1941 the British aircraft carrier HMS *Illustrious* limped into Grand Harbour at Valletta having been attacked and hit several times by Luftwaffe aircraft based in Sicily. Repairs were immediately put in hand, but the presence of this capital ship soon attracted increased enemy attention. On 16 January 1941 the first full blitz against Malta began. It was an attack by over one hundred aircraft, of which about half were bombers. HMS *Illustrious* was the main target, but thanks to an excellent box barrage supplied by the Gunners and attacks by Royal Air Force Hurricanes and Fulmars, the ship was hit only once. However, the densely populated areas surrounding the dockyard were badly damaged. The brunt of the attack was felt by the Three Cities area (Senglea, Vittoriosa and Cospicua) and to a lesser extent by Valletta. For the next few days attacks continued against the *Illustrious* and against the Royal Air Force airfields at Luqa and Hal Far. The ship was not hit but the areas around the dockyard were gradually reduced to rubble. As will be seen later the Germans were using every possible weapon to prevent the repair of *Illustrious*. However, at dusk on 23 January 1941 she sailed from Grand Harbour under her own power and managed to reach Alexandria, a thousand miles away in Egypt. From here she eventually went on to the United States of America for major repairs.

The departure of HMS *Illustrious* brought no respite for the hard-pushed inhabitants of Malta. During the first three months of 1941 there were over 250 air attacks. Little did anyone realize that within a year 250 would become the monthly rate of attack, ie, eight attacks a day every day. In May 1941 a new peril and mode of destruction was introduced. This was the parachute mine, initially intended for the harbour and sea approaches, but as demonstrated during the attacks upon the United Kingdom, a most effective blast weapon against buildings and a major problem when it failed to explode.

Between May and November 1941 there was a short respite as the Luftwaffe was withdrawn from Sicily to take part in the German invasion of the Soviet Union. The Italian Air Force continued their attacks at the rate of about fifty a month but with far fewer aircraft and with a greatly reduced effectiveness. In part this was due to the arrival of reinforcement Hurricanes from the aircraft carriers HMS *Ark Royal, Furious, Victorious* and *Argus*.

In November 1941 the Luftwaffe returned to Sicily in the shape of Fliegerkorps II and the rate of attacks against Malta quickly rose from 78 in November to 263 in January 1942. In these attacks the enemy clearly aimed at military targets in what they thought was the final assault before the surrender of Malta. The airfields at Hal Far and Ta'Qali were prime targets as it was from these that Royal Air Force bombers were striking back at the enemy's sea movements to and from north Africa. In April

1942 there were 282 separate attacks and death and destruction were everywhere. During the single week ending 25 April 1942 well over a thousand enemy aircraft flew over the island and during the whole month a total of 6,834 tonnes (6,727 tons) of bombs were dropped, just under half of which were dropped on the dockyard area.

It was at this low point that His Majesty King George VI sent the following message to Malta on 15 April 1942: 'To honour her brave people I award the George Cross to the Island Fortress of Malta to bear witness to a heroism and devotion that will long be famous in history'.

After the peak of attacks in April 1942, Malta continued to be bombed but at an ever-decreasing rate until the Luftwaffe launched its final fling against the island on 10 October 1942. The attack lasted for ten days and then collapsed. By December 1942 the monthly rate of attacks had dropped to 35 and by February 1943 the rate had fallen to a mere five. On 20 June 1943 His Majesty King George VI visited the island, almost exactly three years after the first bomb fell on an undamaged Malta.

It is against that background of furious air attacks spread over a prolonged period that the activities of the various bomb disposal teams of all three Services must be viewed. They were in the most part self-taught and at the end of a very long supply route when it came to specialized disposal equipment.

As we have seen, the first unexploded bomb was discovered following the very first air attack upon Malta on 11 June 1940. It was an Italian 100 kg (220 lb) bomb and was dealt with by Lieutenant W. M. Eastman, RAOC, Corporal C. A. Brewer, RE, Sapper W. D. Scott, RE, and Sapper D. MacDonald, RE. At this stage there were no qualified Army bomb disposal officers or men on the island. There were, however, two RAOC officers, Captain R. L. Jephson-Jones and the Lieutenant Eastman referred to above, who had both received ammunition training. Captain Jephson-Jones was a regular soldier who was first commissioned in 1925 and had been stationed in Malta since before the Second World War began. Lieutenant Eastman had volunteered in 1939 and had arrived in Malta in March 1940. These two officers had no special equipment, no trained staff and virtually no knowledge of German or Italian bombs. For manpower and technical assistance they obtained volunteers from 24 Fortress Company, RE. Thus an *ad hoc* bomb disposal section was established. It was commanded by Lieutenant Eastman and initially consisted of some fifteen non-commissioned officers and soldiers, all from 24 Fortress Company, RE. Although the records show this section as being commanded by Lieutenant Eastman, it was both he and Captain Jephson-Jones who dismantled every new type of bomb discovered in an effort to understand how they worked. Sapper W. D. Scott, RE, writing of this period said:

'He [Lieutenant Eastman] would make Corporal Brewer and I take cover and then carry out the first stage of defuzing then call us over to see what he had done. He would make Corporal Brewer take notes. This was carried on until the bomb was made safe. Sometimes the operation would take over an hour. Corporal Brewer sometimes helped him if it needed more than one pair of hands. He also designed several tools for defuzing Italian bombs. He and Captain Jephson-Jones must have been responsible for saving many lives in the Middle East Land Forces when they too had to start dealing with Italian bombs. I believe they both retired as Brigadiers.'

Sapper Scott was quite correct for they both survived the war and retired as Brigadiers although, considering their activities during the first six months of the Malta attack, it is a miracle that they survived that period. In recognition of their work they were each awarded the George Cross on 24 December 1940.

In November 1940 the bomb disposal section was put on to a more constitutional footing with a trained and experienced Royal Engineer bomb disposal officer being put in charge. He was Lieutenant E. E. Talbot, GC, RE, who had received his George Cross whilst serving with 103 Bomb Disposal Section in Wales earlier in the year. He brought with him the latest 'state of the art' and the most recently developed equipment for dealing with German unexploded bombs. This was most fortunate as the German onslaught was to begin six weeks later in early January 1941. Indeed, the following members of the bomb disposal section were to be specially commended for the dangerous and valuable work they undertook in dealing with a 1,000 kg (2,200 lb) unexploded bomb in Vittoriosa on 21 January 1941: Lieutenant Talbot, Lance Sergeant R. C. Parker, Sapper D. McCarthy, Sapper L. Miller and Sapper J. Leonard.

Two months later another ten Sappers were to be commended for work on Hal Far and Luqa airfields between 26 February and 5 March 1941.

From the start of the Luftwaffe onslaught it is almost impossible to record the full workload of this Royal Engineer Section. By December 1942 its strength had risen to thirty, all of whom were extremely experienced men. Their type of bomb disposal differed in several ways to that practised in Great Britain. The major difference was occasioned by the nature of Malta's rocky surface. Most unexploded bombs were to be found lying on the surface or buried under the debris of buildings and only very rarely buried in the ground. Most of the work was, therefore, identification, defuzing or rendering safe and finally disposing of the bombs. Once again quoting from Sapper Scott:

'We did not defuze delayed-action bombs because of possible anti-withdrawal devices under the fuzes. Only officers and senior non-commissioned officers dealt with those. The responsibility for defuzing and the removal of unexploded bombs fell mainly upon the non-commissioned officers and in many cases, Sappers. It was a sheer impossibility to work to the procedures used in Great Britain. The officer dealt with what he could, mainly the tricky ones. It was a case of whoever started the job went on to complete it no matter what rank they were. We were all very highly trained in bomb disposal work as most of us were working on unexploded bombs every day of the week and for many of us this went on for three years. Our officers always insisted that we carry out the proper procedures at the bomb and no matter what the backlog was we were not allowed to take short

cuts. We always defuzed German bombs by remote control. We suffered no casualties from actual bomb disposal work. We have to thank our officers for that as they always said our lives were more important than buildings.'

During the three years of constant bombing many hundreds of unexploded bombs with long-delay fuzes and anti-withdrawal devices were dealt with. Similarly, large numbers of Italian and German anti-personnel bombs, designed to explode if they were disturbed, were also cleared. The fact that there were no fatal casualties among the Royal Engineer bomb disposal team reflects great credit upon their discipline, training, experience and professionalism. Sapper Scott, quoted above, was awarded the BEM for his work in Malta and survived the war. He was the Squadron Sergeant Major of an Assault Squadron, RE, in 1953 and has since retired to Devon.

In October 1941 Lieutenant Talbot was offered a ride in a Royal Air Force Wellington bomber on an operational sortie. He accepted and regrettably was killed whilst flying the mission. Command of the bomb disposal section was given to Lieutenant T. W. T. Blackwell, MBE, RE, another experienced bomb disposal officer. One of his men described him thus:

'He was a fine bomb disposal officer who never became excited. He always had that old pipe in his mouth, giving orders slowly and calmly. He did much to keep the morale of the section up during a bad period. When a raid was developing he used to climb on top of the barrack block in Linton Barracks with a local map and plot all the unexploded bombs as they fell. Through this we often had the bomb removed before it was reported.'

On assuming command Lieutenant Blackwell formally established two bomb disposal sections, Nos 127 and 128, as units separate from 24 Fortress Company, RE. The personnel, however, remained the same and still regarded themselves as part of 24 Fortress Company.

At this time Lieutenant Blackwell and his bomb disposal sections were to face the heaviest attacks so far experienced in Malta. The combined strength of his two sections was by that time 32 non-commissioned officers and men. During April 1942 stories of heroism, death and lucky escapes abounded. Yet the escape most remembered by the people of Malta, and on occasions credited with divine intervention, occurred on 9 April 1942. On that day a stick of bombs fell around the huge dome of Mosta Church and failed to explode. An eye witness in the church, the Reverend Salvatore Magro said:

'At about 16:40 hours one of the bombs pierced the dome, bounced twice off the wall, skidded the whole length of the church and finally came to rest without exploding. At the time there were about 300 people attending a service and, while the majority sought refuge in the side chapels, some remained kneeling. The dome was damaged but inexplicably no one was injured.'

When the Sappers who dealt with the bomb were questioned they said: 'It

Above left *Royal Engineer Bomb Disposal Squad. Standing: Lieutenant E. E. Talbot, GC, Lance Sergeant R. Parker, GM, Lance Corporal Hillier, Sappers Miller, McCarthy, Leonard, Reeves and Corporal Brewer. Sitting: Sergeant Piggott, Sappers Turner and Lockyer.*

Right *The dome of the Parish church at Mosta after an unexploded bomb pierced it on 9 April 1942.*

was just one of many. It was a 500 kg (1,100 lb) bomb with a simple impact fuze. It was defuzed where it lay against the wall of the vestry and taken to our bomb dump. The local people asked for the bomb back, so we steamed the explosive out, gave it a coat of paint and handed it over to the Church.' (It is still there.)

This was, indeed, just one of many incidents and in this case there was relatively little danger to the bomb disposal men once the bomb had come to rest. However, in another incident in which Lieutenant Blackwell was personally involved some three months later there was danger throughout the operation. At about 22:00 hours on 30 July 1942 a number of delayed-action bombs (ie, fitted with No 17 fuzes) were dropped in Birkirkara. One of these bombs, by its sheer size and weight, partially destroyed a house in a densely populated and built-up area, burying a number of civilians. The bomb was just visible amid the debris. On arrival at the site Lieutenant Blackwell discovered that the bomb contained two No 17 fuzes, both of them ticking. He could not remove the fuzes, either by hand or remotely, for fear that they were protected by anti-withdrawal devices, which would detonate the bomb and so kill the people buried in the rubble. He, therefore, decided to remove the bomb as quickly as possible, fully appreciating that it could explode at any moment. As no lifting tackle was available he considered the only alternative was to drag the bomb away. It was first necessary to clear a path through the rubble along which the bomb could be pulled. Lieutenant Blackwell, assisted by Police Constable J. Baylis, a local policeman, duly cleared a path. Lieutenant Blackwell then tried to haul the bomb clear using a truck with a rope attached to the bomb. The layout of the street was such that the maximum length of tow rope which could be used was 3.6 m (12 ft). The first attempt failed when the bomb became jammed in the debris. It was then obvious that two persons were required, one to drive the truck and the other to guide the bomb clear of the debris. Police Constable Baylis volunteered to drive the truck and with Lieutenant Blackwell guiding the bomb the operation was successfully completed. The bomb was then taken to a safe place and disposed of. During the process of removing the bomb from the damaged house another bomb which had been dropped at the same time exploded, reminding Lieutenant Blackwell and Police Constable Baylis that the time on 'their' bomb was also running out. For this operation Police Constable Baylis was awarded the BEM and Lieutenant Blackwell the George Medal. Sadly, as the George Medal citation relates, the people buried under the house were dead when recovered. 'The fact that the people buried under the debris of the house on which this bomb had fallen were, when extricated, found to be dead, does not detract from the gallantry of the action of Lieutenant Blackwell and Police Constable Baylis'.

Throughout the campaign against Malta a wide range of Italian and German bombs were used. In the main they were thick-walled bombs designed to penetrate the fortress bastions within which vital supplies of

ITALIAN BOMB 4AR (THERMOS)

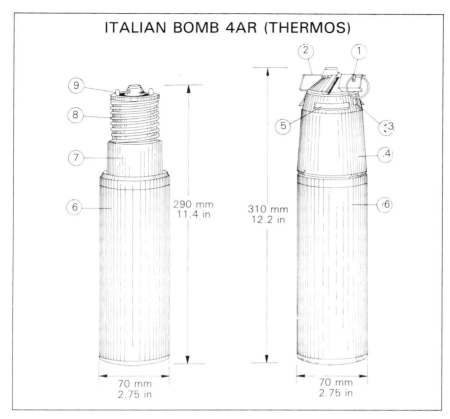

290 mm
11.4 in

310 mm
12.2 in

70 mm
2.75 in

70 mm
2.75 in

The 4 AR (4 kg Armamento Retardato — Delayed Arming) was given the nickname the Thermos Bomb because of its general resemblance, when complete, to a picnic thermos flask.

Description: *The safety pin (1) passes through one of the vanes on the vaned cap (2) and into a slot (3) in the aluminium cup (4). This pin is removed before the bomb is dropped, thus allowing the vanes to rotate as the bomb falls. The cup (4) has three projections (5) formed by cutting the metal and bending the tab outwards.*

Operation: *On release from the aircraft the vaned cap (2) unscrews and falls away, the air catches the projections (5) and pulls the cup (4) from the bomb. The removal of the cup releases the primary safety devices from the Manzolini fuze. The bomb now looks like the left hand drawing. When the bomb hits the ground the secondary safety devices are released and after a period of a few seconds the bomb is fully armed. The bomb will now detonate upon receiving a sudden jerk or jolt. The main identification features of an armed bomb are, the green or sand coloured body (6), the black steel collar (7), the heavy steel spring (8) and the brass fuze cover (9).*

food and ammunition were stored. There were, however, three types of bombs which deserve special mention. First, there were the small anti-personnel bombs designed to slow down repair work on the airfields and disrupt the everyday work of debris clearance, rescue and general sur-vival. Anti-personnel bombs were dropped on Malta by both the Germans and Italians. The German bomb was the SD 2 (Spreng Dickenwand 2 kg

—explosive thick-walled 2 kg), more commonly known as the butterfly bomb. The Italian bomb was the 4 AR (4 kg Armamento Retardato—4 kg delayed arming), usually known as the thermos bomb. Both had fuzes designed so that the bombs did not explode on initial impact with the ground but were subsequently extremely sensitive to any movement. A proportion of each nation's bombs were fitted with a variant of the fuze just described. This alternative fuze contained an additional hazard in that, if left undisturbed, it would explode the bomb at a predetermined period of up to eighty hours after being dropped.

A description of the German butterfly bomb and the problems it caused wherever it fell is provided in Chapter 6. The thermos bomb was so called because it was 310 mm (12.2 in) long, 70 mm (2.75 in) in diameter and had, with a little imagination, the appearance of a small picnic thermos flask. It had a lethality range of approximately 30 m (98 ft) and a maximum fragmentation range of up to 275 m (300 yd). The recommended method of disposal for these bombs was initially to leave them alone for four days in the hope that they would destroy themselves. After four days, or earlier should they be in a location where their removal was essential, the recommended means of clearing them was, in order of priority:

To shoot at them—not very practical if inside a building or in an area where people might be within range of ricochets.

To destroy them by placing a small explosive charge close to but not touching them and then fire the charge—this was not always practical if the bombs were close to a piece of vital equipment such as an aircraft.

To place a loop of string around the bomb, taking care not to disturb it, and then from a distance or from behind cover, jerk it. This method involved a very real risk to the bomb disposal man and suffered from the same shortcomings as placing a charge against the bomb.

In each of the above methods, except shooting at them, it was often necessary to build a small sandbag wall around the bomb to reduce the effect of the explosion, again exposing the working party to a considerable risk. The final option was carefully to carry the bomb to a safe area for disposal. On occasions this was done by carrying the bomb in a horizontal position and not subjecting it to any vibration, an extremely hazardous pastime. There are a number of recorded cases where civilians picked up these nasties and took them to the local police station—and lived. These people were either extremely lucky or the bombs were genuine 'duds'. There were many more cases of people picking up thermos bombs and being killed instantly.

One member of the Royal Engineer bomb disposal team (Sapper C. E. Reeves) who was involved in the clearance of these bombs in Malta recalls that: 'The most disturbing and frightening part of our Section's work was the clearance of thermos bombs. I think they were the most inhuman and unnerving of all the jobs we had to do. I believe that each of the lads who covered those jobs deserved much more recognition than they received— in most cases nil.'

In fact, nearly a third of the section were commended for their work during this period. Unfortunately, when working in a situation where to be brave is normal, it demands a far higher standard to achieve recognition than might be required elsewhere. Sapper Reeves continues:

'I remember one day when we dealt with a large number of these bombs. At that time we were told to blow them up where they were or to move them by remote control, ie, pull them with a piece of string. The first was in a jeweller's window in Valletta. He begged us not to blow it up but to take it to the police station. This we could not do, so we asked him to take out his goods from the window but on no account to touch the bomb. He would not go near it, so one of the lads removed his stock for him and then we pulled the bomb. We made an awful mess but at least his stock was safe. Later at Rabat, the local policeman met us and showed us where the bombs were—we dealt with three. Then another report came in; there was another bomb— on the policeman's own bed! Even by putting down a lot of sandbags it still left quite a mess.'

Sapper Reeves survived his experiences in Malta and by 1953 was Regimental Sergeant Major of 32 Assault Regiment, RE. During this same period one of his Squadron Sergeant Majors was the Sapper Scott referred to earlier.

The second type of bomb worthy of special mention was the German rocket-assisted bomb, the PC 500 RS or the larger PC 1000 RS (Panzer-

German rocket-assisted bomb (PC 500 RS) recovered on 4 January 1942. Key **A.** *AP bomb 500 kg* **B.** *Suspension band* **C.** *HE fuze and gaine holder 4½ lb* **D.** *Side fuze pocket* **E.** *Rocket holder* **F.** *Tail fragments* **G.** *Venturi tubes* **H.** *Tail locating webs* **J.** *End cap 118 lb* **K.** *Rocket container 190 lb* **L.** *Distance piece*

durchschlagscylindrisch 500 kg/1,000 kg Raketensatz—500 or 1,000 kg armour-piercing bomb with rocket attachment). These were armour-piercing bombs to which were attached six rockets. These bombs were originally designed for use against warships or other heavily-protected targets. They were, therefore, ideal against Malta with its many heavily-protected locations. The purpose of the rockets was to increase the velocity of the bomb and so assist it to penetrate its target. They also enabled the bomb to be dropped accurately at low level and yet still hit the ground at the same speed as if it had been dropped in free fall from a much greater height. Its impact velocity was in fact in excess of 1,000 km/h or 900 ft/sec. (Details of this bomb are shown in Annex B.) Eye-witnesses who saw these bombs fall said that they accelerated with a tremendous roar and left a trail of flame about 50 m (54 yd) across the sky.

These bombs were first dropped on Malta on 1 January 1942 and a member of the Royal Engineer team sent to deal with one of the unexploded examples said:

'The bomb call reported that there was an unexploded bomb hole in the pavement outside a church in Floriana. When we arrived we found two holes, not one. After a quick look at both holes, it was fairly obvious that the bomb had gone in one end and out the other but we had to find it or prove that it had exploded. There were no new shrapnel marks on the nearby building, so while the search for the bomb went on we probed the holes. We quickly found an obstruction and started to dig for it. As we dug we found, as expected, parts of a tail fin. Then we became very wary and not a little worried as we came across bits of wire, pipes and components we could not recognize. The usual slick working became slower and more meticulous as we continued to dig. Eventually we unearthed the propulsion unit of our first rocket bomb. The business end of the bomb was found by Lieutenant Blackwell about 137 m (150 yd) away on the top of a very high bastion. Later we heard that these bombs were intended to penetrate the bastions and to demolish the grain stores. I did not know we had any grain at that time. We were living on hard biscuits.'

The third type of bomb of special interest fell on Malta in January 1941 while HMS *Illustrious* was being repaired. As discussed earlier she was a prime target and very many bombs intended for the *Illustrious* fell in the Three Cities area. The story of this particular bomb is best told by Lance Sergeant R. C. M. Parker, RE (later to become Major R. C. M. Parker, GM, RE), a senior non-commissioned officer in the Royal Engineer bomb disposal section.

'A call came to deal with a bomb in the Three Cities area. On arrival at the site we were of the opinion that a bomb had gone off. We believed this because of the amount of damage that faced us. What we later learnt had been a nunnery, had collapsed into a mountain of stone and rubble. Fortunately it had been evacuated prior to the raids. This nunnery was in a narrow street of steps. It had been several storeys high and was originally attached to similar buildings on either side. The adjacent buildings were now also in a very shaky state. It was obvious that we either had something very large in the form of a bomb, or that something large had crashed into it. We considered the possibility of a crashed aircraft or part of one.

Cases had been met of complete engines crashing down and this might be such a case. Initial examination of the area revealed nothing to confirm our views.

At this early stage we were hampered by numbers of wild cats. These were the poor animals left behind by the inhabitants. They were herded together in fear and were starving. They stubbornly barred our way and were very vicious. In the end we had to shoot some of them. We started to dig into the mountain of rubble and stones. This proved very difficult as we had no mechanical equipment. The location up the street of steps would have denied us using any heavy equipment even if we had it. After several days we had still found no evidence of a bomb having exploded. (Evidence had to be found consisting of blast marks or splinters from a bomb before we could abandon a reported unexploded bomb.) The excavation had reached the state of a funnel-shaped hole with steep sides down which occasional large building stones would crash. We had suffered minor bruises and cuts from such falls and I became worried that we might get more serious injuries as we worked in this funnel shape. We were told to get proof one way or the other, so we enlarged the diameter of the funnel-shaped hole, this process being repeated several times as we got deeper. After a few more days and the removal of tons of stone and rubble, we found pieces of cast light alloy, some wire, and what seemed like pieces of electrical equipment. Our thoughts again returned to the possibility of an aircraft crash, or part of one. When seeking buried bombs the first thing to come to light is the tail or part of it. This would be of sheet metal not the cast alloy painted sky blue that we had found. On reporting the situation to our Headquarters with our opinion, we noted that it caused some excitement and were told that we possibly had some sort of new bomb to contend with. We were told to proceed with caution.

Again we decided to enlarge the diameter of our funnel-shaped hole prior to deepening it. At last we got to the ground floor level in our enlarged excavation, finding more of the light alloy blue painted pieces. In the floor was a hole with sky blue paint marks around its edge. At this stage we discovered that there were cellars, and that the ground floor was in a dangerous state, broken through in some places and liable to collapse under the mountain of rubble.

Looking into the hole with the aid of a torch, we could just see a cylindrical shape painted sky blue partly covered with rubble from the damaged floor. We again cleared the area, enlarged the hole, which fortunately was not over the bomb, and got into the cellars. We cleared the rubble from the bomb and found it to be the largest we had seen to date, and of such a shape that we had not before encountered. As the bomb lay we could not see any fuzes. This we reported to our Headquarters who confirmed that it was as they expected, a new type of guided bomb and we were to proceed with great care, doing our best to recover it intact. We propped up the ground floor with timber and enlarged the hole still further to allow us to work in the cellars with some degree of safety.

Our first problem was to render the brute safe by removing the fuzes. We attempted this in the cellars after rolling the bomb over to reveal the fuzes. We found that the fuzes were not of the delayed action type or anti-handling variety. Our efforts to remove the fuzes were unsuccessful as the retaining screw rings had been so damaged when the bomb crashed through the building that we could not move them. We had no wish to use excessive force in the still shaky cellars. I presented these facts to our Headquarters and suggested that we blew the thing up where it stood. To move the bomb would be dangerous and the problem of getting it out of the cellar through the crumbling hole and down the street of steps was immense. There was the problem too of moving it out of the densely built-up area of the Three Cities. We were told bluntly to recover it fuzed or not and take every precaution possible.

The removal of this bomb was a worrying problem. It was an awkward shape, very heavy (we later discovered it weighed 1,400 kg/3,086 lb) and its fuzes were still very much alive. We had to lift it out of the cellar, through the floor and then on to the street of steps. All this with the minimum of vibration. By means of blocks and tackles, the rigging of steel girders across the excavation to adjacent shaky buildings and using brute force where all else failed, we managed at last to get it on to the street of steps. Here we again tried to remove the fuzes as the bomb lay in the street, but without success. Our next problem we had foreseen and had built in our Floriana barracks a heavy wooden sledge. This we used to carry the bomb gently down the street of steps and round a corner. This was achieved using 'hold back' tackles and pulling ropes, all operated from under cover as much as possible. Having got the bomb to a normal road we were at last able to load it, still on its sledge, into a lorry, and drive it out into the country. It was a relief to get away from the Three Cities and the dockyard area where we were constantly being bombed, although to a lesser degree once the *Illustrious* departed. It had been very frightening sitting in that cellar, or working in the hazardous funnel-shaped excavation with bombs dropping around us from time to time. The sense of foreboding in our isolated situation in what seemed a dead city heightened by the wild and starving cats with their pitiful throaty cries was weird and frightening in itself.

At our safer area we at last managed to remove the damaged fuzes. To achieve this we had to resort to hammer and chisels and the normal principles of treating fuzes gently had to be ignored. What a relief it was to get the fuzes and exploders out. We then ceased to call the bomb a beast. We could now admire the bomb and its obvious excellent finish. Our Headquarters told us that the bomb was an armour-piercing type designed to penetrate the armoured decks of capital ships and that when dropped it had stub wings and a tail, permitting it to glide to some degree. They added that when dropped the bomb was capable of being guided by radio from the dropping aircraft. Our bomb had obviously been intended for the *Illustrious*'.

Details of this bomb are given in Annex B, but there is undoubtedly a mystery over this particular one in Malta. Lance Sergeant Parker was awarded the George Medal for the incident and his citation refers to a bomb of a new type. The only bomb which matches his description is the SD 1400 X, a 1,400 kg (3,080 lb) radio-controlled armour-piercing bomb, yet this bomb is not thought to have been used operationally until 1943. As described in Chapter 8 the bomb was used most effectively in September 1943 against both the Italian battleship *Roma* and the British battleship HMS *Warspite*. It must, therefore, be assumed that Lance Sergeant Parker's bomb was a very early experimental version. He cannot be further questioned as, although he survived the war and retired from the Army as a Major, he died in June 1983 aged 66. For the historically interested the Convent referred to in this incident was in Scholastic Street, Vittorioso.

Before leaving the story of the Royal Engineers bomb disposal section

Right *Typical bomb damage in Malta.*

Below *The Royal Opera House in Valletta after an air attack on 7 April 1942.*

School at Senglea destroyed during an attack on HMS Illustrious, 19 January 1941.

in Malta mention must be made again of Corporal C. A. Brewer, RE. He was there assisting with the first unexploded bomb on 11 June 1940 and remained in the thick of it until the last bomb had fallen. When reading of almost any tricky incident relating to army bomb disposal in Malta the name of Corporal 'Busty' Brewer crops up. It is upon such men as these that so much depends when small groups of men are put under pressure. The best citation for Corporal Brewer is that written by Warrant Officer Scott who, it will be remembered, worked as a Sapper with Corporal Brewer and Lieutenant Eastman during those first vital months in 1940 and who stayed in Corporal Brewer's detachment throughout the siege.

'Whenever we speak of bomb disposal in Malta or think about it, 'Busty' is always first in our thoughts. He was a pre-war Corporal who volunteered for bomb disposal the day war was declared. In this work he had at last found his goal. He was an outstanding bomb disposal non-commissioned officer and was given responsibilities far beyond his rank. He was fearless without being foolish. He seemed to us to have an uncanny second sight when it came to fuzes. When at times, after twelve to fourteen hours of dealing with bombs, we felt we could not carry on for another minute, 'Busty' could get that extra effort out of us. He did not suffer fools gladly and was rather outspoken to his seniors if he thought they were wrong. This may be why he remained a Corporal for so long.'

Corporal Brewer was awarded the British Empire Medal in 1942 and

Warrant Officer Scott will be pleased to know that he was eventually promoted to the rank of Sergeant. Sergeant C. A. Brewer, BEM, RE, died on 14 May 1981.

The Royal Air Force in Malta depended, as in Great Britain, very largely upon their armament warrant officers and non-commissioned officers to clear the unexploded bombs from their airfields. Since the airfields were legitimate military targets, they and the dockyards were the primary targets of both the Regia Aeronautica and the Luftwaffe. In the early months their objective was to destroy the Royal Air Force's fighter aircraft and the airfields from which they operated. In later months and years, as Malta became a base for offensive airborne operations, the attacks upon the airfields became even more concentrated.

Under these conditions it is not surprising that detailed records of the bombs dealt with were not always kept. However, it is clear from the records which do exist that the enemy task was not only to destroy the airfields using bombs with direct-acting fuzes—it was also their objective to prevent the speedy repair of damaged airfields. This was attempted by including a large number of bombs with No 17 long-delay fuzes and No 50 anti-disturbance fuzes. In addition, many hundreds of anti-personnel bombs were dropped. Their presence immediately slowed down repair work as men are understandably loath to work in areas where small bombs are exploding at random intervals. In effect this meant that repair work could only be fully completed after the delayed-action and anti-personnel bombs had been removed, detonated or otherwise rendered safe.

With the large bombs the normal practice was to remove the simple direct impact fuzes and take the bombs away to an area where they could be disposed of at a later date. When clockwork long delay fuzes were found they were either destroyed where they were or, if near a critical installation or vital piece of equipment, great risks had to be taken either to move them away or attempt to remove the critical equipment. An idea of what life was like for a Royal Air Force armourer during the first two years of the siege can best be exemplified by the experiences recorded by Flight Lieutenant D. Bishop, GM, RAF.

He arrived in Malta in 1940 as a Sergeant Fitter/Armourer. A few weeks after his arrival at Luqa he was promoted Flight Sergeant and told he was responsible to the Station Armament Warrant Officer for bomb disposal on the airfield. At this stage he had no knowledge of bomb disposal and so was given a day's instruction by his superior, Warrant Officer Woolsencroft. During the next few months Flight Sergeant Bishop continued his armament duties and undertook bomb disposal as a frequent sideline. At this stage he was dealing with only one or two bombs a day. This qualified him as an experienced bomb disposal man and he was promoted to acting Warrant Officer and posted to Hal Far airfield. Whereas Luqa had been a bomber station Hal Far was a fighter and torpedo bomber station and, therefore, a mixed Royal Navy/Royal Air Force base. At Hal Far the tempo of bombing had increased and Warrant

Officer Bishop found bomb disposal a full-time task. He was even allocated a light-tracked vehicle to enable him to get around his parish. In the vehicle he carried a stethoscope borrowed from the Station Sick Quarters, the explosives and accessories necessary to detonate a bomb, a set of hand tools, a red flag and a whistle. The latter two items were to warn both the control tower and anyone in his vicinity that he was going to cause an explosion.

He described his actions when called to a bomb as follows:

'Prior to going on the airfield I would tell the officer in the control tower where I was going. He would then keep a watch on me through his binoculars. When I reached the bomb I would carry out an inspection of the bomb and the fuze. If it was a dud, ie, a No 15 direct impact fuze which had failed to go off, I would remove the fuze, separate the gaine from the fuze and report my findings to the tower. Finally I would tell some of my armourers to go and remove the bomb. If I found the bomb was fitted with a No 17 fuze I would use the stethoscope and listen to hear if the fuze was ticking. It inevitably was, and that meant action at the double. First of all I would have a quick look around the area to see where I could find safe cover for myself at not too great a distance. Then I would prepare a demolition charge and place it on the bomb. I would then wave my red flag furiously until the control tower acknowledged seeing it by firing two red signal cartridges. After a few blasts on my whistle I would light the fuze of the demolition charge and take cover. Following the explosion I would wait for the debris to finish falling and then inspect the scene. If all was clear I would signal the control tower by laying down my flag and they would fire a green signal cartridge indicating that all was clear.'

However, not all actions were quite as simple as that. On 1 May 1942 Warrant Officer Bishop had just gone to bed when he was called out because a bomb had fallen beside a Royal Naval Albacore torpedo bomber and failed to explode. Furthermore, the aircraft had a torpedo on board. He dressed and was driven over to where the bomb had been reported. The bomb, a 500 kg (1,100 lb), lay approximately 6 m (19.6 ft) from the torpedo-laden aircraft, one of three prepared for a mission that night. Using a stethoscope he quickly realized that he had two No 17 fuzes, both ticking. The only answer was to move the aircraft. He returned to the control tower and contacted the Naval Squadron Commander. He told him that there was nothing he could do to the bomb and his advice was to move the aircraft as quickly as possible. This the officer would not do because, as he explained, there were more aircraft available, but there were no more men if the bomb exploded while they were moving the aircraft.

Warrant Officer Bishop was not happy about this and went to have another look at the bomb, knowing full well that it could explode at any moment. This time he noticed that the bomb case was split and that the complete fuze pocket appeared to be free from the bomb. He knew he dare not try removing just the fuze because there was always the risk of an anti-withdrawal device beneath the fuze. This would cause the bomb to explode as soon as he began to remove the fuze. However, there was the possibility that he could remove the complete fuze pocket. Slipping his

'...*so he gave a strong pull and tore the pocket from the bomb.*'

fingers into the crack he located the fuze pocket and began to gently ease the powdered explosive away from the pocket. This took some time and that was something of which he had very little. He therefore removed his hand, grasped the rim of the fuze pocket and tentatively wriggled it. Nothing happened, so he gave a strong pull and tore the pocket from the bomb. He repeated the process with the second fuze pocket and hurried away carrying the two pockets, either of which was still liable to explode, killing him and damaging the aircraft. He ran to a bomb crater and left the fuze pockets in the hole. He then returned to the control tower and spoke to the Naval Squadron Commander, reporting what he had done.

The next morning the Command Armament Officer, Squadron Leader Hardiman, congratulated him on his previous night's work, called him a 'bloody fool' and told him not to dare do that again as he, Bishop, was more valuable to the Armament Section than all the aircraft on the island. Together they visited the bomb crater in which Warrant Officer Bishop had placed the fuze pockets. One had detonated and so damaged the second that it was inoperative. This the Squadron Leader took away for investigation. It was subsequently shown that under the No 17 fuze there was a ZUS 40 anti-withdrawal device. Had Warrant Officer Bishop attempted to take out the fuze rather than the whole pocket he would certainly have been killed and the aircraft destroyed. Two months later he was awarded the George Medal for his bomb disposal exploits.

At the end of 1941 a Royal Air Force Bomb Disposal Squad under the command of Flight Lieutenant H. B. H. Dickinson, RAFVR, was posted to Malta. This team had gained previous bomb disposal experience in Great Britain and visited the three airfields to discuss the local problems. At this stage it was suggested that Warrant Officer Bishop should keep a record of all bombs he dealt with as this would be of assistance to the Air Ministry. This he did and later noted that during the next two months he dealt with just under 200 bombs.

Flight Lieutenant Dickinson and his team arrived just in time to face the renewed attack by the Luftwaffe. It was at this stage that a very close rapport developed between the Royal Air Force and the Army bomb disposal teams, each working in each other's areas of responsibility as the situation demanded. The Army were regular visitors to all three airfields, especially after attacks which involved the use of the small German anti-personnel bomb. Following one attack over 500 butterfly bombs had to be cleared and such an operation was extremely labour intensive. Royal Engineer assistance was requested and willingly given.

In July 1942 Flight Lieutenant Dickinson was awarded the George Medal for his work during this particularly hard period, hard for both Malta in general and the bomb disposal groups in particular. His citation said:

'He has shown outstanding courage, initiative and devotion to duty. He had some experience in dealing with unexploded bombs prior to arriving in Malta and when intensive and almost continuous air attacks were commenced against the island he volunteered for bomb disposal duties. Despite deficiencies of necessary equipment for dealing with the tremendous number of unexploded bombs which had been dropped on the airfields, he succeeded in disposing of all the bombs which would otherwise delay operations and traffic. This dangerous work has been performed while enemy air attacks were in progress. He has displayed remarkable powers of leadership and indomitable courage and the utmost confidence has been placed in him by the members of the bomb disposal squad. He has shown fine initiative and sound judgement in all jobs which have entailed great risk.'

In the Royal Air Force, as in the other Services, there were many members of bomb disposal teams whose names have not been included in unit histories or in books such as this. In Malta, as elsewhere, a number of junior ranks received decorations for spectacular acts of bravery such as saving pilots from the sea or from burning aircraft. But remember too the cool courage needed to assist in the removal of a bomb when all around are under cover and an air raid is in progress. These, the unnamed workers, deserve our recognition and respect.

Like the Royal Air Force, the Royal Navy was responsible for bomb disposal in what can only be described as a prime target, namely the dockyard and its surroundings. The Royal Navy were responsible for a wide range of explosive items deployed by the enemy against Malta and its sea approaches. These included sea mines, torpedoes and the infamous Italian one-man torpedoes. These were dealt with by such gallant officers and men as Lieutenant Commander W. H. Hiscock, GC, DSC, RN (who was killed with his wife only twelve days after his George Cross was gazetted), Lieutenant E. D. Woolley, GM and Bar, RNVR, Petty Officer C. le Bargy, DSM, GM, RN, Chief Mechanic's Mate L. Hanlon, GM, BEM, RN, and Leading Seaman H. A. Gray, GM, RN.

However, this is the story of bomb disposal. As in the United Kingdom, Naval responsibility for bomb disposal was vested in one or more Bomb Safety Officers (BSO) and their small team of assistants. As elsewhere in the world the BSO reported direct to the DUBD at the Admiralty. The BSOs in Malta during the period 1941 to May 1943 were Lieutenant C. Rowlands, RNVR, and Sub Lieutenant C. StJ. Ellis, GM,RNVR. The latter had been awarded the George Medal for work in Plymouth during March 1941. Their actual arrival dates are uncertain but Lieutenant Rowlands was certainly dealing with bombs in January 1941 and Sub Lieutenant Ellis was doing likewise by May 1941. During the period 1941 to 1943 Lieutenant Rowlands was awarded two George Medals for quite outstanding work. Not only did he render bombs safe, he also reported in great detail his findings in respect of new bombs, fuzes or bomb markings. In fact his records still exist and show that after a long day and frequently a long night too, he prepared a full report for the DUBD in respect of each bomb dealt with during the preceding day. These reports showed the type of fuze in the bomb, all markings on the bomb and fuze, where the bomb had fallen (often with a little thumb-nail sketch) and finally his actions in rendering the bomb safe. Sub Lieutenant Ellis produced similar reports and these can only reflect the dedication displayed by these two officers.

The bombs they dealt with ranged in size from 1,000 kg (2,200 lb) down to the deadly 2 kg (4.4 lb) anti-personnel butterfly bomb. The following two stories give a good indication of their respective dedication to work.

On 20 April 1942 Sub Lieutenant Ellis was a patient in the Imtarfa hospital (for what reason history does not record) when a 500 kg (1,100 lb) bomb fell beside the wall of the main hospital block and failed to explode. At that time the April blitz was at its height and Sub Lieutenant Ellis knew that the Royal Engineer bomb disposal sections were fully committed. He therefore, whilst still a patient, went to the bomb, removed the fuze and declared the bomb safe. The bomb was subsequently collected by the Royal Engineers. Lieutenant Rowlands commented on the report written by Sub Lieutenant Ellis, 'This bomb was causing so much inconvenience that Sub Lieutenant Ellis considered his action justifiable. The Army he knew to be busy elsewhere; and being a patient on the spot, there was no delay in rendering it safe.'

Possibly Lieutenant Rowlands felt bound to support the action since he had done a similar thing only two days previously. His report records that on 18 April 1942 at 16:49 hours a 50 kg (110 lb) bomb dropped on to a house at 13 St Margaret Street, Sliema, and ended up lying on the drawing room floor. He commented: 'This bomb was in a house opposite my residence and was dropped by a fighter bomber. As several people would have had to evacuate the area [presumably himself included], I removed the fuze from the bomb and dumped the bomb in Balluta Bay. Disposal completed 18:02 hours. Military informed.'

However, not all bombs were dealt with so easily. On 1 November 1941 Lieutenant Rowlands was tasked to deal with three Italian anti-personnel thermos bombs. One was in the Valletta Museum (which at that time was being used by the Cashiers' Department of HM Dockyard), one was in the Naval Picket House and the third was on the Naval Commander-in-Chief's tennis court. The bomb in the museum was lying on the floor of a top corridor. Lieutenant Rowlands, being fully aware of the danger in handling these bombs, tied a length of line to the nose of the bomb and from a safe distance gave it a violent horizontal jerk. Nothing happened. The line was then passed through a hole in the roof and the bomb given a violent vertical jerk. Again nothing happened. He then decided to carry the bomb out of the building. To do this he prepared a box half filled with sand and made a seating in the sand. He carefully lifted the bomb into the box, maintaining its horizontal position. He then carried the box and bomb down the stairs and through the street to the Naval Picket House. Here the second bomb was lying in a horizontal position just inside the entrance. Again he made a seating in the sand and carefully placed the second bomb in the box. As he left the Picket House a weeping Maltese woman ran up to him and spluttered 'Signor, Signor—bombi', pointing towards her house a short distance away. Knowing that the Royal Engineers were extremely busy in another area of Valletta, Lieutenant Rowlands decided to deal with her bomb. This one was lying in a horizontal position under a chair in the attic. It was impossible to move the chair without disturbing the bomb. He there-fore sawed through the chair at various points and removed parts of it until he could get at the bomb. He picked up the bomb very carefully and carried it down a narrow spiral staircase to the wooden box outside. (The staircase was so narrow that it had been impossible to carry the box up to the attic.) Having made a third seating in the sand he placed the bomb in the box. From here the box plus its three bombs was carried to the tennis court. The bomb on the tennis court could not be fitted into the box, so Lieutenant Rowlands placed a lump of concrete in front of the bomb and tied a line to it. The bomb was then jerked against the concrete block and exploded. The box, with its three bombs still sitting on their bed of sand, was carried to the bottom of Crucifix Hill by the sea wall. The first bomb, the one from the museum, was lifted carefully and dropped into the sea—nothing happened. The second bomb was treated similarly, but exploded on hitting the water. The explosion caused the box containing the third bomb to topple over into the water, when it also exploded.

Apart from the risk of any of these bombs exploding due to violent handling, there was always the risk that they were fitted with a timed self-destruct fuze which could have caused them to explode at any time, however gently they were handled. The fact that two did explode upon hitting the water emphasizes the risks taken by the BSO.

Some bombs could not always be taken away to be sea-dumped even when they had had their fuzes removed or rendered safe. An example of this occurred on 7 April 1942. A 1,000 kg (2,200 lb) bomb had fallen on to a house in Dockyard Terrace. The BSO arrived on the scene and was able to render the fuze safe using a fuze discharger. However, the bomb had come through the side of the house in such a way that it now supported the whole front of the building. To remove the bomb would mean the collapse of the front wall of the house. As was pointed out to the BSO, the front room of the house was used as a dockyard office. It was, therefore, agreed that the final disposal of the bomb would be delayed until 'the present office shortage on the island has improved'.

During the two-year period 1941 to 1943 Lieutenant Rowlands dealt with 85 large bombs, some forty small anti-personnel bombs and a rocket bomb. Lieutenant Ellis also dealt with a large number of bombs. All required a steady hand and a cool nerve. As with all the bomb disposal teams in Malta, large numbers of bombs were disposed of almost as a

Members of the Royal Navy assisted by civilians hoisting a mine ready for disposal.

matter of routine. Some of the bombs appear to have been treated in a most cavalier fashion but the majority of the 'disposaleers' survived to tell the tale. One who unfortunately did not was Commissioned Boatswain L. J. H. Sheldon, GM, RN. Having been awarded the George Medal for assisting Lieutenant Eastman (an RAOC officer) during the initial few months of the attack upon Malta, he volunteered to assist Lieutenant Rowlands with his BSO duties. From April 1941 he took charge of the volunteer party of Naval ratings who assisted the BSO in gaining access to the bombs and removing them once rendered safe. This was no mean task considering that in one month the BSO organization dealt with and dumped at sea over 13,000 kg (12.75 tons) of bombs. As a result of his work with Lieutenant Rowlands he was recommended for a Bar to his George Medal. Unfortunately he was killed before it could be awarded and so he received a posthumous Mention in Despatches. (It was not until 1977 that the George Medal could be awarded posthumously.)

Like so many other soldiers, sailors and airmen, the ratings who made up the BSO's bomb disposal party should not be forgotten—they shared the risks but rarely the recognition. These men were all volunteers from HMS *Fermoy*, an 'Aberdare' Class minesweeper, which had been bombed beyond repair in early May 1941. The following ratings worked with the BSO from 23 May 1941 and were still doing so at the end of the year: Leading Seaman C. Gallop, Able Seamen R. Hunt, C. Richardson and S. Wakefield, and Stoker T. McKenna. They all received instruction on bomb disposal equipment and the general components of the various bombs they were likely to encounter. In this way it was hoped to avoid the problems caused earlier in the year when two officers were killed while rendering safe a magnetic mine. The officers were part of a volunteer party from a destroyer. The ratings with them were unable to say what the officers had been doing when the mine exploded, even in the most general terms. This was simply because they had no idea of the construction of the mine. Lieutenant Rowlands, by his instruction not only made his team more efficient but also avoided the possibility of his being killed without anyone else knowing why, and thus knowing what to avoid in the future.

Throughout the stories of bomb disposal in Malta can be discerned the close co-operation which existed between the three Services and, indeed, the civilian population. The Army helped the Royal Air Force, the Royal Navy helped the Army and the Royal Air Force assisted the Royal Navy. Malta was one of the best examples of inter-Service co-operation at unit and sub-unit level. Each Service had its own bomb disposal organization, but they worked in complete harmony and often in each others' territory when so required. Frequently a special type of equipment would be issued to only one Service, or general purpose equipment would be in short supply (a frequent occurrence). Yet such equipment was made available to whoever needed it at any particular time irrespective of which Service actually held it. No doubt the siege complex helped. When all are exposed to the same dangers petty inter-Service rivalries become pointless and counterproductive.

6

New threats—new answers 1942-1943

The year 1942 was a comparatively quiet one for the bomb disposal organizations in respect of newly dropped enemy bombs—that is, compared with the intense activity of the preceding year. It therefore gave the bomb disposal teams time to catch their breath, readjust their organizations where necessary and clear the vast backlog of unexploded bombs.

The threat of invasion had all but disappeared and plans were being prepared for the counter-attack. Bomb disposal units were beginning to join the armies and garrisons overseas. At the beginning of 1942 there were already bomb disposal sections in Gibraltar, Malaya, West Africa and, as we saw in Chapter 5, Malta. There were also Royal Engineer Bomb Disposal Companies in Northern Ireland (27 Company) and in the Middle East (18 and 28 Companies). In November 1942 another two companies (Nos 15 and 17) landed with the Allied forces in Algeria, and later went ashore in Sicily and Italy with the invading forces. The activities of these companies and the closely associated teams from the Royal Air Force are considered in a later chapter.

The Royal Air Force bomb disposal teams were also spreading their wings. Overseas, wherever there was an airfield, there was also a small bomb disposal team. These teams were particularly active in North Africa and later across into Sicily and Italy. Teams were also in Iraq where they were responsible for all bomb disposal. At home they had changed their organization into 39 separate squads. These were annotated as Type A, A^x, B or C depending upon their role, strength and, to a lesser extent, their equipment. They were each commanded by an officer and their 'other rank' strengths varied between twelve and thirty. This was the intermediate stage prior to the major reorganization which took place in April 1943. At that date the Royal Air Force bomb disposal organization within the United Kingdom came under the control of a single Bomb Disposal Wing Headquarters based at RAF Eastchurch. Later in the year it moved to Eastfield House, Doncaster, Yorkshire, where it was to remain for the rest of the war. The Wing Headquarters had under command six Bomb Disposal Squadrons (Nos 5130 to 5135) which in turn commanded 29 Bomb Disposal Flights (Nos 6201 to 6229). The Wing also had under its command the Royal Air Force Bomb Disposal School which was now co-located with the Wing Headquarters.

Although German raids may have slackened off, the work of the Royal Air Force bomb disposal teams certainly had not. The major percentage of their work was the disposal of Allied weapons, and Allied air activity was increasing each month. For example, during 1943 the Royal Air Force dealt with 43,261 bombs (including incendiary and anti-personnel ones); only 3,092 were of enemy origin.

During 1942 the Royal Engineers were able to clear away many of their outstanding tasks. It was apparent, however, that some unexploded bombs could not be recovered without major engineering effort. Some bombs were also situated such that even if they did explode they would cause no damage. In those circumstances it was agreed that they could be formally abandoned until such time as the engineer effort was available. The authority for this action was delegated by the Ministry of Home Security to the Regional Commissioners.

The real problem lay with those bombs which had fallen, but had never been recorded. These had never been looked at or considered for recovery and had certainly not been officially abandoned. As was seen earlier those German bomb fuzes which depended for their detonation upon the electrical charge held in a capacitor, had a finite life. Certainly, if buried for over a year there was no way they could function as designed. However, bombs which depend upon some mechanical action initiated by a clockwork mechanism, can remain poised to strike almost indefinitely. This was very tragically demonstrated on 6 June 1942. On a warm sunny day the inhabitants of Gurney Street, near the Elephant and Castle in south London, were making the most of the sun and the respite from bombing. There had been no bombs dropped in their area for several months when suddenly there was a large and totally unexpected explosion. Thirty-seven people were killed and many more injured. A weapon, it will never be known whether it was a mine or a bomb, had for no apparent reason detonated. The sad thing is that no one even suspected its existence. Experts viewed the crater and attempted to recover fragments of the weapon, but none were found. The explosion was almost certainly caused by a clockwork mechanism which, having remained stopped for so long, was finally persuaded to begin its deadly countdown. It could have been a large bomb fitted with a long-delay fuze or any one of a number of types of mine. All were equipped with a clockwork device which could have been vibrated free by local traffic or nearby underground trains.

Much later, when V2 rocket attacks began on London, huge explosions with no prior warning such as the one at the Elephant and Castle were to become almost commonplace. However, in 1942 such an incident made everyone more conscious of unexploded bombs. The local bomb disposal company was asked to visit a wide range of suspect holes which might otherwise have been ignored. Following this incident over a hundred sites were visited and 22 bombs recovered.

The year 1943 was a year of surprises in many respects. It was certainly a year of increased enemy air activity. During the year over 2,300 tons (2,341,818 kg) of bombs were dropped on mainland Britain. Not a lot by 1941 standards but certainly a major increase over 1942. 1943 was also the year of the butterfly bomb, and the year in which it was first taken as a serious threat to civilian and military movements and to rural agriculture. It was also the year of the latest German booby-trap fuze, designed to kill the bomb disposal operator. Yet it was also the year in which this latest enemy fuze was countered within seven days of its first arrival. On a lighter note it was the year in which 'Old Bill' arrived in Hull, but more of that later. Finally, it was the year in which the Royal Engineers bomb disposal units were tasked to a job which would test their nerves and determination to the limit. It would cost them one third of the total deaths incurred by them since their formation and would last until well after the war was ended. The task was the clearance of the beach mines around the British coasts.

The story of the German SD2 anti-personnel bomb, or as it was more commonly known, the butterfly bomb, started as early as 1940. However, to those within the bomb disposal organization, 1943 was really the year in which this small bomb came of age and posed a threat which had to be recognized. Before considering the problems caused by the butterfly bomb it is first necessary to understand what it looked like and how it worked. It was a small anti-personnel bomb weighing 2 kg (4.4 lb) and containing just 225 gm (8 oz) of high explosive. Yet this bomb exploding at ground level was lethal to any unprotected person within a radius of 25 m (27 yd) and produced fragments capable of inflicting serious wounds up to a radius of 150 m (164 yd). As with all things explosive though, there are recorded exceptions of people who survived within a metre of a bomb going off and of people who were killed 150 m away.

The butterfly bomb differed considerably in appearance from any other known bomb. It had a cylindrical cast iron body with diameter and length being 80 mm (3.1 in). A light steel case in four sections enveloped the body of the bomb, to which it was connected by a 150 mm (5.9 in) long steel cable attached to the arming spindle of the fuze. The fuze was in a fuze pocket in the side of the bomb. When the bomb was released from the aircraft, or from the container in which it was dropped, the case flew open, sliding up the spindle and cable. The two half cylinders of the case formed a pair of wings or drogue, slowing down the descent rate of the bomb. The two end sections of the case formed a rudimentary propeller, the rotation of which caused the steel cable to turn and hence turn the spindle which was screwed into the body of the fuze. When the spindle had been unscrewed a certain number of turns (the number of turns varied in each type of fuze) the fuze became armed. The wings, cable and arming spindle normally remained attached to the bomb but on occasion did unscrew completely. In that case the components would be found some distance from the bomb, and in such situations the fuze would invariably be armed.

*German SD 2 anti-personnel
bomb (the Butterfly bomb).*

GERMAN SD2 ANTI-PERSONNEL BOMB (BUTTERFLY BOMB)

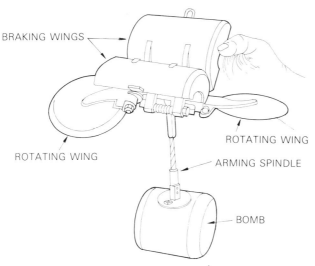

BRAKING WINGS

ROTATING WING

ROTATING WING

ARMING SPINDLE

BOMB

BOMB & CASING IN OPEN POSITION

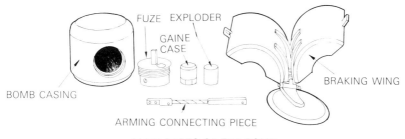

FUZE EXPLODER

GAINE

CASE

BOMB CASING

BRAKING WING

ARMING CONNECTING PIECE

MAIN PARTS OF THE BOMB

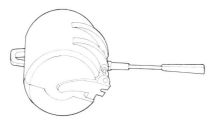

BOMB CASING IN CLOSED POSITION

The butterfly bomb was fitted with three types of fuze. First was the No 41 which had a small switch which enabled it to be set to function in two different ways. In each case the fuze was fully armed by the rotation of the spindle shortly after the release of the bomb. At one setting of the fuze the bomb detonated instantaneously upon hitting the target. At the other setting the fuze functioned three to five seconds after being armed. This could therefore be just before or just after impact, depending upon the height from which the bomb was dropped. The second fuze was the No 67. This was a straightforward clockwork delay which could be set to function at intervals up to a maximum of thirty minutes after the bomb was armed. As with the No 41, the No 67 fuze was armed during its fall to the ground. Finally came the No 70 which was probably the most feared fuze of them all. This was a sensitive anti-handling fuze operated by a simple mechanical device. The fuze was partially armed during its fall by the action of the propeller and arming spindle. On impact a trip lever allowed the mechanism to run for five seconds, after which the fuze was fully armed and in its most sensitive condition. Any disturbance or movement of the wings, cable, arming spindle or bomb body would cause the fuze to function and detonate the bomb after a delay of about half a second.

In addition to the correct functioning of these fuzes there were also genuine malfunctions which only added to the dangers inherent in dealing with these weapons. For example, the No 41 in either mode may have failed to function because of incomplete arming, perhaps due to some slight defect in the mechanism or because the shock of impact was insufficient to cause the fuze to function. In either case the fuze would be in an extremely sensitive condition where any movement of any part of the bomb could cause it to function.

The first reported use of the SD2 against Great Britain was on 28 October 1940 when a number were dropped in and around the town of Ipswich in Suffolk. A few failed to explode. No 8 Bomb Disposal Section of 4 Bomb Disposal Company, RE, was sent to investigate. On arrival it was discovered that several police officers had handled these bombs with fatal results. Second Lieutenant I. N. Taylor, RE, the Section Commander, and his Section Sergeant, Sergeant C. M. Cann, RE, appreciating that these were an entirely new type of bomb which had already caused fatalities, set about destroying them. Whilst doing this, one bomb was found in which the arming spindle had not been unscrewed as far as those on the other bombs. Sergeant Cann, in consultation with and in the presence of Second Lieutenant Taylor, screwed in the arming spindle and then removed the fuze, thus rendering the bomb harmless. As a result of this action, extremely valuable information was gained regarding this new weapon. In fact all the Ipswich bombs had been fitted with No 41 fuzes and so each unexploded example was a true malfunction. As we have seen, this did not stop them from being lethal. For his initiative and courage on this occasion, and for previous bomb disposal work, Sergeant Cann was awarded the George Medal. He remained in bomb disposal until

1945 by which time he had reached the rank of Captain. Second Lieutenant Taylor, who had been in bomb disposal since May 1940, was
awarded a King's Commendation for his work in Ipswich and was to be
awarded a George Medal nine months later for his work in the Tilbury
Docks area.

A few days later another attack occurred on a town in Sussex in which
damage to overhead power lines, telephone lines and trolley-bus wires
were reported. Three empty containers, each known to contain 23
bombs, were recovered, indicating that 69 bombs had been dropped.
Eighteen unexploded butterfly bombs were dealt with—again all fitted
with the No 41 fuze. As a result of these attacks and the information gained
from the unexploded bombs, details of this new threat were circulated to
ARP organizations and bomb disposal units. However, at this time
Britain was being heavily bombed with bombs up to 500 times larger than
the butterfly bomb and so information about them tended to be merely
noted and pushed to one side.

During early 1941, Lieutenant Colonel S. M. Lovell, RE, was a
member of the British military mission to the Soviet Union. He was responsible for offering advice on bomb disposal matters and reported that
the Soviets were very aware of the problems resulting from the use of
butterfly bombs. It was reported that when used in high concentrations
these bombs had cost the Red Army great numbers of casualties and
effectively held up the movement of ground troops.

In the same year the Royal Air Force were also to experience their first
taste of the butterfly bomb. During August 1941 a number of the weapons
were dropped on the Royal Air Force airfield at Harlaxton, near
Grantham in Lincolnshire. Flight Sergeant Handford, RAF, found
eleven of these bombs on Air Ministry property, and there were also some
sixty others in the surrounding countryside which were dealt with by the
Royal Engineers. He decided to drag three of the eleven off the runway.
A line was tied to the first bomb and it was slowly pulled along the
ground—it exploded! The Flight Sergeant decided to destroy the other
two where they were without attempting to do anything to them. This he
did and then turned his attention to the remaining eight bombs. These, he
noticed, had arming spindles which appeared only to have been
unscrewed a small amount. He therefore screwed them back into the fuzes
to prevent the fuzes from operating and returned with them to his
Headquarters at Digby just south of Lincoln. Here he received a 'rocket'
for his foolhardiness but the experts of the Technical Armaments branch
of the Air Ministry received eight new bombs to experiment with and use
as instructional models. Flight Sergeant Handford was extremely lucky
as once again all the fuzes were No 41s. It has since been discovered that
it was not until 1943 that the No 67 and No 70 fuzes were used against the
United Kingdom. It is also now known that it was only safe to screw in the
arming spindles of the No 41 fuze if not more than four threads were
visible. Despite his 'rocket' Flight Sergeant Handford was awarded the

British Empire Medal for his action at Harlaxton on 18 August 1941. A few days after the Harlaxton incident, on 24 August 1941, two non-commissioned officers of 22 Bomb Disposal Company, RE, were killed clearing butterfly bombs at Sarsted in Essex. They were Sergeant Shoebottom and Lance Corporal Farquharson.

During 1942 there were no recorded cases of butterfly bombs being dropped on the United Kingdom, although many hundreds were being dropped in the Middle East. Consequently, the general public was largely unaware of the possible threat posed by these weapons. It can be argued that the public, like the bomb disposal organization or, indeed, almost anyone in the United Kingdom at that time, had other more pressing dangers to consider. Thus any warning, without the materialization of the threat, would have been quickly forgotten or totally ignored.

It was not until March 1943, when over 1,800 butterfly bombs were dropped on London, Kent, Sussex and Essex, that the threat was even partially appreciated. It was during these attacks that the short delay fuze No 67 and the anti-disturbance fuze No 70 were first used. It was after the first attack on the night of 3/4 March 1943 that an announcement was made on the radio, and national newspapers published photographs of butterfly bombs, warning people on no account to touch them. The Ministry of Home Security also republished the warning notice previously distributed to the ARP organizations and on this occasion distributed it to every school and police station in the country. As will be seen this did not prevent a number of totally unnecessary casualties when the next major attack occurred three months later in June 1943.

The Essex raid on the night of 3/4 March 1943 posed a new set of problems, in that the vast majority of the unexploded butterfly bombs fell in rural areas. It might be considered that this presented far less of a problem than would the same bombs in an urban environment, for the countryside was less densely populated and had fewer buildings to be damaged. This is true, for in an urban setting the normal life of the community is practically at a standstill until all unexploded bombs have been discovered and recovered. One dare not open a door, slam a window or enter an attic without fear of detonating a bomb—but in the main they are readily visible. In a rural area they will be hidden in hedgerows, woods and (most important) in growing crops. At that stage of the war Great Britain's food supply was very dependent upon what she could produce from her own resources and any threat to standing crops was clearly serious. The problem therefore was to find, if possible, a means of searching standing crops without exposing the searchers to unacceptable risks and at the same time not damage the crops. An alternative was to leave the crops until just before they were due to be harvested and then search the area. To a bomb disposal man the thought of entering a field of fully grown peas or beans where their tendrils are wrapped lovingly around extremely sensitive anti-disturbance fuzed bombs is one of horror!

Such then was the situation in March 1943, and as usual a compromise had to be made. Hedgerows and areas where the general public had right of access were searched immediately and cleared by bomb disposal personnel. Fields containing crops in which it would be hazardous to search when fully grown were searched at once; other crops were left to be searched just prior to harvesting. Woods and hedgerows not adjoining public roads or rights of way were signed as being dangerous and were left to be searched in the following autumn/winter when the foliage was less dense. In fact, some areas were not finally cleared until the winter of 1946-7, or even much later. Following the showing in 1979 of a television serial *Danger UXB*, one episode of which dealt with butterfly bombs, several were reported to the Royal Engineer Explosive Ordnance Disposal unit. These were reported by gamekeepers, poachers or others who frequented isolated woods and who had noticed these items hanging from the trees but had not considered them dangerous. Several were also reported by householders who had stored them unknowingly in their attics. Major B. Birch, RE, dealt with several of them and they were very definitely still dangerous, providing a tribute to the German craftsmanship of the war years when these small mechanical devices were manufactured.

Returning to 1943: on the night 3/4 March, 346 butterfly bombs were dropped in open country in the area of Mountnessing, Essex. No 22 Bomb Disposal Company, RE, was deployed to dispose of these bombs. Where possible a cord was looped over the bombs and they were given a sharp jerk. In most cases this caused them to explode. In other cases a small charge was placed adjacent to but not touching the bomb (for fear of disturbing it), and it was destroyed accordingly. Many fell into soft ground and had to be uncovered by hand before an explosive charge could be placed close to them. Other risks experienced by members of the company were caused by the necessity of clearing some butterfly bombs from a wood on the edge of a main road. In several cases the bombs were suspended from the trees or caught in the undergrowth and there was a very grave risk of disturbing them as the wood was searched. Between 5 and 8 March 1943, Lieutenant T. Blackshaw, RE, and Sergeant T. Hall, RE, both of 22 Company, dealt with a total of 178 bombs. Both were subsequently awarded George Medals.

During the next three months there was much discussion, debate and downright argument between the Ministry of Home Security, the Ministry of Agriculture and Fisheries, the bomb disposal organization, the Civil Defence Regional Commissions and even the Admiralty. The cause of the debate was the search for solutions to the problems presented by the fall of butterfly bombs in rural areas and in particular in growing crops. No thought appears to have been given to problems which might be caused if these weapons were deployed against an industrial city or even, despite the reports from the Soviet Union in 1941, against concentrations of troops. However, minds were quickly concentrated on these matters following the dropping of over 9,800 butterfly bombs on towns, cities,

Royal Air Force stations and Army camps during June to October 1943.

The first of these attacks, and probably the most publicized in subsequent years, was that against Grimsby and Cleethorpes on the coast of Lincolnshire during the night of 13/14 June 1943. During that night, in addition to high explosive and incendiary bombs, well over 1,000 butterfly bombs were dropped of which three-quarters were discovered unexploded after the attack. The remainder exploded on impact, exploded within half an hour of falling or were disturbed and exploded during the night of the attack. To search and clear the urban areas of Grimsby and Cleethorpes took over 10,000 man hours spread over eighteen days. The total number of civilians killed by these bombs was 61 of whom fourteen were killed during the raid, 31 within the first hour following the raid and the remainder during the next twelve hours.

After the 'All Clear' was sounded on the night of the raid, people began to appear in the streets, mainly to watch the fires. In doing so they stumbled over the bombs, picked them up or disturbed them as they hung on fences or in hedges. This lack of awareness accounted for the high casualty rate in the first hour following the raid. At first light loudspeaker vans toured the towns warning of the dangers and imploring people to remain indoors or be extra vigilant. Despite this there were many foolish or thoughtless acts which killed or badly scarred a number of people. Some anonymous examples are quoted below.

A man had collected three bombs and having been quite incorrectly advised to put them in a water butt started to do so. He found the butt was covered with wire netting and so tried to hand the one bomb he was then carrying to his companion who refused to take it. In so doing the bomb was dropped and exploded, killing both men. The other two bombs, which had been placed by a shelter door, also exploded killing two other people. A school caretaker saw a bomb inside the school and went for an air raid warden. When he returned with three wardens the bomb exploded and all four men were killed.

Some examples had less tragic endings but still make a point. Some days after the raid, when the dangers of the bombs had been widely publicized, a Special Constable carried a butterfly bomb into his Inspector's office as he thought the Inspector might be interested in it! The bomb was removed rapidly to a safe place where it exploded soon afterwards without injuring anyone. On the day following the raid an elderly lady found a butterfly bomb half buried in her garden. She dug it out, but was admonished by her daughter who took it from her. While she was still holding it a soldier in a nearby garden shouted a warning at her and she dropped it. The bomb exploded but both ladies suffered only slight injuries. Many more similar incidents occurred, such as children taking bombs home and being told to put them back where they found them. It is surprising that many more fatalities among the civilian population did not occur.

That was the situation into which Major W. G. Parker, RE, Officer Commanding 3 Bomb Disposal Company, RE, brought his men. At the time of the raid the company were grouped together under canvas in the grounds of Tollerton Hall just outside Nottingham, to where the company headquarters had recently moved. It was the first time the company had been together for some time and so was able to deploy to Grimsby and Cleethorpes with the minimum of delay. With over 750 bombs to be found and disposed of, it is not surprising that there were many stories of individual bravery. Above all, the initiative and improvization in the removal or destruction of these bombs with the minimum of damage was quite remarkable.

Some of the risks taken by the officers and non-commissioned officers of the bomb disposal company were taken entirely to protect property, the loss of which would have had no direct effect upon the war effort. It could be argued that their lives were worth more than any amount of property, but it should be realized that this was, for the local civilian population, the first major attack by a new and frightening weapon. Therefore it was essential to restore normality to the town of Grimsby as quickly as possible and with the minimum of damage. This was not only for the sake of the morale of the inhabitants but to minimize the results of this extremely effective weapon for those who might report them back to Germany. The men of all three Services who dealt with butterfly bombs in a variety of situations did so with the minimum of fuss and one must assume that the apparent ineffectiveness of this form of attack was reported back to Germany. As will be seen later, the United Kingdom fully expected the butterfly bomb or a variant of it to be deployed in large numbers against Allied troops forming up for the invasion of Europe. Yet it was not so, and perhaps lives saved in southern England in 1944 were the result in part of the bravery of bomb disposal men in 1943.

Some of the improvizations used to remove these small (but always dangerous) bombs from the most inaccessible places would have done credit to Mr Heath Robinson himself. For example, one bomb was found at the bottom of a seven-junction drainage manhole. To destroy the bomb where it was would have caused considerable damage to the drainage system of seven separate routes. It was therefore decided to remove it remotely, but first it had to be dug clear of the sludge in which it was buried. This was carefully carried out using a dessert spoon. When this was completed a chimney of straw bales was built round the top of the manhole. At ground level a gap was left in the chimney through which a straw bale could be pulled on rollers. Over the top of the chimney a pole with a pulley block was erected. Through the block was passed a line to which was attached an electromagnet accurately placed over the bomb. From a safe distance the magnet was lowered to the bomb and the power switched on. The magnet with the bomb attached was then lifted until it was above the first layer of straw bales. The bale on rollers was then pulled over the manhole and under the bomb. The bomb was released over the bale and after the required safety time had elapsed it was destroyed. No damage was caused to the drainage system.

Butterfly bomb caught in roof slates.

Similar strings and pulley arrangements were prepared to remove bombs from attics, bedrooms, church organs, timber mill machinery and cinema projectors. Most of the men engaged in this clearance work were involved for four weeks working throughout the daylight hours of each day. There were many well-deserved awards and decorations given during this period. However, all the men of the bomb disposal units who had to deal with these bombs in a variety of situations deserve recognition for their bravery and their ingenuity. There is no doubt that their personal courage and resourcefulness were a major contribution towards the restoration of public confidence and morale at a time when it could have been seriously undermined.

The next major attacks using butterfly bombs occurred during August 1943 when almost 3,000 were dropped on Yorkshire, Lincolnshire and Norfolk. The majority of these incidents were the results of German fighter bombers following returning British bomber aircraft and attempting to put their airfields out of action as the bombers landed. Those bombs which landed within the airfield perimeters were the responsibility of the Royal Air Force teams. Those spread in a wide area around the airfields were the responsibility of the Royal Engineers. By now the Royal Air Force had perfected a drill for clearing these bombs off main runways and the remainder of the airfield involving a combination of pulling and destroying *in situ*. The bombs outside the perimeter fence, however, presented a far greater problem in that corn crops were, at this time, fully grown and either ready for harvest or were in the process of being cut. Cabbage and sugar beet fields were turned overnight into minefields which farm workers were very understandably loath to enter. During the same month, on the night of 17/18 August 1943, Hull was attacked with butterfly bombs. Its inhabitants and ARP services had learnt from their neighbours in Grimsby, and casualties were relatively few.

Similarly, in September 1943 the attacks continued in Norfolk, Lincolnshire and down into Sussex, although the number of butterfly bombs dropped was reduced to approximately 1,500. Of the bombs dropped 757 were dealt with on Royal Air Force property. Again the attackers flew in with returning British bombers but during this month the butterfly bombs were dropped in conjunction with conventional high explosive bombs. This pattern was repeated again in October and by the end of 1943 a total of over 11,700 butterfly bombs had been dropped over Great Britain during that year.

It is amazing that similar or even greater numbers were not dropped during 1944 on one of the best military targets imaginable. Along the English south coast during early 1944 were many thousands of Allied troops in huts and tents preparing for the invasion of Europe. Yet apart from widely dispersed raids and a deliberate attack in May 1944 against military camps in Dorset, the butterfly bomb threat was over. That is, the threat from freshly dropped bombs was over for the threat from those already dropped continued for much longer. No 1 Bomb Disposal Company, RE, was still searching for and finding butterfly bombs in the rural areas of Yorkshire and Lincolnshire as late as November 1946. In some cases they were forced to use flame throwers to destroy hedges as the only way to declare the area safe. Similarly, 20 Bomb Disposal Company, RE, was clearing these bombs in Sussex and Kent during 1945 and 1946. Altogether at least ten separate Royal Engineer Bomb Disposal Companies were involved in the fight against this particularly nasty form of attack, as were the Royal Air Force teams on the majority of operational stations. Indeed, during 1943, 64 Royal Air Force airfields and nineteen non-flying stations were bombed.

As was said at the beginning of this chapter the butterfly bomb was not the only device to threaten the lives of bomb disposal personnel during 1943. The butterfly bomb threatened all who came near to it, yet the next device to be described was designed solely for the purpose of killing bomb disposal personnel.

On the night of 17/18 January 1943 an air raid took place over the Greater London area and a number of 500 kg (1,100 lb) bombs failed to explode. This in itself was not an unusual event and each was looked at and its priority for removal determined. One such bomb had fallen near Lord's cricket ground, then being used by the Royal Air Force. The bomb had penetrated to such a depth that it was buried under the railway track of the Bakerloo line of the London underground system. It had therefore been given a high priority for disposal. A detachment from 5 Bomb Disposal Company, RE, under the command of Captain F. Carlyle, RE, began digging to uncover the bomb. Whilst working the detachment was visited by its Company Commander, Major W. G. Parker, RE. This was the same officer who, when commanding another company, had been responsible for the clearance of butterfly bombs in the Grimsby and Cleethorpes area some five months later. The bomb on the underground railway was quickly uncovered and its single fuze examined. It was identified as a No 25B, a direct-impact fuze very similar to the No 15 already described. Among the many markings on the fuze head was the letter Y, but since most fuzes had a host of subsidiary markings indicating the factory of manufacture, the date, the inspector's stamp, the batch number, etc, this apparently insignificant marking was ignored. A fuze was always identified by the number in the circle; in this case it was 25B.

Major Parker decided to wait while Captain Carlyle discharged the fuze. By now these types of fuzes had their capacitors discharged by putting a conducting fluid into the fuze which would allow the capacitors to discharge but would not conduct sufficient energy to fire the detonator. In this case only a quarter of the normal amount of liquid would enter the fuze. The two officers then jointly tried again but no further liquid could be forced into the fuze. This was odd but not unheard of and since this was a priority task the bomb was deemed safe to move. Major Parker returned to his headquarters and Captain Carlyle removed the bomb to the bomb cemetery at Hampstead Heath. (A bomb cemetery was an open space where bombs safe to move were stored prior to having their explosive contents removed, where inert fuzes were extracted and certain experiments took place. They were so sited that if an accident occurred it would involve only those working with the bomb.) At Hampstead Heath Captain Carlyle fitted a fuze extractor and attempted to remove the fuze remotely. This he could not manage and since he believed the fuze to be inert he removed it by force, ie, he used a hammer, chisel and crowbar.

As soon as he saw the fuze he realized that it was unlike any other fuze he had previously seen. It was longer than normal and the bottom end had a reverse taper with a separate metal ring round the narrowest part. On attempting to remove the fuze from the bomb the ring would slide down the tapered portion of the fuze, effectively increasing the diameter of the fuze and so preventing its extraction. Captain Carlyle removed the gaine and took the fuze to his Company Headquarters. Within the hour the fuze was receiving a scientific examination. Within 24 hours a report had been issued by the research team and a signal sent to every bomb disposal unit in the United Kingdom. This signal warned of the existence of this new fuze (dubbed the Y fuze) and ordered that no work was to be undertaken on any bomb containing a Y fuze or any bomb in which the fuze could not be positively identified. The remarkable thing is that this order remained operative for only five days, that is seven days from when the first Y fuze was dropped. At the end of that period not only were all the secrets of the fuze known and understood, but an initial method of rendering it safe had been circulated to bomb disposal officers.

The initial report on the fuze showed that the top half was very similar to all the other German electric fuzes. It was armed during its fall and on impact a trembler switch completed a circuit, but instead of that circuit firing a flash cap or a detonator it merely completed a secondary circuit. This second circuit was powered by a dry cell battery connected to a detonator and broken by three very sensitive mercury switches, wired in parallel and placed at right angles to each other—one in each directional plane. This meant that after impact the slightest movement of the bomb in any direction would cause it to explode. Furthermore, the life of the fuze was not dependent upon the ability of a capacitor to hold its charge but on the time a dry battery would hold its power when not in use (a year at least). One other aspect of the fuze was that, should the normal discharge procedure be followed, the introduction of the fluid would short-circuit the dry battery circuit and detonate the bomb. Thus the whole fuze was designed solely to kill the bomb disposal operator and to serve no function other than that of a booby trap.

So how did Major Parker and Captain Carlyle avoid being blown to pieces by this unsuspected danger? When the fuze was dismantled it was discovered that there was a break in its initiating circuit and so the secondary circuit containing the dry battery and the mercury tilt switches was never activated. Thus the injection of the conducting fluid and the subsequent rough handling of the bomb had no effect. This fault in the circuit enabled the secrets of the Y fuze to be exposed and undoubtedly saved many lives. Whether it was a genuine fault or, as one would like to think, the work of a friend in the German factory, will never be known.

On the same night that the Lords bomb had fallen another had crashed through the roof of a warehouse in Battersea, South London. This bomb penetrated not only the roof but a pile of packing cases and finally came to rest unexploded beneath the bed plate of a large lathe. The rest of the warehouse was packed with newly arrived (and much needed) machine tools from America. In view of the importance of the warehouse contents this bomb was also given top priority and preliminary work began on the morning of 18 January 1943. The working party was under the control of Lieutenant R. W. Deans, RE.

Luckily, the bomb was difficult to reach and by the time the bomb was uncovered news of the Y fuze recovered earlier in the day was available. On close inspection, the bomb in the warehouse was found to have a very battered fuze but the letter Y was clearly discernible. On reporting this, the Director of Bomb Disposal ordered that every effort be made to establish that this fuze was identical to the one already recovered. There was no known way of rendering the fuze safe and it was too much to hope that this fuze, like the first one, was faulty. It was therefore decided to take a radiographic photograph of the fuze using equipment still in the development stage. This was done by Dr J. A. T. Dawson of the Ministry of Supply

Field photography — pseudonym for radiography — Captain A. B. Waters, RE.

technical staff and Captain A. B. Waters, RE, on the Directorate of Bomb Disposal staff, using photographic plates and a radioactive source. This involved some twelve hours' tedious but dangerous work, rewarded in the end by a good radiograph. This film showed that the fuze was identical to the one recovered earlier. From then on every fuze found within the London area and suspected of being a Y fuze was radiographed by Dr Dawson and Captain Waters to confirm its identity before any render-safe procedure was attempted.

However, at this stage no render-safe procedure existed and the bomb in the warehouse had to be cleared. This task was given to Major C. A. J. Martin, MC, RE, on the Directorate staff, assisted by Lieutenant Deans who had carried out the initial uncovering of the bomb. Equipped with the radiograph and the initial report on the first fuze, they decided to unscrew the base plate from the bomb and remove the high explosive filling. This would then leave an empty bomb case and a relatively small charge in the fuze pocket which, if detonated, would do little damage to the critical machine tools. By midday on 20 January 1943 the base plate was removed and the bomb was found to contain solid cast TNT, which could only be removed by the application of high temperature steam. This 'steaming out' process is normally done by remote control, but in view of the need for accurate temperature control and no movement of the bomb, it was decided to do it by hand. This meant applying the steam nozzle by hand, softening a small amount of explosive, scraping it away and repeating this process until the bomb was empty. At the same time it was necessary to apply cold water on to the fuze to prevent it becoming overheated. At no time during this process could the bomb be jarred. Major Martin and Lieutenant Deans worked continuously from the afternoon of 20 January and all through the night until 08:30 hours the next morning. By this time the bomb had been completely emptied. Throughout that night the two officers had taken it in turns to lie under the bomb in a cramped hole filled with steam and water manipulating the steam hose and scraping away the explosive. This was throughout an extremely dangerous operation requiring cold-blooded courage of the highest order.

While this operation was proceeding, Ministry of Supply scientists and the Royal Engineer technical staff were working to find a technique and equipment to defeat this new fuze. Already nine Y fuzes had been located in London, all of which were waiting until a suitable technique had been perfected. Major J. D. Hudson, MBE, RE, Deputy Assistant Director Bomb Disposal (Technical), was working on the problem in the belief that if the dry batteries could be cooled sufficiently they would become temporarily inert. If this were true then during the inert period the fuze could be extracted from the bomb. Experiments were tried and it was believed that by using liquid oxygen poured over the fuze head the necessary very low temperature within the fuze could be achieved. Since only one fuze had so far been recovered it was impossible to carry out the usual tests before introducing a new disposal technique. Major Hudson therefore decided to continue the experiments on a live bomb. Such a bomb had fallen on the same night as the others and had caused the closure of the Albert Bridge over the River Thames at Chelsea, denying access to a nearby flour works.

So, on 24 January 1943, Major Hudson approached this 500 kg (1,100 lb) bomb prepared to put his theory into practice. Using clay he moulded a cup around the fuze head and filled this with liquid oxygen. The liquid oxygen of course evaporated very rapidly and the cup had to be continuously refilled. Quite apart from the risk of the bomb exploding should it be moved or jarred in any way, working with liquid oxygen in a confined space is far from pleasant. There is, of course, a very high risk of fire in an atmosphere which is almost pure oxygen. Indeed, pure oxygen coming into contact with a number of substances, explosives being one of them, can cause self-ignition. All work must be viewed through a thick fog which forms as the oxygen evaporates and the air temperature falls. Finally, a concentration of oxygen, although to some stimulating, generally produces a feeling of giddiness. Major Hudson had concluded during his laboratory tests that the fuze and its batteries would be sufficiently cooled when the ring of frost forming on the bomb extended for a 12 in (305 mm) radius round the fuze. This was determined when a piece of wet cotton wool froze solidly on the bomb case at a distance of 10 in (254 mm) from the fuze. This was achieved after just over two hours crouching by the bomb, pouring liquid oxygen into the cup, repairing the cup as the clay cracked and checking regularly on the state of the cotton wool. As if he did not have enough to do, he also provided by telephone a detailed commentary on what he was doing and suggested modifications to the process, just in case of accidents. In Major Hudson's view the fuze was now inert and would remain in that condition for approximately twenty minutes without further application of oxygen. He then managed after considerable effort and the use of a jemmy to prise the frozen fuze from the bomb–defeating both the functioning of the fuze and the purely mechanical anti-withdrawal device. After 23 minutes he had the fuze in his hands. He quickly unscrewed the gaine and there was another fuze urgently required for further research.

Instructions on this method of rendering safe the Y fuze (albeit for a relatively short period) were quickly circulated to all bomb disposal units. Those bombs awaiting disposal within the London area were dealt with by those most closely involved with the Y fuze, namely, Major Martin, Major Hudson, Captain Waters, Captain Carlyle and Lieutenant Deans. Although all the bombs were safely dealt with they were not without their moments of excitement.

For example, when Captain Waters was dealing with one which had fallen in the Old Kent Road area of south-east London, he attempted to prise out the fuze. The force used, instead of overcoming the anti-withdrawal device, broke off the head of the fuze. This left the fuze body jammed in the pocket with no way of removing it. In a few minutes the fuze would warm up and be as deadly as ever. The solution arrived at by Major Martin, who was present at the time, was to drip liquid oxygen into the fuze and chip away the frozen fuze components, repeating this as many times as necessary until some part of the firing circuit could be exposed and cut. This was a most dangerous procedure involving a steady hand and steady nerves. Major Martin opted to do the work himself. Armed with the necessary equipment and a detailed drawing of the fuze, he proceeded to pour and chip, describing each move into a microphone, until the task was successfully completed.

Another incident occurred on 4 February 1943 when Captain Carlyle (the officer who recovered the first Y fuze) was working on a similar fuze in a bomb at the bottom of a badly ventilated shaft under a house. As with the previous incident Major Martin was present but not actually down the hole. Captain Carlyle had successfully frozen the fuze and was engaged in prising it out when suddenly he and the shaft were enveloped in flames. The liquid oxygen had come into contact with some substance which had spontaneously ignited. Luckily he was speaking into the microphone at the time which both warned the team at ground level and protected a part of his face. He managed to climb the burning ladder and Major Martin and other members of the team put out the flames and had the badly burnt Captain Carlyle rushed to hospital. Major Martin, despite the obvious risk of another fire or detonation of the bomb, returned to the site and, starting from scratch, refroze the fuze and successfully removed it from the bomb.

Thus the initial threat of the Y fuze had been overcome, but the apparatus was cumbersome and only allowed the fuze to be removed from wherever the bomb had landed. A fear in the bomb disposal operators' minds was that if the Germans discovered that this fuze could be defeated then a ZUS 40 anti-withdrawal fuze might be placed under the Y fuze. To overcome these problems new equipment was designed and in a very few days it was approved and being issued to units. The new equipment enabled the liquid oxygen to be placed in a sealed and insulated container with a pressure release valve. The liquid oxygen was forced, by its own pressure of evaporation, out of the container through a pipe to a collet fitted over the fuze head and then collected for re-use. This avoided the need to build a clay cup and to pour the liquid oxygen directly on to the fuze. Another advance was to design a travelling cup which could be fitted over the frozen fuze. This enabled the bomb to be moved to a demolition area should it be impossible or inadvisable to remove the fuze, for example, if the bomb was found to be fitted with a ZUS 40 fuze. The first officer to use this newly designed equipment was Captain Waters who successfully dealt with a Y fuze fitted to a bomb which had fallen in Lisson Grove, north London. Thus, thanks to the courage of the pioneers and the determination and scientific ability of the specialists this fuze, designed to kill bomb disposal men, claimed not a single victim from those actually working on it. Several soldiers at about this time died while digging close to a bomb but it was never determined whether it was a No 17 long-delay fuze, a No 50 anti-disturbance fuze or the latest Y fuze which caused the bomb to explode.

For their courage and coolness in dealing with the Y fuzes Major Martin was awarded the George Cross and lived a full life until he died in 1973. Captain Waters was made a Member of the Order of the British Empire (MBE) which was followed by the award of a George Medal in 1944 for work on a parachute mine. Major Hudson was awarded the George Medal and, as will be seen later, received a second one for his work on unexploded flying bombs. Lieutenant Deans was also awarded a George Medal.

One short footnote on the Y fuze saga. Liquid oxygen was readily available in the towns and cities of England, but on a battlefield or in the war-torn cities of mainland Europe it would not be. These facts were appreciated by the scientific staff who quickly produced the solution. If compressed carbon dioxide is released from its cylinder into a standard kit-bag it forms a substance known as carbon dioxide snow. This, when mixed with methylated spirit, forms a perfect freezing compound which, packed round a Y fuze, will produce a sufficient drop in temperature to immunize the fuze.

Thus was the Y fuze defeated, initially by luck, or perhaps an unknown helper, then by courage of the very highest order supported by some of the best scientific brains available at that time. It must be remembered, however, that bombs with Y fuzes continued to be dropped on Great Britain until well into 1944, and although methods of dealing with this

particular fuze had been perfected, it still required courage and determination to carry out the procedure.

In addition to the dramatic events already considered in relation to the
butterfly bomb and the Y fuze, and before we consider the awesome task
of beach clearance, there is one other task which was started in 1943. It was
the recovery of 'Old Bill' a 1,000 kg (2,200 lb) bomb dropped in the
Market Place, Hull, Yorkshire, on 24 June 1943. The recovery of this
bomb is thought to be the longest continuous effort in the history of bomb
disposal—certainly in Great Britain. It is a story of dogged determination,
extremely hard manual work, the development of new equipment techniques and the bravery of the men who dug and worked for two and a half
years knowing that somewhere beneath them was a bomb which, if they
hit it, could explode and kill them all.

Today, with modern electronic equipment the position of a buried
bomb can usually be determined to very close limits and when a shaft is
sunk it is very rare for the bomb not to be found within the cross-section
of the shaft at the forecast depth. At the time of the search for 'Old Bill' a
very primitive bomb locator existed which could only detect metallic
masses very close to the surface. Thus with a deeply buried bomb it was
usual to look at the hole of entry and decide in which direction the bomb
was travelling when it hit the ground. It will be appreciated that very few
bombs hit the ground falling vertically. Knowing the size of the bomb and
the general direction it was moving, it was possible to make an estimation
of about where the bomb was in relation to its hole of entry. A shaft was
then dug over this point. If nothing was found it was then usual to move
back towards the point of entry and dig another shaft hoping to pick up
signs of the bomb's passage through the soil (its trace) and then follow it.

The search for 'Old Bill' began in the same way. On 3 July 1943, nine
days after the bomb fell, a standard timber shaft 8 ft (2.4 m) by 8 ft was
started. This was dug to a depth of 19.5 ft (5.9 m), at which depth it was
impossible to proceed owing to the excessive pressure upon the timber
work. No sign of the bomb, its fins or its trace was found. A second timber
shaft only 6 ft (1.8 m) by 3.75 ft (1.1 m) was started on 6 September 1943.
This shaft was positioned with one of its sides over the hole of entry of the
bomb. The bomb trace was followed to a depth of 16 ft (4.87 m) with an off-
set (movement from the vertical) of 4.5 ft (1.37 m). At 18 ft (5.5 m) a piece
of the tail fin was found but the trace was lost. On 22 September a third
timber shaft was started and taken to a depth of 23 ft (7 m). At that depth
silt was pushing through the bottom of the shaft and the ground around
the shaft was beginning to subside. Parts of the bomb fin were found at a
depth of 22 ft (6.7 m).

After three timber shafts, two of which had to be abandoned because of
the soil conditions, it was decided to use a metal piled shaft. This went
down to a depth of 28 ft (8.5 m) and was probed to a depth of 50 ft (15.24
m) but with no result. The fifth shaft was started on 1 June 1944 and went
to a depth of 33 ft (10 m) where pieces of a tail fin were found in line with

the fins found in the third shaft and the original hole. The bottom of the shaft was probed at 9 in (228 mm) centres to a depth of 58 ft (17.67 m) with no result.

By now there was a certain dispiritedness in the men doing the job and a feeling of doubt as to whether the bomb could ever be recovered, or indeed if it was really there. The siting of the first five shafts was based upon the bomb trace and where the parts of the tail fin had been recovered. The officer commanding the company in charge of this work was Major R. A. Shorter, RE, of 1 Bomb Disposal Company, RE, and he felt some trepidation over siting another shaft by the same method as that used for the previous five. He felt an entirely new approach was necessary and in conjunction with the company's Electrical and Mechanical Officer, and Lieutenant F. H. Richards, RE, the officer actually in charge of the site who at that time was in his fifties, a plan was prepared. It was decided to use the existing bomb locator but to lower it down non-magnetic (asbestos) pipes which had previously been sunk into the ground with the aid of water jets. Before this could happen all metal sheeting and piles had to be removed from site to prevent interference with the magnetometer. In all, 22 pipes were sunk into the ground to a depth of 50 ft (15.24 m). The bomb locator indicated from the readings in the 18th to 22nd holes that a large metal object was present at a depth of 36 ft (10.97 m), at a position nowhere near the line of direction in which the fins had been found. It was a man of great faith who gave the order to sink yet another shaft in what was clearly the 'wrong' position. This shaft was started on 25 November 1945 using sheet piling 33 ft (10 m) long and sited such that the centre of the shaft was directly over where the instrument indicated that the bomb lay. On 31 January 1946 the bomb was uncovered in the centre of the shaft at the predicted depth of 36 ft (10.97 m). The fuze was rendered safe and the bomb removed after two and a half years' continuous work. The use of bomb locators in holes drilled into the ground is now commonplace and their readings are accepted as gospel. In 1945 this was a new procedure which gave readings which conflicted with simple logic but once again it only proves the point that no one unaided can predict the manner in which a bomb will behave when travelling underground, there are so many influences at work. The officer and non-commissioned officers in charge of the various aspects of this job were: Lieutenant F. H. Richards, RE, in charge throughout; Sergeant G. H. Quarendon, GM, RE, responsible for finding the bomb with the locator (he was awarded the George Medal for his work in Hull during 1941); Lance Sergeant Lovell, Corporal Welsh, Corporal Townsend and Lance Corporal Woods, responsible for timbering, piling and excavation.

The author has no sense of guilt in writing of this episode although it lacks the dramatic impact and stark bravery of many of the other incidents recorded. It does, however, reflect much of the routine work of bomb disposal in peace or war—and of whatever Service. Hours of searching or digging or a combination of both followed by a relatively short period of activity on the actual weapon tends to be the norm, unless you can arrange for someone else to find the bomb for you!

Searching was the key word in perhaps the most dangerous and trying single task to be given to the Royal Engineer bomb disposal units in 1943. That was the clearance of some 2,000 separate minefields laid on the beaches and cliff tops round the coast of Great Britain as a defence against threatened invasion. Initially the task was to clear selected beaches so that Allied troops could practise their own invasion techniques, but the task quickly grew to include all the 350,000 anti-tank mines laid on British beaches and the exits from them. Technically this was not a bomb disposal task, although it was given to bomb disposal units. Its story should not therefore appear in this book. To tell the story of this work in full and to give due credit to all the officers, non-commissioned officers, Sappers, prisoners-of-war and eventually ex-prisoners-of-war would require a full-length book of its own. However, a few paragraphs must be included to pay respect to the 151 men who were killed on this task between 1943 and 1947 and to the many hundreds of unnamed and frequently unremembered men who worked in constant threat of death even when for others the war was over. Indeed, bomb disposal men will continue to do that just as long as weapons designed to kill are left in the ground posing a threat to life and limb.

The difficulties of this mine clearance task were enormous. The mines had been laid in great haste in 1940, with the result that the minefield records, although showing the general areas in which the mines were laid, contained very little reliable information as to the exact position of the mines or (in some cases) even the total numbers laid. In one classic case the map used was an unamended 1906 edition! Even if the exact position of all the mines had been shown, there were many instances where the action of wind and tide over the years had altered the whole topography of the area. Mines laid a few inches below the surface of the sand or shingle often became buried deep beneath dunes of sand or banks of shingle. It was not unusual to find that mines had been carried by storms to points far along the coast from where they were originally laid. Similarly, mines laid on cliff tops had, as the cliff was eroded, slid to the bottom of the cliff and either been buried under tons of material or washed out to sea only to be returned to another beach which may already have been cleared.

The most modern instruments then available were used to locate the whereabouts of these mines but many were buried beyond their effective range. Furthermore, the instruments were liable to indicate the presence of a mine which, when uncovered, turned out to be nothing more dangerous than a large tin, a length of chain or any one of the many strange metallic objects with which the beaches had become strewn.

Finally, the mines themselves had suffered from long years of corrosion. One of the most numerous mines to be laid was the anti-tank mine known as the B Type C. This depended for its action upon a pressure of 50 lb (22.7 kg) on the edge or 100 lb (45.4 kg) on the centre of its domed

Right *B Type C — British anti-tank beach mine.*

Below and bottom *Water jetting to expose beach mines by a Royal Engineer bomb disposal team.*

top which reversed a simple bow-shaped spring. This spring drove a striker on to a cartridge cap and so fired the mine. After years of corrosion the bow spring became weaker and its supports less strong. This left the mine in a highly sensitive condition and instead of the intended activation pressure the weight of a man's foot or even a handful of sand could be sufficient to set off the 25 lb (11.4 kg) of explosive contained in the mine.

Various forms of mechanical equipment were used to clear the beaches and cliff edges. One method was to carry out a surface sweep with mine detectors, then to use armoured bulldozers to scrape off a layer of sand or shingle equal to the effective depth of the search instrument and then re-sweep and continue this until the required depth had been cleared. Another method was to use powerful water jets to clear away the accumulation of sand and shingle until the mines were exposed. Whatever method was used in the way of mechanical devices the final search had always to be carried out by men armed only with mine detectors and complete faith in the other members of their team.

The work of sweeping for and clearing beach mines must inevitably be a very slow and deliberate operation. Any attempt to hurry was all too likely to be attended by fatal results. This work tested a unit's morale to its limit. It was tedious, dangerous and, except when a mine was recovered or someone was killed, it was boring in the extreme. Between 1943 and 1948 a total of 1,986 minefields consisting of 338,500 mines were cleared. This left eleven small areas, the last of which was cleared in 1972.

The year 1943 was clearly an eventful one for many units and individuals in the bomb disposal organization. In the Royal Engineers there were many men who were involved in the most active way possible with all three major developments of the year, the butterfly bombs, the Y fuze and the clearance of Britain's dangerous beaches. It is perhaps fitting that of the three George Crosses awarded for bomb and mine disposal in the United Kingdom during 1943 one should have gone to each of the armed Services. They were, in the *London Gazette* order of publication, Major C. A. Martin, MC, RE, for bomb disposal work since 1940 culminating in the work described earlier in this chapter in respect of Y fuzes; Wing Commander J. S. Rowlands, MBE, RAFVR, for conspicuous courage in bomb disposal over the previous two years particularly in the experimental aspects and the development of new procedures. (He was referred to earlier in Chapter 2 as a Flight Lieutenant.) The third member of this trio was Lieutenant H. R. Syme, GM and Bar, RANVR, for his work with HMS *Vernon*. He had already been awarded the George Medal in 1941 and a second one in 1942. He was one of that courageous band of Australian Naval officers referred to in Chapter 4.

7

Overseas again

As was referred to in earlier chapters, bomb disposal personnel of all three Services were deployed to all parts of the world where it was considered their expertise would be required. Ports as widely dispersed as Hong Kong, Singapore, Trincomalee (Ceylon—now Sri Lanka), Simonstown (South Africa) and many others had a Naval bomb disposal presence in the form of Bomb Safety Officers (BSO). The BSOs were often left to work on their own and forced to train a support team from either the local force or from volunteer servicemen based at the port.

Some reported back to the Admiralty that the prevailing spirit was 'nobody will drop bombs on us, and even if they do it will cause no real problem'. In that sort of atmosphere—real or imagined—it would have been understandable if the BSOs had lost their enthusiasm and just relaxed and enjoyed their foreign tour, especially as most of them had experienced the more hectic life of a BSO in the United Kingdom during 1940 and early 1941. But far from it; they were keen dedicated men intent upon training their various staffs on what to expect and how to react following an air attack.

In many cases they were not entirely alone as frequently the ports were in, or close to, areas of Army and/or Royal Air Force influence. These Services also had deployed enthusiastic bomb disposal officers, so frequently they were able to give each other mutual support. Of course, much depended upon the personality of those concerned and one can well imagine situations where junior but experienced bomb disposal officers might clash with more senior but less experienced officers.

By November 1941, there were representatives from all three Services in Singapore; Lieutenant A. J. Lilburn, RNVR, Captain Walsh, RE, and Flight Lieutenant W. H. Charlton, GC, RAF. The last had been awarded his George Cross for bomb disposal work during 1940. In the reports from Singapore it was clear that until November 1941 only the Royal Navy had any bomb disposal equipment and that was designed for dealing with German bombs. When the equipment arrived for the other two Services that also was intended to defeat German bombs and fuzes. In October 1941 the Commander-in-Chief China Station had sent the Singapore BSO to Hong Kong to give a series of lectures to ARP personnel and also to officers and men likely to have to deal with unexploded bombs. The BSO commented upon his return that the Army bomb disposal officer in Hong Kong, Lieutenant B. Crowley, RE, was well equipped with all the essential equipment for dealing with German bombs!

Luckily, at this time Flight Lieutenant Charlton (by means unknown) was able to organize an extremely successful visit to the interior of China. He brought back with him a wide range of bomb fuzes removed from unexploded Japanese bombs. He was also able to arrange for a number of Japanese bombs to be delivered to Singapore. He and Lieutenant Lilburn, the BSO, prepared a most useful technical evaluation of these bombs and fuzes for transmission to the Air Ministry; this information was distributed to all interested parties throughout the Far East.

Concurrent with the exploitation of the Japanese bombs and fuzes, another experienced officer, Lieutenant J. H. Rouson, GM, RNVR, on a visit from the Department of Torpedoes and Mines, was instructing the bomb disposal staffs of all three Services on the means of disposal of German parachute mines. He was well qualified to do this as he was one of the team which dealt with this menace in Birmingham during October 1940. Its direct relevance to the situation in Singapore at that time is, however, debatable.

From April 1942 to May 1943 the BSO in Simonstown, south of Cape Town, South Africa, was an extremely experienced and courageous officer. He was Lieutenant J. Bridge, GM and Bar, RNVR. It was here that he trained to be a diver as he was convinced that there was a threat from manned underwater weapons to places like Trincomalee (Ceylon) and Simonstown. As it was he put his newly learnt skills to good effect in September 1943 when he cleared Messina harbour in Sicily. The details of this action, leading to the award of a George Cross, are recorded later.

The Royal Air Force too was establishing bomb disposal squads. On 14 May 1943 fourteen squads, each consisting of one Flight Sergeant and two Corporals, were established in India and Ceylon. In the Middle East, Royal Air Force squads were operating in North Africa, Malta, Gibraltar and later, after the invasions in July and September 1943, bomb disposal Flights were operating in Sicily and Italy.

When Italy declared war on the United Kingdom and France in June 1940 the Army in the Middle East faced a position similar to that faced in the United Kingdom in 1939, namely an unquantified threat from as yet undefined weapons. From the responsibilities defined at home, Army bomb disposal was clearly a Royal Engineer responsibility. To meet this responsibility a bomb disposal company was established around a very small nucleus of officers and senior non-commissioned officers who had experience, albeit very limited, of bomb disposal. The bulk of the company was recruited from volunteers within the theatre and from a wide range of regiments and corps. On joining the company, known officially as 18 Bomb Disposal Company, RE, all entrants were transferred to the

Royal Engineers. This company, like its sixteen predecessors in the United Kingdom (there never was a 13 Company), learnt its skills (by necessity) quickly and often the hard way. Initially the weapons with which the company dealt were of Italian manufacture. Apart from some in East Africa and a great many in Malta, very few Italian bombs had been recovered. The men of the Royal Engineers and the Royal Air Force were therefore, during this initial period, working within a very steep learning curve. Every new weapon or fuze recovered added to the available information and at times it appeared that men were risking, and on occasion losing, their lives purely to gain this information.

Clearly, bombs which fell in the desert and failed to explode could be blown up *in situ*, but on occasion they were dismantled for intelligence purposes. This thirst for information and the desire to try out new methods of fuze immunization reached such a point that operational instructions for all bomb disposal personnel throughout the theatre were issued. These instructed that whenever circumstances permitted bombs were to be destroyed *in situ*. Only in exceptional circumstances were bombs and fuzes to be dismantled.

From March 1941 the nationality of the unexploded weapons being found began to change. Up to that date enemy unexploded weapons had been almost entirely of Italian origin. After the German attack which halted and turned the Allies' westward advance, more and more German weapons were recovered. When the tide turned at El Alamein in October 1942 and Allied forces again moved westward, an ever-increasing amount of German explosive ordnance was encountered. Throughout this period the sections of 18 Bomb Disposal Company, RE, were spread along the coast of North Africa and into the Nile delta in small isolated detachments. Their major role was keeping open the main supply routes and clearing unexploded bombs which fell into vital stores areas and fortified towns. They were also responsible for the many unexploded bombs which fell in Alexandria and Cairo, although this responsibility was shared with the Egyptian Army Engineers.

An example of the sort of work carried out by these isolated detachments is best shown by extracts from a citation written in respect of Captain J. B. Smith, RE. This states that during the period 27 May to 12 September 1941, while based at Mersa Matru, he dealt with several hundred unexploded bombs of all types, sizes and weights up to 1,000 kg (2,200 lb). He dug for and recovered a 1,000 kg bomb from a depth of 8.5 m (28 ft). On 29 August 1941 he investigated two 500 kg (1,100 lb) unexploded German bombs fitted with No 17 long-delay fuzes, both of which were ticking. He took charge of the situation and his timely orders and precautions saved casualties and damage to the fortifications within the fortress area where the bombs exploded a few hours later. Two unexploded Italian sea mines were also safely dealt with, as were many anti-personnel, general purpose and incendiary bombs.

During the period May to October 1941, 18 Bomb Disposal Company,

RE, dealt with 1,403 high explosive bombs. All reports during this period refer to the close co-operation maintained between the Royal Engineers and Royal Air Force. One RE officer is quoted as saying, 'The cordial relations between Royal Engineer and Royal Air Force bomb disposal personnel not only saved many lives at the time but, because of the freedom with which they discussed their work, prevented many casualties later, when the Eighth Army's advance made it necessary to deal with scores of unexploded British bombs'. It is sad that security restrictions prevented the official flow of information on British bombs and fuzes until after the Army had fought its way halfway up Italy.

By December 1941 the increased availability of bomb disposal equipment from the United Kingdom was sufficient to enable 18 Bomb Disposal Company, RE, to split and form a second company, 28 Bomb Disposal Company, RE. This enabled the complex command, control and administrative problems experienced by 18 Company to be eased a little. As with every law of supply and demand the responsibilities of the two companies grew to meet the increased manpower. The geographical area of responsibility now included Cyprus, but not Iraq for which the Royal Air Force accepted full responsibility.

A year after 28 Bomb Disposal Company's formation, ie, in December 1942, the battle of El Alamein was over and the final Allied drive to the west had begun. This stretched the bomb disposal resources to the limit. Many vital areas had to be cleared of unexploded bombs, booby traps and mines. Many German, Italian and British bomb and ammunition dumps had changed hands several times and it was a brave man who would dare to enter them until they had been declared free from booby traps and demolition charges. In fact, most were abandoned to be dealt with later when the pace of battle had slowed.

At about this time the theatre was increased by three additional bomb disposal companies, Nos 8, 15 and 17, from the United Kingdom. These landed in Algeria with the Allied invasion force of November 1942 and were fully occupied in that area. They would eventually move on to Sicily in July 1943 and then on to Italy. These three companies were both well-equipped and well trained in the skills of German bomb disposal. Prior to the Algerian landings they had also received instruction on Italian bombs and fuzes. However, as the final battle raged in North Africa it became clear that there were insufficient Royal Air Force technicians to deal with their own unexploded bombs. Consequently, Army bomb disposal sections were being called upon to deal with as many British and American bombs as enemy ones. The details of these bombs and their associated fuzes had not been released to them in the United Kingdom. The reasons, as expressed by the Air Ministry, were firstly that it was not the Army's responsibility to clear Allied bombs and secondly it was a question of security. The same types of bombs and fuzes were being dropped on north-west Europe and the fewer people who knew the secrets of their fuzes and how to render them safe the better. Certainly the Germans did not have a monopoly on nasty fuzes. Some of the British long-delay and anti-disturbance fuzes, although working on different principles, were just as deadly as any produced by Germany, if not more so. So quite naturally the Royal Air Force was loath to broadcast their secrets too widely.

There were reasons to suspect that security within and around the bomb disposal organization as a whole had, during its earlier days, been less than perfect. Indeed, it had reached the stage where the Director of Bomb Disposal, Major General Taylor, requested a total press blackout on all bomb disposal activities. He believed it was far from a coincidence that almost every countermeasure produced for a German fuze was met by a counter-countermeasure. For example, the first German direct action fuze, the No 15, was countered by the Two-Pin Plug Discharger as already described. The No 15 fuze was then followed by, or replaced by, the No 25 and No 35 fuzes which required different techniques to discharge them. Then there was the No 50 anti-disturbance fuze which caused the bomb to explode if an attempt was made to use a pin discharger. When a fuze extractor was perfected for the No 17 fuze the enemy started to fit the ZUS 40 anti-withdrawal fuze. When the No 17 clockwork long-delay fuze first appeared it had a relatively loud tick which could be heard with the use of an electric stethoscope, or even under ideal conditions with a doctor's stethoscope. But following the issue of an electric stethoscope a new No 17 fuze appeared on the scene which had an almost silent movement. Except in almost total silence, this fuze could not be heard ticking with the stethoscope then issued. The list could be continued with almost every fuze, but the point made by the Air Ministry was well founded. It is for that same reason that the reader will not find in this book details of modern bomb disposal equipment.

Nos 8, 15 and 17 Bomb Disposal Companies, RE, had not been in the theatre long enough to build up a rapprochement with their opposite numbers in the Royal Air Force. Consequently, because of this security restriction they were forced to treat British and American bombs as if they were enemy ones, ie, deal with them without any prior technical information. Sadly this led to some casualties.

In view of the impending invasion of Sicily and Italy which would be supported by heavy British and American bombing, representations relating to this security embargo were made to the highest levels of command. Allied Headquarters in North Africa finally issued an operational order stating that British Army bomb disposal units would be responsible for Allied as well as enemy bombs which fell outside areas of Royal Navy or Royal Air Force responsibility. On the strength of this order, equipment to deal with American bombs was demanded and technical instructions on British bombs and fuzes were sought from the Air Ministry. The Air Ministry would not agree to the request and a series of letters passed between the various Whitehall departments. A compromise was finally reached. The Air Ministry would provide a technical armament non-commissioned officer, bomb disposal-trained, to work with each RE bomb disposal section as its technical advisor on British and American bombs. However, the Air Ministry agreement to provide one officer and 21 Flight Sergeants to work with the RE bomb disposal sections was not issued until early November 1943. By this time Sicily had been captured, Italy had been invaded two months earlier and Naples had fallen. However, with the invading troops there had been two Royal Air Force Bomb Disposal Flights to cover the normal Royal Air Force responsibilities. As is normal at grass roots level, bomb disposal men get on well together whatever their uniform and a certain cross-flow of information took place.

The situation did not close there, as the Army immediately requested a large number of Royal Air Force technical staff to work and train with the five bomb disposal companies within 21 Army Group preparing for D-Day. Technical staff were also requested to train representatives from all Royal Engineer units in 21 Army Group on British and American bomb recognition. Eventually, after further correspondence the War Office and the Air Ministry issued a memorandum on the disposal of Allied bombs, just three months before D-Day. After defining the new responsibilities it was agreed that the Air Ministry would give the Army access to all Royal Air Force publications and instructions relating to bombs and fuzes at present in service. It would also make available to the Army specimens and drawings of equipment for disposal of bombs. Finally, the Air Ministry would accept a small number of Army officers and non-commissioned officers for training at their bomb disposal school and with Royal Air Force bomb disposal units.

In fact on D-Day and immediately afterwards the Royal Air Force provided, in addition to their own Bomb Disposal Squadrons, 94 bomb disposal-trained non-commissioned officers to be attached to the Divisions and Corps of 21 Army Group. The five Royal Engineer bomb disposal companies were not permanently allocated to any Corps or Divisions but were deployed as Army troops. These 94 members of the Royal Air Force, consisting of 72 senior non-commissioned officers and 22 Corporals, stayed with 21 Army Group from D-Day, 6 June 1944, until September 1944.

We are now ahead of ourselves, but it was necessary to clear the position of responsibilities before considering the events in both Italy and North Africa.

The invasion of Sicily started on 10 July 1943 and with the invading troops were elements of bomb disposal units from all three Services. As far as the Royal Engineer bomb disposal companies was concerned Sicily, and later Italy, were totally different from any other area of operation so far encountered as the company headquarters had very little direct control over the individual bomb disposal sections. This was due mainly to the distances involved and the lack of communications. Bomb disposal sections had by their very nature to be totally mobile and capable of deploying rapidly to wherever they were most needed. Thus the company headquarters acted as a focus for the receipt and distribution of bomb intelligence and ensured that the sections were provided with their essential requirements. It was also at company level that official liaison with bomb disposal units of the other Services was established.

In Sicily sections were initially sited to cover the approaches to ports, airfields and main routes towards Italy. During those initial two months before the invasion of Italy two Royal Engineer bomb disposal sections, Nos 53 and 58, dealt with 59 German and 448 Allied unexploded bombs. This did not include the large number of small anti-personnel bombs of German and Italian manufacture which were scattered around the island in a most haphazard way. In addition, they were frequently required to carry out tasks which were not strictly of a bomb disposal nature. These included clearing mines and booby traps and the removal by explosive demolition of road blocks and unsafe buildings. Or in a simple phrase, normal Royal Engineer combat engineering tasks.

As can be seen from the statistics quoted, the single largest problem was that of unexploded Allied bombs. Sections frequently worked as a number of sub-sections under the command of a junior non-commissioned officer and it was at this level that bomb disposal techniques had to be known. It was at this level that the Corporal or Lance Corporal was expected to be able to cope with almost anything which might be recovered. The dangers from certain Royal Air Force bomb fuzes were well appreciated, but these junior ranks dealt with the situation admirably. It is sad that more of them were not given the recognition they deserved, but as in other combat situations when all around you are risking their lives, bomb disposal is merely another form of risk.

Some acts of bravery must, however, be mentioned. Perhaps some of the most daring acts in relation to bomb and mine clearance were the clearance operations carried out at ports in Sicily, Italy and later in north-west Europe. These were frequently joint Royal Navy and Army operations with the Navy leading on the underwater aspects and the Army leading on the mine and booby-trap aspects. Both were capable of operation in the other's environment and there are many recorded cases of Royal Engineer divers clearing underwater obstacles and explosive charges. This was particularly true of the operations in Europe after D-Day when every bomb disposal company had a complement of officer and other rank divers.

The clearance of Messina harbour on the north coast of Sicily, between 25 August and 2 September 1943, completed just one day before it was required for the invasion of Italy, was a totally Naval operation. The Royal Navy Port Clearance Party No 1500 (P 1500) arrived in Augusta, Sicily, on 11 August 1943, having previously spent its time clearing ports on the North African coast. A few days after its arrival it had two BSOs, Lieutenant A. R. J. Firminger, GM, RNVR, and Lieutenant J. Bridge, GM and Bar, RNVR, both experienced officers. Lieutenant Firminger had been engaged in bomb, mine and torpedo recovery at Bone and

Philippeville on the Algerian coast from 1 February to 12 July 1943. During this period he had personally rendered safe seventeen enemy bombs, five German sea mines and an Italian circling torpedo. Lieutenant Bridge, it will be remembered, was BSO Simonstown where he learnt to dive. In fact in Simonstown he did a lot of useful underwater work.

The officer in charge of P 1500 sent Lieutenant Firminger and a small party with instructions to enter Messina as soon as it was reasonably safe to do so and to carry out a reconnaissance of the harbour area. On arrival the party found large numbers of depth charges with a wide variety of fuzing arrangements lying around the port. In the actual harbour were more depth charges and a number of unidentified objects. The water was very clear and at the end of the jetty it was possible to see a group of depth charges wire-roped together with another unidentified cylinder. Lieutenant Firminger arranged for a hook to be placed through the wire rope holding the depth charges together and for the end of the rope to be passed over a pulley on the jetty and fixed to the back of a vehicle. The vehicle was then slowly driven off and the depth charges were lifted clear of the water. Lieutenant Firminger, Warrant Officer Bratley and three Able Seamen were on the end of the jetty watching the depth charges and the additional cylinder lifted clear of the water when the depth charges hit the underside of the pier. There was a huge explosion which destroyed the pier and killed all who were on it. One Able Seaman on the shore was so injured he spent some months in hospital and the driver of the vehicle escaped with injuries which detained him in hospital for three weeks.

It was into that situation that Lieutenant Bridge was sent with orders to find out how the earlier party had been killed, what the present situation in the harbour was and how he proposed to clear the harbour and dockyard. He arrived in Messina with a small party on 26 August and took until 29 August 1943 to complete his ground survey and prepare a plan. Throughout this period the harbour was under intermittent shelling from Italy which did not help the situation. On 30 and 31 August Lieutenant Bridge, assisted by two Naval divers, Warrant Officer Stone and Petty Officer R. M. Woods, RN, carried out an underwater reconnaissance and discovered two more groups of depth charges with booby-trap attachments and a number of individual depth charges. In all there were over 250 depth charges scattered around the quays, in pump houses and in sub-stations. There were a further forty depth charges in the harbour excluding the two booby-trapped groups. Lieutenant Bridge, assisted by Warrant Officer Stone, Petty Officer Woods and Able Seaman T. P. Peters, RN, managed by 11:30 hours on 2 September 1943 to clear the harbour and port area. Lieutenant Bridge made a total of 28 dives on to the booby-trapped groups accompanied by Able Seaman Peters and with Petty Officer Woods acting as diver's attendant. As a result of this work, Messina harbour was used to ferry troops to the invasion beaches of Italy from 04:00 hours on 3 September 1943. For their outstanding courage Lieutenant Bridge was awarded the George Cross, Petty Officer Woods and Able Seaman Peters the George Medal and Warrant Officer Stone received a commendation.

This type of action was repeated throughout the Italian campaign as each successive port, airfield or garrison town was captured. The Royal Air Force bomb disposal Flights were faced with huge bomb dumps within which were deliberate booby traps, demolition charges fitted with time delay fuzes and every conceivable device designed to prevent the clearance of the dumps and the subsequent use of the airfields. The port of Naples posed a major problem to the Royal Navy and the city provided an equal problem for the Royal Engineers. An example of this was the work carried out in Naples by one section of 17 Bomb Disposal Company, RE. The section was commanded by Lieutenant J. G. Allen, RE, and during the period 9 to 15 October 1943 it cleared 85 booby-trapped and mined buildings and searched many more. At Prince Piedmont Barracks, which had previously been declared safe by other troops, an explosion occurred which killed 25 American soldiers. Lieutenant Allen and his section were then asked to clear two other barracks and in doing so disconnected and neutralized a German firing mechanism connected to 725 kg (1,595 lb) of high explosive.

Naples was considered bad by those involved, but by the time the campaign had moved northwards to Leghorn (Livorno) on the north-west coast of Italy the Germans had improved their techniques still further. The port itself was a mass of Teller mines (a German anti-tank mine containing between 4.5 and 5 kg (10–11 lb) of explosive and capable of being laid with a booby trap)—19,000 were cleared from the port area alone. The harbour was blocked with sunken and booby-trapped ships, demolition charges, depth charges and other nasties. One of the problems was that if one charge was detonated several others in the area might also be detonated as a result of the first explosion. Indeed, in Leghorn when the first demolition charge was fired, a mine went off by sympathetic detonation and this in turn fired an explosive charge under the lighthouse. This sent several tons of masonry 100 m (330 ft) into the air. Later a small anti-swimmer charge set off a sunken lighter full of explosives and a demolition charge fired to clear a berth set off over 1,000 kg (2,200 lb) of explosive buried in a nearby quarry. These frightening and fatal occurrences meant that a very complex control organization had to be established into which all bomb and mine clearance teams had to be fitted. 'A' must not set off a mine while 'B' has divers in the water and 'C' must not fire his demolition charge until those clearing the pump house have been evacuated. Thus a degree of organization was established but there was no control over the intermittent explosions caused by enemy shells which continued to fall throughout the clearance operation. The George Medal citation for Petty Officer W. R. I. Davey, RN, of No 1 Mine and Bomb Disposal Unit, RN, is typical of a number of awards given for this operation and reflects the work carried out by all, including those who did not necessarily gain official recognition.

At Leghorn he was involved in the operations involving clearance of demolition charges and land mines including sixty large demolition charges, 721 Teller and other mines and a number of unexploded bombs and sea mines. He is recommended for outstanding zeal, initiative and unfailing devotion to duty whilst clearing the port area at a time when the ground being cleared was under shell fire.

It was not all major clearance work which was undertaken in Italy, for many of the incidents involved individual bombs or groups of bombs, as in the United Kingdom. The only difference here was that all roads tended to be packed with military convoys and there was little scope for diversions. The congestion on the roads can be understood when it is remembered that the Royal Engineer field units built over 2,500 Bailey bridges in Italy to replace those destroyed in the fighting or by withdrawing troops. Lieutenant Allen, RE (referred to earlier for his work in Naples), spent one week in Salerno. There he had defuzed and removed seven British bombs fitted with long-delay fuzes and anti-handling devices. The bombs had been adjacent to the Salerno/Naples road and the Salerno/Naples railway and their presence was impeding military operations. It was most important that they should not be allowed to explode *in situ*, either by the delayed action of their fuzes or by deliberate demolition. The removal of this type of fuze had in the past caused a number of casualties and the Air Publication for this combination (not then available to Lieutenant Allen) laid down that all such bombs should be destroyed *in situ*. Knowing the dangers but appreciating the urgency of clearing the bombs, Lieutenant Allen accepted the task and successfully removed the bombs without causing an explosion. A month earlier in September 1943 another section commander, Lieutenant K. Lanham, RE, had dealt successfully with six similar bombs in Taranto on the instep of Italy. As with the other bombs they had been given top priority and could not be destroyed or allowed to detonate *in situ*. One bomb was by a main aqueduct, four were on the railway and one was in a gas works.

This, then, was bomb and mine disposal in Sicily and Italy as carried out by the teams from all three fighting Services, but what of North Africa? As the battle flowed back and forth along the coast of North Africa from El Alamein in the east to Tunisia and Algeria in the west, the bomb disposal forces of both the Royal Air Force and the Royal Engineers were stretched to the limit. Their joint role was to keep the Army mobile and the Royal Air Force flying. The Royal Navy had a role also; they were responsible for keeping the ports open. Without the ports and their ability to unload the multitude of stores required by the Army and the Royal Air Force, the aircraft, tanks and men would have come to a grinding halt.

The Royal Navy had similar responsibilities to those in the United Kingdom except that the dividing line between the BSO and the RMS teams was less finely drawn. If you were the only Naval representative present you were expected to be able to deal with anything nautical wherever it was found. Within the actual port you were expected to deal with anything that the enemy or the Allies cared to deliver, whether by sea or air. One example is that of Petty Officer W. Barker, RN. Whilst based at Mersa Matruh, halfway between El Alamein and the Egyptian/Libyan border, he was called to deal with a British magnetic parachute mine which had been discovered in the middle of an anti-personnel minefield. Owing to the nature of the mine it was impossible to clear a path to it using mine detectors because of the fear that their presence could cause the mine to detonate. Petty Officer Barker therefore prodded and felt his way into the minefield three times carrying demolition stores to make up a counter-mining charge. He knew that a false move would mean his death or muti-lation. He successfully fired the charge and by his action allowed the Royal Engineers to clear the minefield.

One hazard which Naval personnel did not have to deal with other than in the Middle East was that of the Italian circling torpedoes. These, when dropped in a harbour by parachute, were designed to run in a spiralling circle until such time as they hit something or ran out of power. They were equipped with three separate detonating systems so that when their run was completed they became a floating mine. If they landed on a ship or on land they had a self-destruct mechanism which made them extremely sen-sitive to any movement. A 1945 publication issued to US mine disposal officers stated in respect of these torpedoes, 'Never attempt rendering safe by disassembly. The extreme sensitivity of the inertia exploders when armed makes such a procedure suicidal. The armed or unarmed condition cannot be determined from exterior examination.' A number of Naval personnel were killed attempting to render safe those torpedoes which had been towed ashore. On occasions these torpedoes were dropped on land and the rendering safe was comparable or greater in risk to rendering safe a parachute mine. Two Naval personnel who cleared many circling torpedoes were Lieutenant Commander N. M. Waldeman, RNR, and Petty Officer P. J. Holdstock, RN. Lieutenant Commander Waldeman worked in Tripoli during the period March/April 1943 when Tripoli received some of its worst attacks. Petty Officer Holdstock ranged along the coast west of Tripoli and between March and September 1943 dealt with over a hundred enemy devices found around the coastline. During the attacks on Tripoli in March and April 1943 he towed a number of torpedoes clear of Tripoli harbour. Both were subsequently awarded well-deserved George Medals.

The first Italian circling torpedo to be rendered safe was on 15 January 1942 some 18 km (11 miles) east of Alexandria. One had been recovered earlier but it had exploded, killing the complete render-safe party from HMS *Medway*. The torpedo recovered on 15 January 1942 was rendered safe by Lieutenant G. H. Goodman, MBE, RNVR, assisted by Petty Officer W. B. Filer, RN, and Painter A. J. Russell, all from HMS *Nile*. Lieutenant Goodman was subsequently awarded the George Cross for this action and his two assistants were both awarded George Medals.

Once the battles had ceased in North Africa a clear-up of the loose explo-sive in the form of bomb and ammunition dumps had to be considered.

Many of the dumps were deteriorating having been exposed to North African climatic conditions for up to four years. Many of the smaller dumps were becoming buried by loose sand and there was a fear of losing them. Some dumps were being systematically plundered by the local population for their own purposes and in one or two cases there appeared to have been spontaneous explosions. Many more were reported as spontaneous but upon investigation the remains of trespassers were found; all reasons that justified a major clearance programme.

Prior to 1944 no large-scale effort had been made to clear the dumps that the enemy had left behind in the desert, although several Mobile Ammunition Laboratories, Royal Army Ordnance Corps (MAL) had been working on ammunition dumps. In early 1944 the Royal Air Force bomb disposal unit, now consisting of 27 trained men (one officer, one Flight Sergeant, five Sergeants and twenty Corporals), began the demolition of certain selected bomb dumps sited on or close to operational airfields. By April 1944 GHQ Middle East recognized the need to clear all the bomb and ammunition dumps for the reasons quoted above.

A joint Army/Royal Air Force co-ordinating committee was established, initially consisting of the officer commanding 18 Bomb Disposal Company, RE, Major P. J. Hands, RE, Command Bomb Disposal Officer (RAF) Flight Lieutenant C. A. Smith, RAF, and a member of the Ordnance Survey Branch of GHQ. This small committee laid down the basic rules and responsibilities for the clearance operation and the units involved. It was agreed that 18 Bomb Disposal Company, RE, would carry out all the reconnaissance work and that these reports would form the basis for all future tasking. No 352 (Indian) Bomb Disposal Company, RE, being the largest unit employed and yet the least mobile, would work on large dumps or areas where a number of dumps were close together. Three MALs, each under the command of a warrant officer and reporting direct to the Inspecting Ordnance Officer, would deal with ammunition dumps. The Royal Air Force bomb disposal personnel would form three mobile demolition parties and be responsible for clearing all dumps on or close to Royal Air Force airfields or installations. Thus the overall responsibilities were: Royal Engineers— all general bomb dumps; MAL—all ammunition dumps; and Royal Air Force—all dumps on or near their own property.

These responsibilities later had to be modified because, as the reconnaissance work progressed, it became clear that bombs and ammunition were often in the same dump and the great distances involved made some area responsibilities necessary. Eventually the clearance became a genuine combined operation with many of the sub-units working under the officer in charge of the particular demolition, who might be Royal Engineer, Royal Army Ordnance Corps or Royal Air Force.

This work took place between April and November 1944 and as the work progressed the co-ordinating committee grew from the original three to a group of eight men with representatives from a number of GHQ staff branches. On completion of the task the total weight of explosive disposed of amounted to 46,858 tonnes (46,118 tons) of which approximately one-third was in bombs and the remainder in all other types of ammunition. (It should be noted that these weights are the nett explosive content and not the total weight of the bombs and ammunition which would be at least twice the weights quoted.)

This task may appear at first not to have much relevance to bomb disposal but such a thought would be totally wrong. Many of these dumps were in a dangerous condition, many were near sensitive sites which should not be damaged if at all possible and many were still booby-trapped. They therefore required the expertise of experienced bomb disposal officers and men. In fact this was the first of many battle area clearance tasks which were to face bomb disposal units and which continue to face them over forty years later. The most important reason for considering this task, however, is that it demonstrates the co-operation which is possible between Services and arms within a Service when all are competently trained and working to a common aim.

8

Preparation for D-Day and the battle of the missiles

Throughout the latter half of 1943 and during early 1944 the whole of the United Kingdom was becoming an armed camp. Preparations overt and covert were being made for the launching of the largest armada ever assembled—the invasion force due to sail on that unknown date referred to as D-Day.

As far as bomb disposal units were concerned there were three main activities during this period. The first was routine bomb disposal (if any bomb disposal can be described as routine). For the Royal Air Force this was a particularly busy time as more and more bombers were nightly delivering their bomb loads upon mainland Europe. Consequently, more and more damaged aircraft were jettisoning their loads or returning with bombs 'hung up', all needing the attention of bomb disposal personnel. The second activity was the redeployment of Royal Engineer bomb disposal units, with an attached Naval officer, to various areas in southern England. This was done to protect the thousands of troops massing along the English south coast, should the enemy use small anti-personnel bombs or parachute mines against this perfect target. The thought of the carnage which would be wrought by the explosion of a parachute mine in the centre of a tented camp was horrific. Finally, there was the selection and specialist training of those units destined to move with the invasion force.

During early 1944 there was an upsurge in enemy air activity over the United Kingdom and an increase in the number of unexploded bombs. This presented no real problem, although January did see the advent of a new German bomb. It was a light cased, parachute-dropped blast bomb which to the casual observer looked nothing like a bomb. It was made of sheet steel, had an oval cross-section 800 mm (31½ in) wide, was 420 mm (16½ in) high and had an overall length of 1,675 mm (66 in). It was the 1,000 kg (2,200 lb) SB (Sprengbombe—blast bomb) and presented no particular problem to the bomb disposal man as it was fitted with a simple direct impact fuze. When it detonated, however, it was an extremely efficient blast bomb because over 72 per cent of its total weight was explosive.

One interesting point about bomb disposal activities during 1943 and early 1944 was the increased presence of American personnel within the British units. Throughout this period Americans were attached to British bomb disposal schools and units for 'on job' training. British personnel were also sent to the United States as instructors and for liaison. This arrangement continued throughout the war and indeed continues today. The present British Joint Service Bomb Disposal School, or to give it its proper title The Defence Explosive Ordnance Disposal School, not only has instructors from all three Services, it also has instructors from the United States. Similarly, British bomb disposal personnel continue to visit the United States as instructors and students.

Returning to 1944, early in that year the disposition of Royal Engineer bomb disposal units underwent a change. Units were concentrated along the south coast of England in the areas of heavy troop concentration and at possible embarkation ports. At that time there were a number of so-called 'tip and run' raids when a single enemy aircraft would fly low over the coast, drop one or two bombs, and return to base. These raids were a nuisance, but caused little damage except to the inhabitants of such towns as Eastbourne, Hastings and Brighton. However, it was thought that they might be the harbingers of more concentrated raids against the massive military target being established along the coast. It was for this reason that the bomb disposal units were redeployed—the fear of a massive attack using butterfly bombs or parachute mines was very real. As it happened these attacks did not materialize but no satisfactory explanation for the enemy's failure to exploit this situation has ever been given. The writer would like to think that it was due to the efficient clearance operations carried out in 1943, when the true potential of the butterfly bomb was hidden from the enemy by the bravery and skill of individual bomb disposal personnel.

While all these overt activities were taking place there was a great deal of covert and semi-covert training taking place. The selection and training of those bomb disposal units landing with the invasion force fell into the second category of semi-covert.

In July 1943 five Bomb Disposal Companies RE (Nos 5, 19, 23, 24 and 25) were transferred from under command Home Forces to 21 Army Group in preparation for the invasion. Apart from the essential requirement of 100 per cent physical fitness, their training was extended to include the disposal of all known types of German land mines, buoyant mines likely to be found in rivers and canals and all known forms of underwater and land-based booby traps. To enable these skills to be acquired it was agreed that two officers per company should attend shallow-water diving courses to be run by the Royal Navy at Chatham. Courses in sea mine disposal were also offered, accepted and in all cases over-subscribed. Soon it was realized that two trained officer divers per company were not enough. Therefore, all officers who were medically fit to dive and who had volunteered for the training were permitted to be so trained. In the majority of companies this meant that all the officers were trained shallow-water divers and capable of doing minor engineering tasks underwater. That is, providing you can consider removing demolition charges from bridge piers and using underwater cutting equipment as engineering tasks.

This increased scope of training meant that the Royal Navy's Army training programme had to be moved to HMS *Vernon* at Portsmouth. Here also non-commissioned officers and Sappers were trained as divers' mates— essential for any diver. Thus, thanks to the co-operation of the Royal Navy, the Royal Engineer bomb disposal units of the invasion force had a much increased flexibility and capability to deal with enemy devices. Their ability, however, to deal safely with Allied bombs and fuzes was in considerable doubt until early 1944. In January a Royal Engineer technical instruction on British bombs and fuzes was issued to bomb disposal units, followed by a second one in February 1944. It was not until March 1944 that the Air Ministry formally released the necessary Air Publications and began the intensive training of Royal Engineer bomb disposal units in the recognition and disposal of Allied bombs.

When the five bomb disposal companies first joined 21 Army Group they had a total of fifty bomb disposal sections. During the preparations for D-Day, intelligence forecasts of the enemy's air potential indicated that not so many bomb disposal sections would be required. Consequently, by June 1944 the five companies contained a total of 33 bomb disposal sections. Their activities after D-Day are considered in a later chapter.

The Royal Air Force bomb disposal units were preparing for D-Day too. Three bomb disposal squadrons (Nos 5137, 5138 and 5139), containing a total of eight self-contained mobile bomb disposal Flights each of one officer and 26 men, were earmarked for the invasion force. There were additionally, within the three squadrons, seventeen bomb disposal sections each of two to three men. With the exception of the underwater commitment the role of the Royal Air Force bomb disposal units was very similar to that of the Royal Engineers. The Royal Air Force, however, spent the majority of their time clearing captured airfields and Luftwaffe installations. The problems they faced were very similar to those elsewhere, enemy and Allied bombs, land mines and booby traps. Their activities after D-Day are also considered in a later chapter.

Thus the bomb disposal units of the Royal Air Force and the Royal Engineers were prepared for their role in the invasion force. But what of the Royal Navy? Once again their bomb disposal work was carried out mainly by the 'P' Parties. Their very name has become synonymous with courage and daring of the highest order following their clearance of the deadly wreckage left behind in the European ports. Their training, however, was of a more covert nature and their action rather than their training will be considered in a later chapter.

During this period prior to D-Day, preparations were not only being made for the invasion of mainland Europe, but some farsighted plans were also being made for the battles yet to come in the Far East. In March 1944 preparations for the war against Japan were being considered in respect of Royal Engineer bomb disposal units. In that month all bomb disposal personnel in the United Kingdom under the age of 32, other than those in 21 Army Group, were medically examined to determine those who were fit enough to become divers. We have seen already that the officers of the five bomb disposal companies in 21 Army Group were trained as shallow-water divers, but diving was nothing new to the Royal Engineer bomb disposal units. A number of non-commissioned officers had been trained at Chatham in 1941 as shallow water divers to assist in beach obstacle clearance in support of commando raids against the enemy coast. Additionally, in 1942 there is a record of Captain A. G. Polson, RE, carrying out 'copper helmeted' diving in the King's Cross gasholders in north London to recover an unexploded bomb.

In October 1944, from those officers and men who had passed the necessary medical examinations the previous March, ten Bomb Disposal Platoons (Light), RE, were formed. It should perhaps be noted that all Bomb Disposal Sections, RE, were renamed Bomb Disposal Platoons, RE, in September 1944. There was no change in their actual establishment and the parent companies retained their title of company. In May 1947 there was another renaming of both platoons and companies but that will be dealt with in the appropriate point of the narrative.

In the title Bomb Disposal Platoon (Light) the only new terminology was the word 'light'. These new light platoons had a modified establishment which included for the first time two officers, a Captain and a Subaltern, and were designed to be the fighting equivalent of two Royal Naval Landing Craft Obstacle Clearance Units. All ranks were trained to use underwater swimming equipment, which required a very high standard of physical fitness and endurance. They were also trained in Japanese, British and American bomb disposal. The officers and senior non-commissioned officers received training in normal pressure-suit diving (copper helmeted) and the disposal of anti-ship mines of all relevant nationalities.

From the trained light platoon personnel a Company Headquarters and four platoons were formed into a unit in April 1945; this unit moved to India in June 1945 but travelled no further east. The remaining light platoons were sent to north-west Europe and employed on general diving tasks. The principal role of these platoons was beach obstacle clearance but thanks to the cessation of hostilities they were never used in their main role against the Japanese mainland or indeed anywhere else. Thus these bomb disposal men were trained for their dangerous and exacting task but were never needed. One would like to think that today's training for the future will have the same outcome.

Again we have moved forward of our story but it does illustrated that even before D-Day preparations were being made for the next major step.

Likewise, before D-Day there were many rumours and eventually reasonably good drawings (and indeed photographs) of the next problems which were to face the bomb disposal man—the unmanned flying bomb and the long-distance rocket—the V1 and V2.

Under the terms of the Treaty of Versailles in 1919, Germany was forbidden to manufacture heavy artillery. To compensate for this, much of the inventive flair within the German nation was directed towards liquid- and solid-fuelled rockets which could carry a warhead as large or larger than any heavy artillery shell. As we have seen in the development of bombs in 1914 and the development of magnetic mines in the mid- and late 1930s, there was keen rivalry between the German armed Services. This was equally true in relation to the development of guided missiles.

In 1945, when Allied technicians visited the rocket research establishments in Germany they found a large number of guided weapon projects in various stages of development. They ranged from the huge A-9/A-10 rocket designed for the bombardment of the United States of America, to the small X-7 or Rotkappchen (Little Red Riding Hood), a wire-guided anti-tank rocket which must surely have been the ancestor to all the many wire-guided anti-tank missiles which exist today. In between these two extremes were a range of rocket-powered air-to-air, ground-to-air and air-to-ground missiles being developed by agencies on behalf of either the German ground or air forces. Of this range of missiles only four had actually been brought into service although several others had passed their proving flights and were on the verge of becoming operational.

The first two to come into service were the Ruhrstahl SD 1400X and the Henschel Hs 293. Reference has already been made in Chapter 5 to the SD 1400X. It was a 1,400 kg (3,080 lb) armour-piercing bomb with four stubby wings added to the bomb body. Added to the rear was an after body containing a radio receiver and gyroscope and to this was fitted the tail assembly. The four cruciform fins in the tail assembly (hence the X in its title) were fitted with steering controls and solenoids to move them. Thus when the bomb was released from an aircraft it fell in a shallow glide. The direction and steepness of the glide could be controlled by the bomb aimer by the use of a joystick in the parent aircraft which, via radio signals, activated the steering solenoids in the bomb.

The second missile, the Hs 293, was technically a rocket-propelled 500 kg (1,100 lb) bomb, but unlike the SD 1400X it retained little of the appearance of a conventional bomb. It was in effect a small glider 3.5 m (11.5 ft) long with a wing span of 2.9 m (9.5 ft) in the forward end of which was fitted the 500 kg bomb. Behind the bomb, within the fuselage, was fitted a radio receiver similar to that in the SD 1400X and guidance controls for the tail assembly. Suspended from the body was a rocket motor designed to give the missile a greater range and additional velocity to aid penetration upon impact and to escape anti-aircraft fire. This missile was controlled by the bomb aimer in the same manner as the SD 1400X.

German Hs 293 (rocket-propelled, radio-controlled bomb).

From the German point of view the first successful action using these missiles was the sinking of the British corvette HMS *Egret* in the Bay of Biscay with an Hs 293 on 27 August 1943. This was followed on 9 September 1943 by the sinking of the 42,000-ton Italian battleship *Roma* and the crippling of her sister ship the *Italia* en route to Malta following the Italian surrender to the Allies that day. On the night of 9/10 September, attacks started against the Salerno beachhead and by 16 September 1943 the British battleship HMS *Warspite* had been crippled and direct hits had been registered on the cruisers HMS *Uganda* and the USS *Savanna* using SD 1400X missiles.

These weapons continued to be a serious threat to Allied vessels for some months, but by February 1944, when the German counter-offensive to the Anzio landings was at its peak, an effective countermeasure had been devised. It was a simple form of radio jamming. Since the majority of these missiles were aimed at maritime targets, those which missed tended to fall into the sea and so presented no further problem. Those which fell on the land were treated like any other bomb and since the fuzes were designed solely to detonate the weapon after penetrating the target, they contained no traps for the wary bomb disposal teams and so were relatively easily disposed of.

During the period August 1943 to April 1944 there were reports of just over a hundred SD 1400Xs and some ten times that number of Hs 293s having been used operationally in the Mediterranean, the Atlantic and the North Sea. On the night of 30 April 1944 there were also a small number of SD 1400Xs launched against the city of Plymouth, Devon, on the English south coast.

The other two missiles to see operational service will be well known to the residents of London and south-east England in 1944 and equally well known to the residents of Antwerp, Belgium and some other mainland European towns and cities. These missiles were the so-called *Vergeltungswaffe* or Vengeance weapons, better known as the V1 (the flying bomb or doodle-bug) and the V2 (the long-range rocket). These missiles were designed and built for the use of the German Air Force and German Army respectively. The saga of their development from the early A2 rocket first fired in December 1934 from the island of Borkum in the North Sea is an interesting but complex story which has no place in this book, where the main interest must lie with the weapon which lands and fails to explode. Although they will be referred to as the V1 and V2 it is interesting to note their German nomenclature. The V1 was initially known as the Fieseler Fi 103 after Gerhard Fieseler of Fieseler Flugzeugbau who had overall responsibility for its design and development. This was quickly replaced by the official Luftwaffe title FZG 76. The letters FZG were an abbreviation for *Flak Ziel Gerät* (anti-aircraft target apparatus) to hide the weapon's true purpose from Allied intelligence personnel. This stratagem was a total failure as everyone, including Germans not in the know, assumed that the letters were the abbreviation for *Fern Ziel Gerät* (long-range target apparatus) which is exactly what it was. The V2 was known as the A4 rocket, being the direct descendant of the A1, Aggregat 1 (Unit 1). The A2 was first fired in 1934, the A3 in 1937 and the A4 on 3 October 1942. At this early stage all were prototypes and no large-scale production had been considered.

The German anti-invasion plans included a massive conventional and V1 attack upon the gathering invasion forces. This attack was planned for December 1943. However, during the period August to November 1943 the Royal Air Force attacked the Peenemünde research establishment, the Fieseler main works at Kassel and all the known V1 launching ramps. Consequently, by January 1944 all that could be mounted was the so-called 'Little Blitz' using conventional aircraft and bombs. London, Hull on the east coast and Bristol on the west coast were the main targets and these attacks caused a considerable amount of extra work for the bomb disposal organization, as did the attack against Plymouth on 30 April 1944 which was also the final appearance of the SD 1400X.

It was not until the night of 12/13 June 1944 that the first V1 crossed the coast of Great Britain, seven days after the invasion it was designed to prevent. On the night of 12/13 June 1944 it had been the German intention to fire two salvoes each of seventy V1s, but on that first night only ten weapons were launched. Of these ten, five crashed shortly after launch, one crashed into the sea and four crossed the English coast. All four exploded on impact, one in Sussex, two in Kent and one in Bethnal Green (east London). No more V1s were launched until 15 June 1944 when, using fifty-five separate launching sites, a total of 244 missiles were launched within 24 hours. This rate of launch was not maintained but nevertheless, throughout August 1944 an average of 155 missiles a day was launched, the worst day being 3 August when 224 crossed the coast of which 103 hit London. The cease-fire was ordered on 1 September 1944 when the German forces began to withdraw from the Pas de Calais area. This did not, however, signal the end of the bombardment as modified V1s were launched from modified Heinkel He 111 bomber aircraft. Between 5 September 1944 and 14 January 1945 these aircraft launched approximately 1,200 V1s from off the east coast of Britain and V1s fell as far afield as Manchester and areas of Cheshire. From 14 January 1945 all V-weapon operations came under SS control and after that date a further 275 V1s, modified yet again to give them a longer range, were launched against London from sites near Delft in the Netherlands.

The V1 was a small pilotless mid-wing monoplane with a single fin and rudder and was propelled by a pulse jet motor mounted over the rear end of the fuselage. The missile had an ovverall length of 7.75 m (25.4 ft) and a wingspan of 4.9 m (16 ft). It carried a warhead containing 850 kg (1,870 lb) of high explosive. Its duration of flight was controlled by an air log (a small two-bladed propeller geared to a counter). After a preset number of revolutions (distance travelled) two small detonators were fired which, by means of a trip lever, locked the elevators in a diving position. This change of angle shut off the fuel supply and the V1 glided towards its target where in most cases it exploded on impact causing a large area of blast damage.

It was equipped for three fuzing systems although on occasions only the following two were fitted. The first was the 80A, a simple mechanical spring-activated 'all-ways' acting device with a number of sensitive spring-loaded strikers. This fuze was designed to fire the warhead regardless of the direction in which the missile hit the ground. The only safety device was a pin pulled from the fuze head as the V1 was launched. The second fuze was an extremely sensitive electrical impact fuze, the 106X. This obtained its electrical power from a battery situated in the rear of the

German FZG 76 or V1 flying bomb.

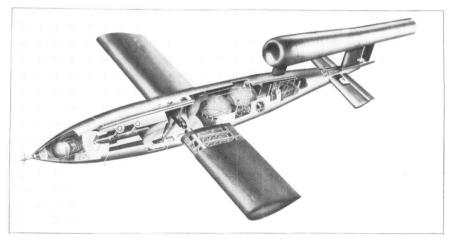

Warhead of German V1 flying bomb.

fuselage. The safety mechanism in this circuit was removed by a switch connected to the air log and was not removed until the V1 had travelled approximately 65 km (40 miles). Another source of power in the firing circuit of the 106X fuze was a small onboard generator which slowly charged a capacitor. Thus, should the battery be destroyed or become separated, there was sufficient electrical energy in the capacitor to fire the detonator when the firing circuit was completed. On impact the circuit was completed either by an inertia switch within the fuze or by one of two pressure plate contact switches situated on the belly of the missile and in its nose. The third fuze, not always fitted, was a clockwork self-destruction fuze intended to operate should the other two fail. It was similar to the No 17 long-delay fuze used in conventional bombs but without the electrical components. The clock was started by a pin being withdrawn during the launching and could be set for any period up to two hours after launching.

The first V1 which failed to explode upon hitting the ground landed in a wood at Fairlight near Brighton, Sussex, on 17 June 1944. Due to its relatively frail construction it was badly damaged and fragments of the missile were scattered over a wide area. Despite the damage, details of the 106X electrical impact fuze and the 80A mechanical impact fuze were discovered and provisional methods of immunization determined. It was not

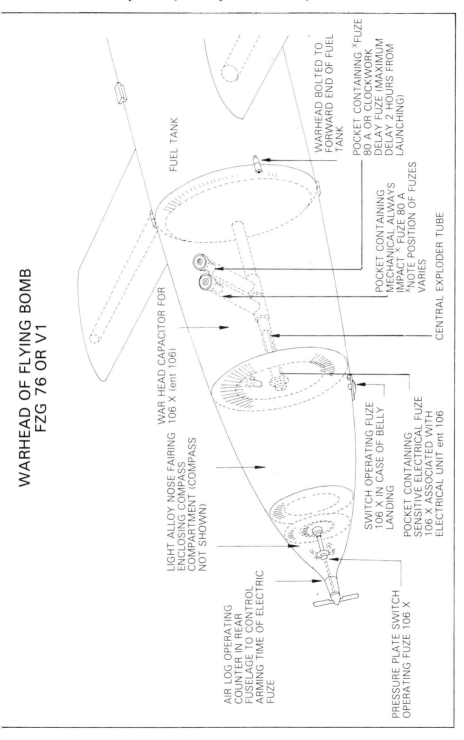

WARHEAD OF FLYING BOMB
FZG 76 OR V1

FUEL TANK

WARHEAD BOLTED TO FORWARD END OF FUEL TANK

POCKET CONTAINING ×FUZE 80 A OR CLOCKWORK DELAY FUZE (MAXIMUM DELAY 2 HOURS FROM LAUNCHING)

POCKET CONTAINING MECHANICAL ALWAYS IMPACT × FUZE 80 A ×NOTE POSITION OF FUZES VARIES

CENTRAL EXPLODER TUBE

WAR HEAD CAPACITOR FOR 106 X (ent 106)

LIGHT ALLOY NOSE FAIRING ENCLOSING COMPASS COMPARTMENT (COMPASS NOT SHOWN)

SWITCH OPERATING FUZE 106 X IN CASE OF BELLY LANDING

POCKET CONTAINING SENSITIVE ELECTRICAL FUZE 106 X ASSOCIATED WITH ELECTRICAL UNIT ent 106

AIR LOG OPERATING COUNTER IN REAR FUSELAGE TO CONTROL ARMING TIME OF ELECTRIC FUZE

PRESSURE PLATE SWITCH OPERATING FUZE 106 X

until 23 June 1944 that the first reasonably complete V1 was discovered after landing at Strawberry Hill Farm, Staplecross, Sussex. It was clearly a bonus for the bomb disposal organization and a very strong team was therefore sent to exploit it.

The team was headed by Major J. D. Hudson, MBE, GM, RE, who it will be remembered, received his George Medal for his work on the Y fuze (recounted in Chapter 6). He was assisted by Dr J. A. T. Dawson (also referred to in Chapter 6) and Mr R. Hurst, both scientists with the Ministry of Supply and responsible for much of the research and development of the early bomb disposal radiographic equipment. There were also a small party of Sappers but history does not record their names.

Before recounting the actions of this team it is necessary to understand the general configuuration of the V1 warhead. In the part of the fuselage where the wings joined the body was the main fuel tank. Immediately forward of the fuel tank and bolted to it was the warhead in the shape of a truncated cone, 1,195 mm (47 in) long. Forward of the warhead was attached a light alloy fairing going to a point where the air log propeller was fitted. Within the fairing was the V1's gyro compass and very close to the forward end one of the two electric contact switches for the 106X fuze. The actual 106X fuze was in the centre of the forward end of the warhead and therefore inaccessible from outside without first gaining entry to the forward compartment. The other two fuzes were fitted transversely into the side of the warhead as in most German bombs. These were, therefore, both accessible from outside the missile.

The team arrived at Strawberry Hill Farm on 24 June 1944 and Major Hudson began an immediate investigation. He quickly identified two of the three fuzes as being the same as those which had been recovered from previous incidents, namely the 106X in the front of the warhead and an 80A in the forward of the two transverse fuze pockets. These he dealt with as described in a later incident. The third fuze contained in the rear fuze pocket was unmarked and of an unknown type. Major Hudson reported this to the Director of Bomb Disposal and was told to recover it intact without fail. The fuze was radiographed by Dr Dawson and it was seen to have a clockwork movement similar to that used in German long-delay fuzes. The radiograph was not clear enough to determine the exact working of the fuze or whether there was any form of booby trap or anti-withdrawal system. It would have been relatively easy to withdraw the fuze remotely and trust to luck, but had the fuze operated and the V1 exploded the fuze would have been lost. The instructions did say it had to be recovered intact without fail.

An attempt was then made to obtain a clearer radiograph by placing an improvised film holder in the forward of the two side pockets (after extraction of its fuze) but this was unsuccessful. It was then decided to remove a portion of the warhead casing either side of the fuze pocket, then to dissolve some of the explosive with a view to placing a film plate on one side of the fuze pocket and a radioactive source on the other and so obtain a radiograph of maximum clarity.

The fuze was presumed to be in an armed condition and to have a short time setting; both assumptions later proved to be correct. It was known that the clockwork mechanism was not ticking but that any movement or vibration could start or restart the clock. The warhead casing could not, therefore, be cut using a hacksaw, file or any mechanical device and it was decided to cut into the case using a fine jet of acid. Before attempting this method on the warhead an experimental cut was tried on a portion of another V1 which proved successful. The warhead casing was accordingly cut into using an acid jet and portions of the casing removed. This operation took a total of five hours' work, and was carried out in relays by Major Hudson and Mr Hurst. Throughout they were aware of the risk from the fuze itself and also of the danger of allowing the acid to come into contact with the explosive. Consequently, the metal was cut away until the thickness of metal remaining in each cut was only paper thin. The cut was then completed using a sharp knife.

Explosive from around the fuze pocket was then washed away with warm acetone by Major Hudson, Dr Dawson and Mr Hurst, working in turns. This operation took a total of thirteen working hours and the toxic fumes generated resulted, according to a contemporary report, 'in dizziness, vomiting and extreme lassitude on the part of the operators coupled with ashy pallor and blueness of the lips'.

Dr Dawson then set up the radiographic equipment inside the warhead with the photographic plate on one side of the fuze pocket and the radioactive source on the other. He obtained a very clear set of radiographs which, when compared with a German 17(B) long-delay fuze, established that the fuze in the V1 held an identical clockwork mechanism giving a maximum time setting of two hours. They also showed that there was no anti-withdrawal device fitted. It was not possible, however, to determine the time setting on this particular clock or how long, if at all, it had already run.

The next step was the extraction of the fuze. Clearly this could not be done without vibration and any movement was likely to start the clock with perhaps only seconds to run. Should that be the case, the safe removal of the fuze, followed by the detonation of its gaine before any of the team could reach the V1, would destroy the fuze and negate all their efforts. Major Hudson and Mr Hurst, therefore, improvized a form of remote extraction equipment utilizing cords, pulleys, blocks and a magnetic clock stopper so that, as the fuze was extracted it swung into a strong magnetic field which would effectively prevent the fuze from restarting, or almost instantly stop it should it start due to the jerk of extraction. While Mr Hurst listened using a remote control stethoscope from a trench some 45 m (50 yd) from the V1, Major Hudson manipulated the cords from a distance of 90 m (100 yd). The fuze was safely extracted and Major Hudson removed the gaine. When the fuze was subsequently tested it was found to be fully armed but not started and was set to function after 32 minutes.

The complete operation started on 24 June 1944 and proceeded almost continuously during daylight hours until 17:00 hours on 2 July 1944. Intermittently throughout this period V1s were being attacked overhead by fighter aircraft and being brought down in the neighbourhood, a most disturbing factor for those working on the crashed V1 and trying to avoid any disturbance which might start the clock.

For this action Major Hudson was awarded a Bar to his previous George Medal and Dr Dawson and Mr Hurst were also awarded George Medals.

Thus were the fuze secrets of the V1 discovered, but this knowledge did not always prevent death, danger and anxiety to bomb disposal operators. The V1s by their nature did not bury themselves deeply into the ground and if they failed to explode they tended to scatter their components over a wide area. This area always had to be searched by bomb disposal personnel, not only to remove hazardous components but also to check whether some new fuze was being employed. Such an event took place at Hopton in Suffolk on 15 October 1944 when Major T. J. Deane, GM, RE, officer commanding 10 Bomb Disposal Company, RE, and two of his officers, Captain H. Yard, RE, and Lieutenant C. J. Bassett, RE, were investigating a V1 crash site. The missile had almost totally disintegrated and the warhead had shattered to such an extent that the fuzes in their pockets were separated from the main charge but still adjacent to it. Clearly they had to be moved—this was done and the fuze pockets were laid to one side. While the search continued one of the fuze pockets exploded killing Lieutenant Bassett and injuring the other two officers. No reason for this explosion was given but a possibility was that a clockwork fuze, despite not operating when the missile disintegrated, started after the relatively gentle movement of being removed from the area of the warhead.

Another instance of a V1 crashing and remaining in a relatively undamaged state occurred at lunchtime on 28 July 1944 when one crashed at Southborough in Kent. The missile was in a residential area and several hundred people had been evacuated from their homes. The officer tasked to deal with this missile was Lieutenant E. W. Sivil, RE, of 20 Bomb Disposal Company, RE. He was an experienced bomb disposal officer with over 200 bombs to his credit and some months' experience of clearing beach minefields, but this was his first V1. In view of the circumstances, and in particular of the pressure which was likely to be applied to a junior officer when hundreds of people were keen to have the job completed and be able to return home, Lieutenant Sivil was accompanied by his company commander. On arrival at the site the officers checked the evacuation distance and then investigated the missile. The two most common fuzes were quickly identified as the 106X and the 80A, with the third fuze pocket closed by an unmarked bakelite cap. The radiographic equipment was sent for and Lieutenant Sivil, realizing that nothing could be done until the spring-loaded mechanical impact fuze had been immunized and removed, set about rendering the 80A fuze safe. This he did by injecting a fast-setting resin into the mechanical intricacies of the fuze, thus preventing any mechanical action taking place.

By this time the radiographic equipment had still not arrived, but because of the large numbers of people evacuated and the general interest being taken, the Commander Royal Engineers of that particular bomb disposal group, a Lieutenant Colonel R. O. StJ. Marshall, had arrived on the scene. He, in consultation with the company commander, decided that Lieutenant Sivil should continue without the radiographic equipment especially as the police were pressing for the work to be completed as soon as possible for the evacuation was causing considerable dislocation within the town.

(This type of pressure is frequently applied to bomb disposal teams even today. Unless there is a valid operational or life-saving reason for 'pressing on', unnecessary risks should not be incurred by bomb disposal operators merely to save other people inconvenience. There are enough in-built risks for the operator without adding unnecessary ones.)

Lieutenant Sivil withdrew the now jammed 80A fuze and turned his attention to the unknown fuze covered with the brown bakelite cap. He was reasonably confident that there was no fuze under the cover but he could not be sure. He unscrewed the locking ring, at the same time pressing down on the fuze cap. As the locking ring was slackened off he cautiously lifted his finger to determine whether the cap was spring-loaded or not. It was not and lifting the cap he realized that it was merely a cover for a fuze pocket containing only a roll of corrugated cardboard. Despite that, it had been a nerve-racking few minutes. All that remained now was the 106X fuze and its complete wiring circuits where the closure of any one could cause detonation. Aided by two Sappers, Brooks and Evans, the circuits were traced, cut and taped and the 106X fuze removed. The V1 was now relatively safe and all that remained was the removal of the two detonators in the tail to allow the residents of Southborough to return to their homes.

The other Vengeance weapon, the V2 or A4 long-distance rocket was, to those at the receiving end, a most frightening weapon as there was absolutely no warning of its approach and consequently casualties per incident tended to be high. It was at eleven minutes to seven on the evening of 8 September 1944 when the long-anticipated attack by high-altitude supersonic rockets began. There was a huge explosion and eleven houses in Staveley Road, Chiswick, in south-west London ceased to exist. Three civilians died, the first of over 2,700 to be killed by this new menace from the air. Less than a minute later a second V2 exploded at Epping in Essex, 33 km (20 miles) north of London.

Between 8 September 1944 and when the last V2 fell on 27 March 1945, a further 517 were to fall on London and a total of over 1,100 were to explode on England as a whole. Of those 1,100-plus incidents only four V2s failed to explode on impact although several others disintegrated in the air, showering the ground with components and vital clues as to their fuzing system. That so few failed speaks well for the fuzing system even considering the size of the weapon and its velocity on impact. It was 14 m (45.9 ft) long, 1.6 m (5.4 ft) in diameter and hit the ground at speeds approaching 4,828 km/h (3,000 mph). Contrary to popular belief the V2s recovered in England were not fitted with proximity fuzes.

By January 1945 parts of two warheads had been recovered from rockets which had broken up in the atmosphere and some tentative picture of the fuzing system had been built up. It was not, however, until 11 March 1945 that the first unexploded V2 was reported. Since this was only sixteen days before the last V2 was to fall on the United Kingdom (although at the time this was not known), it is clear that this weapon posed no serious bomb disposal problem. Despite this the work carried out on the four unexploded rockets is worthy of attention, especially as they all fell in Essex and their disposal was the responsibility of the same bomb disposal officer.

These incidents not only demonstrate the cool nerve required when dealing with a totally new weapon, they also emphasize the problems faced by many bomb disposal men when required to deal with a weapon in which a great many people are interested. Whether it be a new type of weapon, as in these cases, or a routine task in a very public place, it often requires as much nerve and certainly more tact to keep the officials at bay than to deal with the object causing the interest.

The first unexploded V2 fell in a field near Paglesham in rural Essex during the night of 11/12 March 1945. The officer detailed to investigate the site was Major L. Gerhold, GM and Bar, RE, the company commander of 22 Bomb Disposal Company, RE. On arrival at the remote farm he found a most impressive hole of entry some 1.8 m (6 ft) in diameter and approximately 5.4 m (18 ft) deep. Major Gerhold was lowered down the shaft where he found traces of material which convinced him that an unexploded V2 lay beneath his feet. He therefore arranged for men from his company to begin the massive excavation work which would be required to reach the warhead. The hole was likely to be at least as deep as the length of the rocket plus the depth of the visible hole, an estimated 20 m (65½ ft). The excavation was carried out by members of 22 Bomb Disposal Company, RE, who fully understood that they were working on top of almost a ton of high explosive, 994 kg (2,191 lb) to be exact, connected to a fuzing system which had never before failed.

Six days later, on Sunday 18 March 1945, the excavation was still continuing when news arrived that a second unexploded rocket had fallen at Hutton near Brentwood, again in Essex and within Major Gerhold's area of responsibility. He left immediately for Hutton and discovered that this time the rocket had not penetrated deeply and the warhead was clearly visible and accessible from the surface. Despite it being Sunday afternoon, the news of this find within easy travelling distance of London and in a situation where it could be viewed without too much difficulty brought a flood of visitors. Representatives from various War Office staff branches, the Royal Air Force and the Ministry of Home Security, all wanted to see this object the like of which had caused so much damage during the past six months. Luckily Major Gerhold was, on this occasion, accompanied by his commander Royal Engineers, Lieutenant Colonel S. C. Lynn, OBE, RE, and between them they managed to convince the

Recovering the nose cone of a V2 rocket.

onlookers that this was a dangerous spot to be and by last light had cordoned off the danger area and posted military guards. These guards were supported by the local police and the site was secure for the night.

The fuzing system in the V2 was relatively simple in concept. It was an electrical circuit connected to an igniter which, when the current flowed, caused the booster charge (or gaine) to detonate which in turn detonated the main charge. The electrical power came from a 32-volt battery in the rocket, which not only powered the circuit but also charged a capacitor in an electrical 'bag of tricks' known as the Sterg Unit. Thus, if the battery became disconnected from the circuit, power was still available from the capacitor. This was most important to the bomb disposal man since it meant that disconnecting the battery did not make the circuit safe. There were additionally five simple switches in the circuit, the closing of any one of which would fire the igniter. One was a simple contact switch in the extreme tip of the nose. Two inertia switches were mounted on the front of the warhead at right angles to each other and another two, also at right angles, were mounted on the rear of the warhead. Thus any sudden change of direction, reduction or increase of speed or the lightest contact on the nose would cause detonation and in most cases did. The Sterg Unit also acted as a safety device so that should the rocket motors fail during launch all power to the firing circuits would automatically be cut off.

Next morning Major Gerhold, assisted by one of his company officers, Lieutenant W. C. Swinson, GM, RE, another SD2 veteran, set about clearing the debris from around the warhead and locating the Sterg Unit.

They were aware of its basic function and so appreciated the need to trace every wire they came across and check that there were no areas free of insulation since a short circuit could cause detonation of the warhead and certain death. Eventually all wires were traced and each one leading to the Sterg Unit cut and the ends safely taped. The two sources of electrical power had now been separated from the firing circuits and the basic fuze system was safe. All components then had to be radiographed to ensure that no lurking booby traps existed for the unwary and when this was confirmed the final dismantling could take place. The final stage was to remove the explosive from the warhead using high-pressure steam. This whole operation took a total of three days' continuous work.

On the same day that the work was being completed on the Hutton V2, another rocket fell and failed to explode. This one fell in Northumberland Avenue, Hornchurch, Essex, just 29 km (18 miles) from the centre of London. However, it too was in Essex and was, therefore, within the area of responsibility of Major Gerhold. By the time he arrived in Hornchurch several hundred people had been evacuated and visitors from what he considered every staff branch of the Admiralty, War Office and Air Ministry had begun to arrive. Those who could not visit the site tried to contact him by telephone and he began to develop a definite persecution complex. Not the ideal condition for anyone about to attempt a dangerous operation, and all so totally unnecessary. Those with a genuine 'need to know' such as heads and technical staffs of other bomb disposal organizations and the scientific research staffs, would all receive any relevant information within hours of it being discovered, as had happened on countless previous occasions. Those who were just curious or 'happened to be passing by' were a nuisance and had to be treated as such, although, of course, with great tact.

On this occasion, with the rocket in a densely populated area it was necessary to render it safe with the greatest possible expediency. When Major Gerhold inspected the site he discovered that what had actually hit Number 45 Northumberland Avenue was only the front half of the rocket; presumably the fuel tanks had exploded in mid-air and the front half of the rocket had continued on its course. The force of impact had broken open the warhead and lumps of the explosive filling could be removed by hand, but first the fuzing system had to be rendered safe. Clearly the battery was not connected since that was in the half of the rocket which was missing. The only threat, therefore, was from the Sterg Unit which was quickly identified and all wires from it disconnected and their ends insulated. The Sterg Unit and the remains of the warhead were removed from the site and the people allowed to return to their homes.

The fourth unexploded V2 also fell in Major Gerhold's 'patch' and he, as the now acknowledged expert, dealt with it without any problems. The first rocket, the one at Paglesham, was finally reached on 7 April 1944, 27 days after it fell. The warhead, much to everyone's surprise, was removed at a depth of only 11.5 m (37.5 ft). In this case the Sterg Unit was removed and the complete warhead recovered for research purposes.

Thus ended the V1 and V2 attacks upon the United Kingdom in which

German V2 on launching site.

8,958 people were killed and over 24,500 seriously injured. The most seriously damaged part of London was Croydon where 75 per cent of all houses were damaged or destroyed. What is not always realized, however, is that the V weapons fired against the United Kingdom represented less than half of the total number fired against various targets. For example, during the four-month period September to December 1944, Antwerp was attacked with 8,696 V1s and 924 V2s, Liege received 3,141 V1s and 27 V2s, Brussels 151 V1s and ten other towns and cities received a total of 119 V2s.

Despite the misery and suffering brought about by these missiles, none of them posed a serious bomb disposal threat—neither the size of the warhead nor its means of delivery were of any special importance. To the men of the bomb disposal organizations the question is always, 'What makes it go bang?' A simple fuze in 10,000 kg of explosive is always preferable to a booby-trapped fuze designed to trap the unwary in 1 kg of explosive.

For the historically-minded the very last German guided weapons to be used during the war are thought to be those launched in April 1945. During that month twelve Do 217 aircraft carrying Hs 293s attacked and destroyed bridges over the Rivers Oder and Vistula. The exact locations of these bridges are unknown but it is reported that they were quickly replaced by equipment bridges built by the Soviet Army engineers.

9

Europe and the clear up

From D-Day, 6 June 1944, until the end of hostilities bomb disposal units of all three Services were fully occupied in dealing with all manner of explosive devices. Bombs certainly, but also land mines, beach obstacles, missiles, projectiles and abandoned weapons of war. Many were booby-trapped to make their clearance more difficult and dangerous. After VE Day (8 May 1945) the fighting may have stopped in Europe, but the clearance of explosive objects certainly had not and was to continue as a major task for a further two years. Indeed, it still continues today over forty years on. In 1986, British and American bombs are still being recovered from the countries of north-west Europe and bombs of German origin are being recovered in the United Kingdom. Although the bomb disposal units of the three Services had separate responsibilities they frequently worked together, respecting each others' expertise and specialist skills. However, in this chapter, purely for clarity, their various activities will be considered separately.

On D-Day, 21 Army Group had under its command five Royal Engineer bomb disposal companies (Nos 5, 19, 23, 24 and 25) with a total of 33 bomb disposal sections. Throughout the campaign the Royal Engineer bomb disposal companies were deployed on the basis of one company to each of the two Armies and three companies for operations and tactical reserve under the command of HQ L of C (Lines of Communication). To support the forward Corps and Divisions each Corps and Divisional Field Park Company, RE, had a small number of bomb disposal trained personnel and their associated equipment, to deal with operational bomb disposal within their respective areas. Owing to the lateness of the Air Ministry's decision to disclose the details and methods of dealing with British and American bombs it had only been possible to train bomb disposal personnel actually in bomb disposal units. Consequently, the bomb disposal personnel in the forward areas at Division and Corps level were not trained to deal with Allied bombs and fuzes.

In order to fill this gap 72 senior non-commissioned officers and 22 Corporals, Royal Air Force, bomb disposal qualified, were attached to the various Field Park Companies to deal with Allied bombs in forward areas.

From contemporary reports this did not appear to be a happy arrangement. Difficulties were experienced both in administration and in finding any form of employment for the Royal Air Force personnel within an Army environment when they were not actually engaged in the disposal of Allied unexploded bombs. After the break-out from the Normandy bridgehead the need to deal with unexploded Allied bombs within the forward areas became less pressing. The Royal Air Force bomb disposal personnel were, therefore, relinquished and the Corps and Divisional bomb disposal commitments were taken over by the Royal Engineer bomb disposal companies in September 1944.

During the course of the campaign disbandments of bomb disposal platoons (sections were renamed platoons in September 1944) were carried out. This was mainly due to manpower considerations and to the absence of enemy air attacks. The final strength of Royal Engineer bomb disposal personnel within 21 Army Group was five companies of 25 platoons. This strength was maintained until almost the end of active operations. Towards the end of the campaign permission had been sought and given by the War Office to disclose to Allied governments the details of United Kingdom bomb disposal techniques and methods. This was released to the French, Belgian and Netherlands governments in order that they could undertake the disposal of unexploded bombs in their own countries. Two bomb disposal companies then based in those countries were freed for other work. They were withdrawn from HQ L of C and placed in support of T Force for special duties. (The role of T Force and the activities of the bomb disposal companies in it are told later in this chapter.)

From 6 June 1944 to 25 August 1945 the five Royal Engineer bomb disposal companies within 21 Army Group disposed of 939,061 unexploded bombs, mines, missiles and other dangerous objects. This figure does not include unexpended or unused bombs, mines, V weapons and ammunition found in captured stores dumps, neither does it include the countless numbers of booby traps detected and removed.

In February 1946 a senior officer writing a report on the campaign commented in his section on bomb disposal: 'The activities of Bomb Disposal Companies, RE, throughout the campaign have been remarkable for the lack of high priority operational demands for bomb disposal owing to the almost complete lack of enemy air opposition, and for the extraordinary variety of tasks both allied and foreign to bomb disposal which they have undertaken'.

It is clear that some of these activities should be looked at a little more closely. As in Italy bomb disposal sections were constantly detached from their parent company headquarters. As Army troops, they were at the disposal of Army Headquarters and consequently tended to be attached in small self-contained groups (sections or even half sections) to subordinate commands as the operational situation demanded. They were frequently looked upon as the experts in respect of almost any unknown explosive object. 'Is this dangerous?' 'What do you think of this?' 'Get that thing away from my billet!' These requests were perfectly acceptable and certainly preferable to the call to clear a building or a unit area after someone had picked up an object and it had either killed or maimed him. Initially, far too many men had displayed a fatal tendency to collect souvenirs or let their inbred curiosity overcome their newly-taught suspicion of any unfamiliar object.

It was not only the unfamiliar object which caused problems, the familiar could also spoil one's day. On 21 June 1944, Captain A. B. Waters, MBE, RE, of 23 Bomb Disposal Company, RE, was asked by Flight Lieutenant Gillett, RAF, to assist him in clearing a German Type C parachute mine. The mine was lying some 10 m (32.8 ft) from a main military route just outside Banville in the Department of Calvados, France. Captain Waters was an experienced bomb disposal officer (some of his exploits were recounted in Chapter 6) and he was fully aware of the dangers of dealing with this mine without the proper equipment. However, to send for a Royal Navy BSO with the necessary equipment would take at least two hours. The road could not possibly be closed for that length of time and to leave it open would run the risk of the heavy traffic causing the fuze to function. Should the mine explode with the road open there would certainly be many casualties and the very real risk of the road being almost permanently blocked. Captain Waters therefore decided, in spite of the personal risk, that the course least likely to hinder the advance was for him to attempt the render-safe procedure by removing the fuze. He told Flight Lieutenant Gillett to run out the cord for removing the bomb fuze by remote control, and ordered him away to a safe distance. (He was the senior officer present.) The road was closed and Captain Waters approached the mine. He was unable to apply the standard fuze gag but prepared it in all other ways for remote removal. He then pulled it out by remote control from a distance of approximately 100 m (109 yd). The fuze came out and nothing happened. After a suitable waiting period Captain Waters again approached the mine and found the fuze well clear of the mine but ticking. He turned to move but the fuze and its associated gaine exploded, severely injuring his foot. There is no doubt that his swift decision and acceptance of responsibility and risk prevented a major line of communication from being blocked.

Many other similar swift decisions followed by decisive action were made by bomb disposal personnel of all ranks. Three months later in the same department of France, members of another bomb disposal company engaged in clearing the area were involved in an incident where courageous decisions were made. In September 1944 a platoon of 5 Bomb Disposal Company, RE, was engaged in the clearance of mines and booby traps from a village in the neighbourhood of Orbois in the Department of Calvados. In the village there had been a number of accidents involving civilians and other soldiers due to booby traps. Among the platoon non-commissioned officers was Corporal W. Jones, RE, who during the period 3 to 7 September 1944 had been responsible for clearing eleven armed booby traps, two of which were in an extremely sensitive condition. On 7 September 1944 captured German documents revealed the presence of a field of Schumines in an orchard at Orbois and the platoon was tasked to clear them. The Schumine was a small plywood box 128 mm × 98 mm × 46 mm (5 in × 3.86 in × 1.8 in) with a hinged lid. It contained 200 g (0.44 lb) of explosive and any pressure on the lid caused the mine to explode. It could also be made to explode by attaching a trip wire to it or by fastening the wire to the ground and waiting for some unwary soldier to lift or move it. It was a very effective anti-personnel mine and treated with the greatest respect by those expected to clear it.

The platoon had previously suffered casualties in the clearance of Schumines and a certain apprehension existed in the minds of the men in the platoon. This was heightened by their doubts over the effectiveness of the Mark 4 Mine Detector to identify a mine with only a very small metal content. Lieutenant R. G. Walker, RE, the Intelligence Officer of 5 Bomb Disposal Company, RE, volunteered to work with the Mark 4 Mine Detector in this field in order to restore confidence in its use throughout the company. So on the following morning, accompanied by the Platoon Sergeant and Lance Sergeant, he started work in the minefield. The misgivings of the men were quickly strengthened when a mine exploded blowing off Lieutenant Walker's left foot and blinding his right eye. The Sergeant and Lance Sergeant received minor injuries.

This courageous act, although inspired by the need to restore confidence in the equipment, unfortunately had the reverse effect and morale was not at its highest. Corporal Jones was now effectively in charge of the clearance operation and on the following day, 9 September 1944, he entered the minefield with a clearance team. They eventually cleared the orchard which, in addition to Schumines, also contained Tellermines. The platoon continued with the clearance of the village where almost every house and outbuilding had been mined or booby-trapped. On 12 September 1944 a Lance Corporal was killed and a Sapper injured rendering safe a booby-trapped Schumine. This then is the type of additional work carried out by the bomb disposal units of all three Services when not engaged on true bomb disposal. In this instance Corporal Jones, throughout an extremely stressful period, inspired confidence in his men and is typical of many other non-commissioned officers who, unlike him, did not get their exploits recorded. Corporal Jones and Lieutenant Walker were both subsequently awarded George Medals.

There were, however, plenty of conventional bombs to deal with although they were more likely to be Allied ones than German and not always in easily accessible locations. No 23 Bomb Disposal Company, RE, encountered just such a situation in November 1944. On 6 November at Hassault in Belgium, the reconstruction of a demolished railway bridge over the Albert Canal was halted when the presence of an unexploded bomb was suspected amongst the debris. Lieutenant G. H. Gaylor, RE, went down in a diving suit and located the bomb half buried in the mud, underneath torn and twisted railway lines, steel girders and other wreckage. It was covered by 9 m (30 ft) of water. To find the bomb he had had to squeeze himself between damaged girders, running the risk of tearing his diving suit or fouling his air or life lines. In spite of nil visibility, he managed to identify the bomb as an Allied one and perhaps more importantly he identified the tail fuze and by touch confirmed that it was armed and in a dangerous condition. Since remote withdrawal equipment could not be used underwater he decided to remove the fuze by hand. He fully appreciated the dangerous condition of the fuze and that any sudden jar was liable to cause the fuze to operate and detonate the bomb. However, he safely unscrewed the fuze and then attempted to ascertain the condition of the nose fuze. Due to the mud, zero visibility and the mass of metal around the bomb, he was unable to identify the nose fuze or even determine if one was fitted. The following day he again dived to the bomb and after fitting a suitable lifting tackle slowly guided the bomb through the network of girders as it was lifted from above. For Lieutenant Gaylor this was a slow and nerve-racking task as the bomb was lifted inch by inch through the debris. He knew that any sudden movement or bang against the metal lattice work might cause the nose fuze to function. When the bomb was finally brought to the surface and the mud cleared away it was found not to have been fitted with a nose fuze, but this in no way detracted from the determination and courage shown by Lieutenant Gaylor. He was later awarded the George Medal for his exploits and after the war returned to the United Kingdom and was engaged in clearing the minefields around the coast of Britain. Sadly, on 7 August 1946 whilst with 11 Bomb Disposal Company he and two other soldiers were killed by a British mine at Rattray Head, north-east Scotland.

When 23 Bomb Disposal Company, RE, landed at Normandy in June 1944 all the officers and a number of non-commissioned officers were trained shallow-water divers. These diving skills were soon put to the test when the large number of damaged bridges over the various waterways of Europe had to be cleared of explosive devices and made ready for recon-struction work. When Lieutenant Gaylor had finished his task at Hassault, he moved to Stockroye accompanied by Lieutenant A. P. Bryce, RE. Here another bridge over the Albert Canal was being cleared by a company of Royal Canadian Engineers and Lieutenants Gaylor and Bryce spent a month working on the clearance of underwater debris of both an explosive and unexplosive kind. At about the same time two other officers of 23 Bomb Disposal Company, RE, were working in support of another Canadian Engineer company. Lieutenants Fairhall and Blackwall spent over two months diving amongst the wreckage of a bridge at Beringen.

After VE-Day the reconstruction work continued and more non-commissioned officer divers were required. With the Royal Navy's agree-ment that Cuxhaven harbour could be used for diver training the first course for seven volunteers was established. The instructors were Lieutenant Bryce and Sergeant H. Mitchel, RE, of 26 Bomb Disposal Platoon. Of the initial seven volunteers five qualified and became the first of many Royal Engineer divers to be trained in north Germany. From then on divers of 23 Bomb Disposal Company, RE, were spread along the lengths of the Rivers Weser and Aller in Germany. Their work was not only underwater engineering but also the clearance of all types of unexploded ordnance dropped on, fired at or floated towards the various bridges and their piers. A total of eleven divers worked for periods ranging from a few days to several months on four bridges over the Aller and five over the Weser. The bomb disposal aspects of these tasks were, as always, hazardous but additionally the diving work was made exceedingly difficult owing to the strong currents which exist in both rivers. At Verden on the Aller special shields had to be used to prevent the divers being swept off their work. In many cases two divers had to descend together, one to do the work and the other to hold him in position.

As explained earlier, as the liberated nations accepted responsibility for much of the bomb disposal within their respective countries, two bomb disposal companies were withdrawn from under command HQ L of C and placed in support of T Force. Each of the two British Armies within 21 Army Group formed a T Force which was of Battalion Group size and had in support of it a bomb disposal company. T Forces, or Technical Forces, were those special units designated to move immediately behind the attacking infantry, seize specified targets of technical interest as they were discovered and guard them until they could be fully examined by scientific investigators. Most technical targets were known beforehand but occasionally one was discovered unexpectedly and T Force troops had to move in quickly. The role of the Royal Engineer bomb disposal company in each T Force was to examine the targets for booby traps and prepared demolition charges and to remove or neutralize them. They were also required to open locks, force entrances and blow open strong-rooms and safes as required by the technical investigators.

It was in early January 1945 that the two companies were warned of their new role but it was not until March 1945 that they finally deployed. During those two months they continued training the bomb disposal forces of the liberated nations, undertaking routine bomb disposal in their respective areas and most importantly, officers and selected senior non-commissioned officers were returned to the United Kingdom for specialist courses. A course designed to teach someone how to pick a lock, open a safe or strongroom or look for hidden valuables or documents might be considered by some to be an ideal pre-release course. There is no indication, however, that the members of T Force turned to safebreaking any more than any other soldiers used their wartime acquired skills for illegal purposes.

One of the companies selected for T Force was 19 Bomb Disposal Company, RE, which was placed in support of 2 Army T Force with effect from 7 March 1945, but did not actually deploy operationally until 2 April 1945. Between that date and the formal disbandment of T Force on 10 June 1945, 19 Bomb Disposal Company, RE, had opened 95 safes. Many safes contained classified documents but the best haul was considered to be the find of 4,000,000 marks at Unterluss. More often the finds were of a larger and more technical nature and required a detailed search before being declared safe for the technical officers to investigate. One such example was at Hesedorf where a large bomb dump was found to contain glider bombs with demolition charges amongst the radio control apparatus. In some other dumps Type C parachute mines had been placed in position fitted with J Feder 504s (a 21-day clock designed to activate a demolition charge). Over twenty such charges were discovered during the subsequent search but luckily none had been started. On one occasion on 4 April 1945, the Platoon Commander of 53 Bomb Disposal Platoon, RE, plus six Sappers, managed to reach their particular target in Osnabruck some two hours after the town had surrendered but due to the fog of war, well before the infantry of the attacking force had arrived. They occupied their target, a copper and aluminium works, cleared out the displaced persons who were enjoying themselves smashing up the machinery and placed guards. It was some hours later that a British fighting patrol turned up which proved to be the Commandos clearing the area. It was not until 17:00 hours the following day that the target was fully cleared and handed over to T Force.

Such, then, was the work of Royal Engineer bomb disposal units in north-west Europe from D-Day until well after VE-Day. They were specialist trained bomb disposal operators but they demonstrated that they were Sappers also and could turn their hands to a wide range of tasks both allied and foreign to bomb disposal.

The Royal Air Force, like the Royal Engineers, deployed a relatively large number of bomb disposal personnel with the forces fighting through France, Belgium, the Netherlands and on into Germany. On D-Day itself 42 Royal Air Force personnel landed across the beaches of Europe, to be followed by many more until there were over 400 all ranks engaged in bomb disposal.

The main activity of the Royal Air Force Bomb Disposal Organization within the Second Tactical Air Force (2 TAF), was the clearance of explosive objects from captured airfields to make them safe and serviceable, and the clearance of any area to be occupied by units and personnel of 2 TAF. In addition, there were a number of small detached sections of two or three men known as Wing HQ Sections attached to Royal Air Force Wing HQs. These sections were responsible for the clearance of bomb 'hang ups' on returning aircraft and the clearance of bombs from aircraft which crashed on the airfield from which the Wings were operating. They also accompanied the Wing reconnaissance parties when carrying out forward reconnaissances of newly captured airfields and dealt with the initial clearance problems. There were also several specialist attachments; for example, 6237 Bomb Disposal Flight of 5138 Bomb Disposal Squadron, RAF, was attached to the Royal Canadian Engineers to deal with Allied bombs and anything else which turned up.

The story of Royal Air Force bomb disposal in north-west Europe must be divided into two separate phases. The first phase was from D-Day until the actual fighting ceased in May 1945. The second was the vast air disarmament operation involving the physical disarmament of the Luftwaffe in the field. This required a special organization involving many more men than were deployed on operational bomb disposal in phase one. Records of the extremely busy period immediately following D-Day are difficult to obtain and those which are available are frequently contradictory. In May 1944 twelve bomb disposal Flights were transferred from under command HQ Bomb Disposal Wing to 83, 84 and 85 Groups of 2 TAF in preparation for the invasion. Following D-Day there were three Bomb Disposal Squadrons (Nos 5137, 5138 and 5139) deployed in mainland Europe with under command eight bomb disposal Flights, sixteen Wing HQ Sections and a specialist section.

The first squadron to land after D-Day was 5137 Bomb Disposal Squadron, RAF, commanded by Squadron Leader D. Strachan, RAF, consisting of 6220 and 6225 Flights. No 6225 Flight had a disastrous start to the campaign. On 7 June 1944 (D-Day + 1) they embarked for Normandy, France, in a Landing Craft Tank (LCT) but at about 04:00 hours on 8 June they were attacked by German 'E' Boats and shelled by coastal batteries from Le Havre. Their craft was hit and sank within two minutes. The survivors were picked up by another LCT and landed on 8 June. Of the 27 men in the Flight seven died, six were admitted to hospital, one was taken prisoner and the remaining thirteen got ashore safely. Ninety per cent of their bomb disposal equipment was lost. Because of their misfortune the Flight was made non-operational and the survivors were attached to 6220 Flight pending replacements. However, by 4 July 1944 they were again operational and from then on operated in France, Belgium, the Netherlands and Germany. On VE-Day they were based at Lübeck in north Germany.

The second Flight of 5137 Bomb Disposal Squadron, RAF, No 6220, fared better and landed safely on 8 June at Graye-Sur-Mer in France and temporarily merged with 6225 Flight. It too operated from France through the Low Countries and by VE-Day was in Schleswig, north Germany. Both Flights, together with 5137 Bomb Disposal Squadron HQ, took part in air disarmament operations in Norway from June to December 1945.

No 5138 Bomb Disposal Squadron arrived in France on 6 August 1944, consisting of three bomb disposal Flights (Nos 6214, 6228 and 6237) and seven Wing HQ sections. The activities of this squadron will be looked at in detail to show the type of work all the Royal Air Force bomb disposal personnel were engaged in during the advance across Europe. Nos 6214 and 6228 Flights were working in direct support of the Royal Air Force and 6237 Flight was working in support of the Royal Canadian Engineers and were very much front line airmen. During August 1944, 6237 Flight dealt with 5,783 unexploded missiles, cleared large areas of domestic buildings of mines and booby traps in Caen and managed to capture two prisoners during the fighting in the Falaise Gap. Teams from this Flight were moving with the Canadian Armoured Division and so were in the forefront of the battle. In September, still with the Canadian Army, the Flight dealt with 6,560 unexploded missiles and in the following month with 2,444. This drop in numbers of missiles dealt with may have been because in October 1944 the Flight was with the Canadian airborne troops in the Arnhem bridgehead. On 5 November 1944 a detachment from the Flight under the command of Flight Sergeant Simons, RAF, was called to assist 20 Canadian Field Company, RCE, who had discovered twenty 50 kg (110 lb) French bombs attached to a bridge abutment at Loenhout in the Netherlands. The bombs were under four feet of water and had been wired for demolition. They were dealt with without the aid of diving suits and one can imagine the water temperature in a Netherlands waterway in November. This was their last task for the Canadian Army and 6237 Bomb Disposal Flight, RAF, under the command of Flight Lieutenant N. T. King, RAF, returned to the United Kingdom for disbandment.

The other two Flights of 5138 Bomb Disposal Squadron RAF spent much of the same period clearing airfields of bombs, mines, booby traps and crashed aircraft. No 6214 Flight under the command of Flight Lieutenant R. C. Rulf, RAF, spent most of August to October 1944 clearing the two airfields at Lille, France. It worked in conjunction with an Airfield Construction Company, RE, and its attached Royal Engineer bomb disposal section. Many tons of bombs and rocket heads were cleared or demolished. A number of bombs were found in deep shelters placed there as demolition charges. One shelter was over 24 m (80 ft) deep and removing 500 kg (1,100 lb) bombs from this depth presented quite a problem.

During the same period, August to October 1944, 6228 Flight under the command of Flight Lieutenant A. McIntosh, RAF, had been busy clearing Merville airfield, also in France. Here many tons of bombs were rendered safe and put into store and unserviceable ones demolished. During October a small party was sent to Fort-de-Houthuht in Belgium where an American aircraft had crashed with six 1,000 lb (454 kg) bombs. These bombs were relatively easily dealt with, but not so those disposed of by the Flight between 15 and 23 October 1944. Vimy Ridge of World War 1 fame had been used as a dumping ground for German bombs fitted with No 17 long-delay fuzes and recovered from airfield bomb dumps. Although the bombs had not been armed they were fitted with ZUS 40 anti-withdrawal devices and therefore were considered dangerous. They were collected and demolished, there being a total of 27 250 kg (550 lb) bombs.

November 1944 continued as a busy time for both 6214 and 6228 Flights. No 6214 Flight spent much of the month clearing an airfield at

Gilze Rijen in the Netherlands. Here many of the bomb dumps had been partially demolished and those which remained were scattered with armed SD2 anti-personnel bombs which had, of course, to be cleared before any work could start on the main bomb dumps. Whilst clearing a heavily mined area at Gooreind to make room for an air stores park, a mine detonated amputating an airman's left leg. His life was saved by the very prompt action of a Corporal Johnson, RAF, who was working with him. No 6228 Flight cleared mines and unexploded bombs from Woensdrecht airfield in the Netherlands. Hundreds of demolition charges had been placed across the airfield, consisting of unexploded British, French and German bombs together with 256 French anti-tank mines.

This, then, was the routine of the Royal Air Force bomb disposal Flights of 5138 Bomb Disposal Squadron, RAF, during the first four months of their activities in north-west Europe. With the exception of 6237 Flight attached to the Canadian Army, this routine was to continue until VE-Day, not only for this squadron but also for the other two squadrons involved. Occasionally the routine would be changed by the discovery of a V1 flying bomb or an airfield with missile components stored within it. Occasionally too, work would be carried out well away

'Occasionally the routine would be changed by the discovery of a V1 flying bomb . . .'

V1 — piloted trials version.

from aircraft or airfields. Such a situation occurred for 6206 Flight of 5139 Bomb Disposal Squadron, RAF, at Blankenberghe in Belgium. The main square of the town, the Place de la Gare, was required for use by a Royal Air Force unit to accommodate its large number of specialist vehicles. Unfortunately, the whole square had been mined and 6206 Flight was required to clear it as it was the only location available for these vehicles. The Flight Commander, Flight Lieutenant H. Cox, RAF, discovered on arrival that the whole area was covered with torn-up cobble stones under which were German Holzmines (wooden-cased anti-tank mines 330 × 305 × 115 mm (13 × 12 × 4½ in) containing 5.2 kg (11.4 lb) of explosive). Beneath the loose stones the concrete foundation of the square had been cut to accommodate the mines, all of which were booby-trapped with anti-lift devices. A total of 132 mines was discovered and all except seven were neutralized, disarmed and hand-lifted. The seven exceptions were considered to be too dangerous and were demolished *in situ*. A further six Tellermines were lifted from an adjoining pavement where there was a risk that the vehicles might run over them. No further work was necessary to meet Royal Air Force requirements but the rest of the pavement was cleared by Belgian Army personnel. Unfortunately, they came unexpectedly against a Holzmine and a Belgian soldier was killed.

The incidents quoted above reflect only a general impression of the work carried out by the Royal Air Force bomb disposal Flights and sections as they moved across France, the Low Countries and into Germany.

They were all involved in a dangerous and nerve-racking task as they cleared the airfields, air installations and other areas so that 2 TAF personnel could operate and live in a reasonable degree of security. Many huge bomb dumps on or close to operational airfields, once cleared of obvious booby traps or demolition charges, had to be left for removal or destruction until after the battle had moved on (in most cases this meant after VE-Day). In addition, of course, they continued with the routine but equally dangerous task of the clearance of Allied bombs from crashed aircraft or those returning from operational sorties with damaged or 'hung up' bombs.

Early in 1944 (prior to D-Day), it had been realized that the disarmament of the German forces and the collection and disposal of their equipment, weapons and ammunition was likely to be a major problem. However, it was not until October 1944 that the size of the problem was fully appreciated. As far as the Royal Air Force was concerned its responsibility was the disarmament of the Luftwaffe and an Air Disarmament Staff was established as part of the Supreme Headquarters Allied Expeditionary Forces. This staff having made its plans, United Kingdom-based units were warned and trained for their various specialist roles. The planned organization was to consist of a Disarmament Executive based at Headquarters 2 TAF (later to be Air Headquarters British Air Forces of Occupation) with under command thirteen Air Disarmament Wings formed into three Disarmament Groups. Each Wing contained its specialist units but in this story we are only concerned with the bomb disposal units. Initially there were five Bomb Disposal Squadrons (Nos 5130, 5132, 5135, 5138 and 5140), commanding a total of eighteen Bomb Disposal Flights allocated to the air disarmament role. Later this was increased to 21 Flights making a total of 39 officers and 651 other ranks out of a total disarmament force strength of 8,005 all ranks. Of these units 5138 Bomb Disposal Squadron and the Flights from 5137 Bomb Disposal Squadron were already in position; the remainder were all to come from the United Kingdom.

A major problem for the Royal Air Force Disarmament Organization, which it promptly passed to the bomb disposal squadrons, was the disposal of all captured stocks of Luftwaffe explosives and munitions. In addition to it being a very large physical task it was extremely hazardous and the risk grew greater as the condition of the munitions deteriorated with the passage of time. As we have seen already, to embarrass the advancing Allies the Germans had carried out partial destruction of bomb dumps leaving them in a most dangerous and confused state. They had also adopted many ingenious means of booby-trapping bomb dumps and individual bombs which had not always been discovered by the initial clearing parties. The action of some Allied personnel and local civilians had not helped the situation either. The first action of Allied personnel in capturing a bomb dump was to call in the bomb disposal section to render any fuzed bombs safe. This was frequently done by removing the fuzes, but unfortunately this was usually done by front-line teams who were in a hurry and the fuze pockets were not sealed after the fuzes had been withdrawn. Subsequently, the filling of the bomb gradually exuded through the fuze pocket and, after exposure to the air, crystallized and made each particular bomb more dangerous than if the fuze had remained fitted. Similarly, many bomb dumps had been interfered with by local civilians, displaced persons and even British troops, in search of wood, parachutes from planes and even propellants from ammunition for use as fire lighters.

The first air disarmament personnel were established in Belgium in December 1944 but bomb disposal personnel did not begin their work until May 1945. The total disarmament process as far as bomb disposal was concerned took part in three stages. The first, from May to August 1945, was the period when bombs and general munitions were collected, sorted and selected items prepared for shipment to the United Kingdom and elsewhere. At this stage the destruction of explosive ordnance by demolition was confined to such items considered to be dangerous, potentially dangerous or constituting a threat to either the occupation forces or the local population. Despite these conditions the state of many of the bomb and ammunition dumps necessitated the demolition during those first four months of over 12,000 tons (12,192 tonnes) of munitions.

The second stage from September to December 1945 was the period when those items required for intelligence, historic purposes or even re-use, had been removed and general demolition approved. With the vast tonnages involved and the impossibility of disposing of all the items by demolition, this stage merged into the third stage which lasted from January 1946 to mid-1947. During this period much of the work was the preparation of munitions for deep sea-dumping. This phase, although the disposal of bombs, is not truly bomb disposal and with the exception of one incident will not be considered further.

As was seen earlier, Royal Air Force bomb disposal Flights began work in Belgium in May 1945 with the arrival of 6206 Bomb Disposal Flight. This Flight remained for one month before being replaced by 6229 Bomb Disposal Flight and moving on into Germany. In the Netherlands the first Flight (No 6223) started work on 18 June 1945 and then it too moved on to Germany and was replaced by 6234 Bomb Disposal Flight. The greatest problem for the bomb disposal Flights in the Low Countries was the lack of adequate facilities for large-scale demolitions. This was mainly because of the built-up nature of the countries and the density of the population. The history of disposal work in these countries is, therefore, one of hard work and the constant hunt for demolition areas whose use did not bring in a flood of complaints concerning broken windows and cracked ceilings. At the end of 1945 it was suggested and agreed that any remaining work should be handed over to the respective Belgian and Dutch forces, subject only to the disposal by the Royal Air Force of certain bombs which posed great potential hazards. Following this agreement the bomb disposal

Flights in the Low Countries were alerted for departure. This was delayed until June 1946 to allow time for these countries to obtain the necessary specialist equipment (from the United Kingdom) and to train sufficient personnel.

(As a point of interest the author was recently in the Headquarters of the Netherlands Explosive Ordnance Disposal Organization and was shown some of the original Royal Air Force equipment donated to the Netherlands bomb disposal unit some forty years earlier. Similar equipment is still being used to deal with British and American bombs which continue to be unearthed in the Netherlands.)

One example of a group of bombs which posed a particular hazard and which had to be disposed of by the Royal Air Force was found at the Steenockerzeel bomb dump near Brussels in November 1945. Eight 500 kg (1,100 lb) and fourteen 250 kg (550 lb) bombs were located amongst 700 tons of other bombs. Suspicion was raised as each bomb was fuzed with two No 17 long-delay fuzes under any of which might be concealed a ZUS 40 anti-withdrawal device. The bombs clearly could not be demolished *in situ* with 700 tons of other bombs in the immediate vicinity. To add to the problem the bomb dump on the outskirts of Brussels was only 200 m (219 yd) from a main road and tram track and close to the main Brussels airport and Royal Air Force Station Melsbroeck. The fuzes could not be removed remotely in case a ZUS 40 was in position and any attempt to move the bombs to another area was potentially hazardous.

It was known that the mechanism of a No 17 fuze was liable to corrode during bad storage (as in the case of these bombs). Thus any sudden jolt could cause the fracture of a corroded pallet pin within the clockwork mechanism and cause the bomb to explode. The Unexploded Bomb Committee, when asked in early 1945 how best to dispose of a No 17 fuze in an old bomb, had said in its minutes: 'To summarize its discussion the meeting agreed that it could not recommend, in the present state of knowledge, a completely safe method for dealing with No 17 fuzes in old bombs, and emphasized that there is an appreciable risk in any method other than destroying *in situ*'.

Under these circumstances the Air Headquarters (Disarmament) British Air Forces of Occupation wrote to the Air Ministry O.10(BD)—the controlling branch for Royal Air Force bomb disposal—and asked for advice. The reply was a letter stating that Wing Commander L. H. Harrison, GC, RAF, and Squadron Leader T. M. Clark, RAF, would arrive on or about 22 February 1946 and would personally carry out the defuzing. Wing Commander Harrison, having taken over from Wing Commander J. C. Stevens, OBE, RAF, in June 1945, was the head of Royal Air Force bomb disposal and Squadron Leader Clark was on his staff. On 25 February 1946 these two officers were joined by an officer from Air Headquarters, Squadron Leader H. C. Wilson, RAF, and the disposal of the 22 bombs began. Surrounded by 700 tons of bombs and working in the snow and ice of a Belgian winter the team radiographed each fuze pocket to determine the presence or not of a ZUS 40 fuze. They then proceeded to immunize each No 17 fuze and where necessary the ZUS 40 beneath it and then remove the fuzes whenever it was possible. The technique used was still in the development stage and had been designed by the Wing Commander's predecessor, Wing Commander Stevens. The whole operation took three weeks of hazardous work from dawn to dusk, although during some of the preliminary work Wing Commander Harrison managed to get away to visit bomb disposal units. In his letter to Air Headquarters telling them that the bombs had been rendered safe, Wing Commander Harrison reported that all fuzes had been removed from seventeen of the 22 bombs and in respect of the remaining five the fuze pockets were in such a state of corrosion that it had been impossible to remove the ZUS 40 fuzes. These he had immunized, thus making the bombs safe to move and he recommended that they be removed for demolition as soon as possible. Of the 22 bombs, all had two No 17 fuzes fitted, nine also had two ZUS 40 fuzes, nine had only one ZUS 40 and four contained nothing under their No 17 fuzes (except, of course, explosive!). In a report of the incident written by order of Air Marshal Sir Philip Wigglesworth, KBE, CB, DSC, Air Officer Commander in Chief, British Air Forces of Occupation, it is stated:

'It is the considered opinion of those officers in the British Air Forces of Occupation who are competent to judge, that the rendering safe of these 22 booby-trapped bombs at Steenockerzeel comprises an outstanding feat in the annals of bomb disposal and deep gratitude is felt to the two Air Ministry officers who voluntarily undertook this dangerous task, which was completely beyond the unaided technical resources of the British Air Forces of Occupation.'

(For those who wish to be pedantic only eighteen of the 22 bombs were technically booby-trapped with a ZUS 40 fuze although all were in an extremely hazardous condition.) As a result of this safely concluded but hazardous incident, Squadron Leader Clark was appointed an Officer of the Order of the British Empire (OBE).)

In Denmark the disarmament of the Luftwaffe began in May 1945 and was undertaken by 8403 Air Disarmament Wing with under command 6211 Bomb Disposal Flight. The Wing had completed its task and withdrawn by 31 December 1945, but at the request of the Danish government the bomb disposal Flight was retained to help clear the remaining German bombs. It completed this task by 30 March 1946.

The Air Disarmament of Norway was carried out by 8801 Wing with under command 6218 Bomb Disposal Flight, starting work in June 1945. Initially it was intended that only one Flight should be deployed to Norway but the workload was such that 5137 Bomb Disposal Squadron and its two Flights (6220 and 6225) were sent to assist in September 1945. This squadron, as was recounted earlier, had already been on mainland Europe since D-Day + 2. A total of 4,332 tons of unserviceable or damaged explosive ordnance was destroyed by demolition. In addition, the bomb disposal Flights assisted in the destruction of some 471 aircraft and hundreds of aircraft engines. The complete operation was planned to take six months and the completion date was met—just, withdrawal from Norway took place in December 1945.

The Air Disarmament work in Germany was, as far as the bomb disposal units were concerned, similar to the work in the liberated countries. The only difference was that they were also called upon to destroy with explosives large quantities of Luftwaffe equipment, such as aircraft, aircraft engines, radar and wireless installations in addition to the normal explosive ordnance. Disarmament generally was completed by September 1946, but considerable stocks of ex-Luftwaffe munitions still remained. Consequently, the bomb disposal units were retained until June 1947, although much of the work was making munitions safe to transport to the ports from where the sea-dumping programmes were operating. The necessity for this work was emphasized by an incident which occurred on 20 August 1946.

On that date German high explosive bombs were being loaded into barges at Lubeck, north Germany, for disposal at sea, the work being supervised by members of 6214 Bomb Disposal Flight. Two train loads of bombs weighing approximately 1,100 tons (1,118 tonnes) were drawn up at the quayside. Whilst loading was in progress a 50 kg (110 lb) bomb was accidentally dropped a few feet on to the ground by the German loading party. The bomb exploded, killing six of the loaders and injuring twelve other persons of whom one was Flight Sergeant J. R. Ings, RAF, the supervising senior non-commissioned officer. The bomb, which was one of twelve similar bombs being handled at the time, was fitted with a telescopic nose extension connected to a German experimental fuze. This equipment had been designed to detonate the bomb a fraction of a second before the main body hit the ground. However, the fuzes in these bombs had not been armed and had been certified fit to handle and travel to the port.

Squadron Leader H. Dinwoodie, OBE, MC, RAFVR, officer commanding 5140 Bomb Disposal Squadron, arrived on the scene and sought to determine what had happened. The area was in a shambles with bombs scattered everywhere and a great feeling of unease among those present. Squadron Leader Dinwoodie, in an endeavour to determine the cause of the explosion, cleared the area and proceeded to dismantle a bomb similar to the one which had exploded. He found that the accident, apart from the dropping of the bomb, was due to a defect in the fuze. It was possible, therefore, that the remaining ten bombs of this batch could be similarly affected and thus dangerous to handle. Squadron Leader Dinwoodie, assisted by Corporal R. N. Garred, BEM, RAF, and Leading Aircraftsman J. W. Halton, RAF, both of 5140 Bomb Disposal Squadron, removed the potentially dangerous fuzes from the remaining ten bombs. This was carried out in an atmosphere of great tension as no one was quite sure whether the action of defuzing the bombs would in itself cause an explosion. Should that occur there was every possibility that some or all of the 1,100 tons of bombs in the immediate vicinity might also explode.

There is no doubt that Squadron Leader Dinwoodie and his assistants displayed courage and coolness in a situation of great potential danger. For their work on this day at Lubeck, Squadron Leader Dinwoodie was awarded the George Cross, Corporal Garred the George Medal and Leading Aircraftsman Halton the British Empire Medal.

On completion of the air disarmament bomb disposal work in June 1947 there were now only three operational bomb disposal Flights on the Continent (Nos 6203, 6210 and 6212), the remainder having been disbanded a month earlier. By November 1947, when the Air Ministry was formally notified that the air disarmament task had been completed, only 6210 Bomb Disposal Flight remained. This Flight, by then based at Celle in north Germany, was finally disbanded in 1948 and no other Royal Air Force bomb disposal units were to serve abroad until late 1952.

The importance of the role of the Royal Air Force bomb disposal units in the disarmament of the Luftwaffe can best be shown by a few simple statistics. Between May 1945 and June 1947 they disposed of over 163,000 tons of high explosive bombs, 13,500 tons of pyrotechnics and 195,500,000 rounds of ammunition, much of which was in a highly dangerous state when first encountered. This was not done without loss, however, as ten bomb disposal personnel were killed and nine seriously injured during the disarmament phase. This does not, of course, include the casualties incurred by bomb disposal units during the period D-Day to VE-Day.

While the clearance of unexploded ordnance and the disarmament of the Luftwaffe continued across north-west Europe, similar operations were taking place in the Central Mediterranean Force area including mainland Italy and Greece and the islands of Crete, Sicily and Sardinia. Likewise, similar operations were being carried out by the Royal Air Force in Austria, Yugoslavia and some of the battle areas of the Far East.

We must now return to June 1944 and consider some of the activities of the Royal Navy during this onslaught upon Fortress Europe. To many, the battles across Europe would appear to be entirely ones involving air and land forces with no requirement for Naval forces. This would be far from the truth. The thousands of men fighting on the ground or in the air required vast quantities of ammunition, equipment and general stores, most of which had to be delivered by sea and off-loaded through captured ports. Similarly, as the battle progressed more and more men poured into mainland Europe. Hence the acquisition of ports was a priority task.

Initially the invasion forces were supplied across the prefabricated jetties of the Mulberry Harbour built from the shores of Normandy, but as the build-up of forces continued more permanent harbours and ports with deep water berths were required and the destruction of most of the harbour by a storm emphasized the need. The Germans, appreciating this, did everything possible to make the ports which they were forced to abandon as inhospitable as possible. We have seen what was done at Messina in Sicily and Leghorn in Italy, and the same situation existed in the European harbours and ports. Sea approaches and entrances were heavily mined or blocked by sunken ships, dockside equipment was destroyed or booby-trapped and quays and other land-based facilities within the port area were landmined and/or prepared for demolition. Each fresh harbour or port acquired by the Allied forces was inoperative and a virtual death trap until cleared by Naval 'P' Parties and construction or repair work completed by the Port Construction Companies, RE.

Although not strictly bomb disposal a few examples of the work carried out by the officers and ratings involved in the clearance of the ports from D-Day onwards deserve a mention. Since the ports and harbours were needed so urgently, the time factor was always pressing and, consequently, large risks were run continuously, and willingly, so that clearance could be achieved with all haste. An early example of this was on D-Day + 1 at Ouistreham when Royal Navy 'P' Party 1502 was clearing this small port. The work was under the command of Lieutenant R. H. Saull, RNVR, assisted by Sub Lieutenant Kirkland, RNVR. Together they discovered and rendered safe demolition charges placed on the port's lock gates and bridge and a number of other explosive devices at the lock entrance. They also dealt with a controlled minefield in the harbour entrance and removed a number of demolition charges and booby traps from craft and strong points within the port area. (A controlled minefield is one laid in a harbour approach or estuary in which all or selected mines may be fired by an observer on the shore.) Also working in Ouistreham at this time was Lieutenant W. Bailey, DSC, GM, RNVR, of Naval Party 1574. He had earlier, in 1942, been awarded a George Medal for underwater mine clearance in Gibraltar and was continuing with the good work in Ouistreham. He was also to be noted for his bravery whilst helping to clear the ports of Boulogne, Calais, Flushing and Antwerp.

Two members of Naval Party 1571 should also be mentioned: they were Lieutenant Commander J. L. Harries, GM, RCNVR (Royal Canadian Naval Volunteer Reserve) and Able Seaman M. H. Woods, RN. They were both decorated for gallantry and devotion to duty during mine searching and clearance operations in the liberated ports of Cherbourg, Dieppe, Le Havre, Rouen and Antwerp.

Even after the ports became operational explosive objects continued to be found. Such an incident occurred on 12 October 1944, in the Hospital Ship Berth, Avant Port, Dieppe. At 11:20 hours, a Royal Engineer diver from 963 Port Construction and Repair Company, RE, reported an object sticking out of the mud and resembling a large bomb. By 11:50 hours, Sub Lieutenant R. M. Orr, RNVR, had dived to the object and identified it as a Type C magnetic mine. The area was cleared and for three hours Sub Lieutenant Orr attempted to locate the fuze, but with the mine showing only 18 in (460 mm) above the sea bed and with nil visibility because of the stirred-up mud, this was not possible. The Naval officer in charge,

Lieutenant P. C. Grant, RNVR, was approached and it was agreed that the mine should be lifted free by a crane, the driver of which volunteered. Sub Lieutenant Orr once again dived to the mine and secured a non-magnetic shackle to its lifting lug. The diving boat was moved away and the mine lifted on to the quay. The mine was rendered safe by Lieutenant Grant who discovered that instead of the usual fuze the pocket was fitted with a wooden bung. When the bung was removed, a detonator attached to a six-day demolition clock was discovered. All were removed and the remainder of the render-safe procedure completed.

As the last incident indicated, Royal Engineer divers from the port construction and repair companies were involved in the underwater engineering work and as trained Sappers (non-bomb disposal) they were competent to deal with underwater demolition charges. Indeed, one Sapper, T. L. Walker, RE, a member of 963 Port Construction and Repair Company, was awarded a George Medal for underwater mine disposal at the following liberated ports—Dieppe, Flushing, Bergen-op-Zoom and Beveland. However, it is due mainly to the courage of the Naval 'P' Parties that the ports were cleared with such speed and that the Army and the Royal Air Force were at no point in serious danger of out-running supplies during the swift advance from Normandy.

Thus, as the fighting in Europe drew to a close, followed three months later by the surrender of Japan, most members of the Armed Forces breathed a sigh of relief and thanksgiving, and prepared for a less hazardous life. Not so for many members of the bomb and mine disposal units, for no cease-fire or peace treaty could make the many thousands of items of unexploded ordnance littering Europe and elsewhere any less lethal. These items were all designed to kill and would do so if given the opportunity, whether disturbed by friend or foe, child or soldier.

10

Post-war years

Following the end of the war there was an immediate decrease in manpower within the three Services as the 'hostilities only' personnel were released to continue their civilian lives interrupted anything up to six years previously. As a result there was a similar and rapid rundown and disbandment of bomb disposal units. 'No more bombs are being dropped so there is no need for bomb disposal' seemed to be the general cry—how wrong they were!

The tasks which faced the few remaining bomb disposal units in the 1950s and '60s were very similar, in many respects, to today's peacetime roles, although in 1950 no thought was being given to training for any future war and terrorism was very much a fringe activity. The first of these tasks was the clearance of Allied and ex-enemy bombs. This included those bombs whose locations were known and which had been abandoned during the war, but which were now once again sought. Others were those known to exist within areas designated for the emergency jettisoning of Allied bombs by damaged aircraft or in areas deliberately established as decoy targets to attract enemy bombs. Finally there were, and still are, those bombs whose presence is totally unknown until uncovered on a building or civil engineering site.

The second task was the clearance of large tracts of land used as training areas, bombing ranges or military installations, all of which had to be cleared of live ammunition and explosive objects to enable the areas to be handed back for public use. These tasks, although situated in the United Kingdom were, and still are, known as Battle Area Clearance (BAC) tasks. In the case of the Royal Engineers there was the additional task of completing the clearance of the land mines laid on or close to the beaches of the British coastline.

We will consider first the activities of the Royal Engineers who underwent the greatest post-1945 contraction in numbers. Immediate post-war cuts reduced the number of bomb disposal companies dramatically until by April 1948 there were only nine bomb disposal squadrons. (In May 1947, together with all other Royal Engineer companies, the bomb disposal companies with their bomb disposal platoons under command had been renamed squadrons and troops respectively.) These nine squadrons were commanded by HQ Bomb Disposal Unit (UK) RE situated in Ashley Gardens, Victoria, London. The original Directorate of Bomb Disposal had become a branch of the Engineer-in-Chief's staff in the War Office and had in turn had been reduced to a part-time job for one officer on the formation of the HQ Bomb Disposal Unit (UK) RE.

By that time (April 1948), with the reduction in military staff, German prisoners-of-war (PoW) had been brought in as replacements for British troops. However, in June 1948 PoWs were being repatriated or were alternatively being permitted to continue on bomb disposal work as paid civilians. A ceiling of 500 civilians was established and that resulted in the disbandment of a further two squadrons. During August 1948 three more squadrons were disbanded and the remaining four consisted of a Plant Squadron and Nos 2, 7 and 16 Bomb Disposal Squadrons, RE. On 1 January 1950 these squadrons were also disbanded and the Royal Engineer bomb disposal organization was restructured into a single unit consisting of five operational troops and a plant troop (the plant troop held and operated all the heavy digging and specialist equipment). This was later reduced still further to the HQ (by then based at Broadbridge Heath Camp, Horsham, Sussex, having moved from London in August 1950) and two operational troops. These two troops, No 1 based at Whestone Camp in north London and No 2 based at Fort Widley, Portsmouth, between them covered the Royal Engineer bomb disposal requirements for the whole of the United Kingdom. No 1 Troop was later to be based at Mundesley, near Cromer in Norfolk, to be responsible for clearing the wartime minefields still remaining at Mundesley, Trimingham and Sidestrand, leaving No 2 Troop to deal with all ex-enemy bomb incidents throughout the country.

In 1962 HQ Bomb Disposal Unit (UK), RE, assumed responsibility for all Army BAC and inherited part of the organization and some of the manpower which until then had been commanded by HQ Battle Area Clearance Unit (UK) based at Newhaven in Sussex. This unit was renamed No 3 BAC Troop and consisted of one Captain, one Sergeant Major, three Staff Sergeants, three Corporals and 113 civilians. These civilians were all Ukrainians who, originally PoWs, were now unable or unwilling to return to their homeland. These Ukrainians had been clearing minefields since 1946 and six still continue to work for the Royal Engineer bomb disposal organization on BAC tasks. Their camp leader, Mr Steve Marynuik, works as an executive officer in 33 Engineer Regiment (EOD), the direct successor of HQ Bomb Disposal Unit (UK), RE. These Ukrainians have given many years of loyal and faithful service to bomb disposal and in most cases have spent the greater part of their working life swinging a mine detector or bomb locator in areas suspected (and frequently proven) to contain live unexploded ordnance. This work has been carried out in all weathers and over some of the more exposed and desolate areas of the United Kingdom. It was the author's privilege and pleasure to command the unit of which they were a part and a more friendly, phlegmatic body of men it would be difficult to find. The Royal Engineer bomb disposal organization owes them a great deal.

From the low point, numerically speaking of the late 1950s, the Royal Engineer bomb disposal organization began once again to expand. In 1965 a Bomb Disposal Squadron was formed to command the operational troops and a year later it was given the number 49. In 1969 the HQ Bomb Disposal Unit, RE (it having already lost the 'UK' from its title) was redesignated HQ EOD Unit, RE. This was to comply with a NATO agreement whereby all bomb disposal was renamed Explosive Ordnance Disposal (EOD) as being more descriptive of the actual work done. This meant that 49 Bomb Disposal Squadron, RE, was now 49 EOD Squadron, RE. Later still, on 16 May 1973, HQ EOD Unit was redesignated once again, this time to the title it still holds today, 33 Engineer Regiment (EOD). From then on the regiment grew to its current establishment, the organization of which will not be discussed. It is sufficient to say that it is equipped and trained to deal with any eventuality.

From 1950 to the present day there have been, in addition to the regular bomb disposal units, a wide range of volunteer forces. These have been known variously as Army Emergency Reserve (AER), Territorial Army Volunteer Reserve (TAVR) and the Territorial Army (TA). At their peak they consisted of three AER bomb disposal regiments. Today Bomb Disposal Squadrons, RE (V), are trained to the same level as their regular counterparts and fill a vital place in the current order of battle. (A brief history of the volunteer bomb disposal units is given in Annex C.)

While all these reductions, changes, reorganizations and subsequent growth were taking place, what actual work was being carried out? The answer, of course, is every task within their role. As far as actual bombs were concerned there was no great shortage, for between 1950 and 1958, 140 were recovered and in the next eight years a further 75 were dealt with. Those German bombs with fuzes which had depended for their operation upon the charge retained in a capacitor were, as far as the fuze was concerned, safe but because of the possible deterioration of both the fuze and the contents of the bomb they were in many cases more dangerous than when first dropped. Those with a No 17 clockwork long-delay fuze were, as described in the previous chapter, extremely dangerous. As examples of the sensitivity and unpredictability of these fuzes, consider the following instances. The first occurred on 8 August 1948 when for some inexplicable reason a German bomb, probably a 250 kg (550 lb), exploded spontaneously in front of the Vickers Supermarine Works at Southampton. The only possible explanation is that the bomb was fitted with a No 17 fuze and the vibration of passing traffic started the clock. Considering that the bomb probably fell in September 1940, its detonation certainly illustrates the hazards and uncertainty associated with clockwork fuzes. Another incident occurred thirteen years later when it was not even possible to blame traffic vibration. At 07:25 hours on 24 April 1961 an explosion occurred in a field at Woodsmithies Farm, Hurndall, in Derbyshire. The only occupants of the field were sheep, one of which was killed. The bomb left a crater 10m (33 ft) across and 3.5 m (11.5 ft) deep. Following a detailed search of the area, fragments of a No 17 fuze were recovered. Here it must be assumed that a pallet pin rusted with age, finally broke and allowed the clock to rush through its sequence to detonation. The farmer said that after hearing a low-flying aircraft in October 1942 he had found a hole in the field but had done nothing other than fill it in. Thus the bomb had exploded 18½ years after being dropped. It is not surprising therefore that bombs found with No 17 fuzes, even today, or perhaps especially today, are treated with the greatest respect.

An example occurred on 1 July 1959 at Lower Richmond Road, Putney, London. Workmen carrying out excavations alongside a sewer discovered a large bomb and reported the incident to the police. As a result, Major A. B. Hartley, RE, and Captain B. Dace, RE, from the Bomb Disposal Unit at Horsham, arrived on the scene in the late afternoon and confirmed the bomb to be a German 250 kg (550 lb) fitted with two No 17 fuzes. The area was evacuated and the work of immunizing the fuzes began. This was carried out in most unsavoury as well as extremely hazardous conditions. During the operation the base of the excavation had collapsed, allowing raw sewage to flow into the hole and resulting in both officers having to work up to their knees in sewage. By 05:00 hours on 2 July 1959, the fuzes

Major A. B. Hartley, RE, and Captain B. Dace, RE, 'steaming out' the Putney Bomb on 1/2 July 1959.

had been immunized, the bomb filling steamed out and the fuze pockets demolished on site.

It is not always the surroundings which cause odours, it is frequently the smell of decomposing explosive which tends to overcome the operator. This can also indicate an increased sensitivity of the compounds within the bomb. Two examples are given here but there are many such incidents which could be quoted from almost any year between 1950 and the present. The first occurred in March 1961 and involved Major R. H. Hough, GM, RE, and Captain C. N. Thompson, RE. (Major Hough had been awarded his George Medal in 1953 for crawling into a live minefield together with Warrant Officer E. E. Thomas, RE, to recover what they thought was an injured man following an explosion whilst a minefield at Mundesley-on-Sea was being cleared. The injured man, Corporal Braddock, was unfortunately dead when they reached him.) However, on 21 March 1961 the two officers were called to Ham River Gravel Works, Woodley, near Reading, where a suspect bomb had been unearthed whilst gravel was being excavated. The bomb was quickly identified as a German 1,000 kg (2,200 lb) fitted with a simple impact fuze.

Arrangements were made to evacuate people from nearby houses and to control the flow of traffic on the nearby main Paddington (London) to Cornwall railway lines. The bomb was located approximately 2.5 m (8.2 ft) below the surface and because of bomb and fuze damage it was extremely difficult to remove either the fuze locking ring or the bomb base plate. However, by mid-afternoon on 22 March 1961 the base plate was removed revealing that well-known dark brown mush and liquid which, before deterioration due to natural decomposition and the ingress of water, had formed the powder filling in the rear half of the bomb. As always in these circumstances the smell of ammonia was overpowering and indicated the probable formation of a highly dangerous, heat-sensitive compound on the interface between the solid cast TNT filling in the front of the bomb and what remained of the powder filling in the rear. This meant that it would be very risky to attempt to steam out the cast filling unless very special precautions were taken. Nevertheless, the fuze and filling were eventually dealt with and people were allowed to return to their homes.

Another example, where in this case deteriorating explosive filling was linked to the presence of a No 17 long-delay clockwork fuze, occurred in 1969 in Sussex. This bomb also represented the type of situation where the existence of the bomb had been known for a long time but the search had earlier been abandoned and the bomb was once again being sought. In the spring of 1941 a stick of German bombs fell on marshy ground at Rotherbridge Farm, Petworth. Three bombs exploded, killing some cows, and the fourth failed to explode. Efforts were made to recover it at the time but because of complex shafting problems caused by an excess of water and the need to deal with more urgent tasks the bomb was temporarily abandoned. Land reclamation requirements in 1969 made it necessary to relocate and recover this bomb and the task was allocated to 2 Troop, 49 EOD Squadron, RE, under the command of Captain C. E. Nicholls, RE. After relocating the bomb, shafting started on 4 August 1969 and considerable difficulties were encountered, particularly from water, before the bomb was located some 6 m (19.7 ft) down, five days later. The bomb was identified as a 250 kg (550 lb) one fitted with a No 17 fuze which appeared, despite the water, to be in perfect condition. An electronic stethoscope was applied to the fuze and it was confirmed not to be ticking. Normally a constant stethoscope watch would be maintained on the bomb but this was impossible due to the noise made by the waterr pumping sets which, if stopped for more than a few minutes, would have allowed the shaft to flood and perhaps collapse.

The whole area was evacuated and Captain Nicholls, assisted by Warrant Officer S. D. Hambrook, RE, immunized the fuze and then removed the bomb base plate. This revealed that the powder explosive filling had deteriorated to such an extent that some 9 litres (2 gallons) of nitroglycerine (an exceedingly unstable explosive) had been formed and that the remaining 90 kg (198 lb) of powder explosive was floating in it as lumps, or sticking to the inside of the bomb casing. This combination could only be removed by hand. Apart from the extreme risk of explosion which could be caused by any small shock or friction, working conditions were made appalling by the fumes which caused constant retching and nausea. By the time the explosive was finally removed the team had worked continuously for 29 hours without rest and had been exposed to extreme danger for eleven hours. Thus the dangers of bomb disposal continue to exist even from bombs which have been buried for over 28 years.

Another bomb with a similar fill, but a simple impact fuze, was re-

Right *Lieutenant D. Marshall, RE, and Lance Corporal Gregory, RE, fit a magnetic clock stopper.*

Below left *Warrant Officer S. D. Hambrook, RE, (right) and Sergeant R. Bromley, RE, working on a German unexploded bomb.*

covered at Westerham, Kent, near the centre line of the then proposed M25 motorway. This bomb (its presence known beforehand) was searched for, finally located and then removed from extremely marshy conditions during the period July to November 1976. The M25 had another bomb on its route on 18 May 1979 when an earth-moving vehicle uncovered a 250 kg (550 lb) bomb fitted with a No 17 fuze. After evacuation of the construction site and some nearby houses, Captain D. Marshal, RE, of 49 EOD Squadron, RE, safely immunized the fuze which had stayed very firmly stopped despite the rough treatment it had sustained at the hands of the plant operator. This was most fortunate for the outcome could have been vastly different for both the site workers and the nearby inhabitants of Aveley, South Ockenden, Essex.

BAC tasks carried out by the Royal Engineers during the post-war period ranged over the length and breadth of the United Kingdom, from the Highlands of Scotland to Devon, from north and south Wales to the rural areas of Surrey and Sussex. Initially the work was to clear wartime ranges and field firing areas so that they could once again be enjoyed by the general public. Later the work was in response to isolated 'finds' which frequently necessitated the searching of quite considerable areas, or in Wales or the Highlands to enable re-afforestation to take place.

One of the most publicized BAC tasks and one which necessitated the establishment of a special unit was the clearance of Maplin and Foulness Sands in the River Thames estuary. For many years there had been a major obstacle to the development of this particular area. In 1844 the War Office had established an artillery practice and testing range at Shoeburyness on the north Thames coast east of Southend and firing had taken place over the Maplin and Foulness Sands ever since. Consequently, the area was littered with the remains of over 125 years of experimentation and practice firing. In July 1971, after the announcement by the British government that a third London Airport would be built on Maplin Sands, the task of clearing these sands fell upon the Royal Engineer EOD organization. Consequently, on 1 July 1972, 71 EOD Squadron, RE, was formed up at Shoeburyness under the command of Major R. I. Radford, RE. The total establishment of the unit was four officers and twelve other ranks, all Royal Engineers and EOD-trained. In addition, there were four Royal Air Force non-commissioned officers (also EOD-trained) and a Royal Navy clearance diver. The main labour force was civilian, of whom approximately seventy were explosive ordnance searchers and another sixty were drivers, plant operators and administrative staff.

Work started at once with the squadron divided into sixteen half sections (gangs), each under the command of a Corporal Bomb Disposal Engineer (the basic EOD trade in the Royal Engineers). Each gang consisted of seven searchers, a JCB tractor and operator. Each two gangs (one section) shared a cargo vehicle which served not only as transport for the men and stores but also as a shelter for meals on the otherwise bleak sands. All section vehicles were equipped with a radio, windproof bodies, cooking stoves, lockers, etc.

Work continued for the next 21 months until on 20 March 1974 the government announced that it would authorize no further work on the Maplin project pending a complete review. As a result, the squadron was forbidden to start work in any new areas but continued to work in those areas already started until April 1974, when the order was received to disband the labour force. A small labour force was retained to collect and prepare for sea-dumping the several hundreds of tons of inert ordnance which had been collected into piles but not yet disposed of and to demolish the small quantity of live ordnance still awaiting demolition. All work finally ceased on 27 June 1974, just three days short of two years since work first started. During those two years the unit had searched and cleared all items to a depth of 1.5 m (5 ft) and larger items to a depth of 3 m (10 ft) over a number of areas totalling 450 hectares (1,112 acres) and a further 137 hectares (338 acres) of water-covered areas to a depth of 0.4 m (1.3 ft). In all, 63,452 items of ordnance had been located of which 14,180 items were demolished explosively and 1,341 tonnes (1,320 tons) of inert items were sea-dumped. Working conditions were often bleak and working hours on

Above *Maplin Sands, 1973. Warrant Officer S. Chadwick, RE, (71 EOD Squadron, RE) beside a pile of World War 1 trench mortar bombs.*

Below *Maplin Sands. Lieutenant R. Veck, RE, (kneeling on left) and Major R. I. Radford, RE, (kneeling on right) with some of the civilian explosive ordnance searchers of 71 EOD Squadron, RE.*

the sands were dependant entirely upon tides, the hours of daylight available and how far offshore the search area was situated. Inshore areas were accessible for up to seven hours a day, 24 days a month, whereas offshore areas might only be accessible for 2½ hours a day, eight days a month in summer and even less during the short winter days.

An interesting 'spin-off' of this work was the recovery of a magnificent collection of historic ordnance spanning over a century of development. Items included round shot, many early experimental rounds, Armstrong and Whitworth shells and bolts (term for solid shot), studded shells up to 13 in (330 mm) diameter, Hale and other Victorian war rockets, World War 1 trench mortar bombs and a selection of modern rounds. All were presented to Service museums relevant to their origin.

Although the proposed airport was never built on Maplin Sands, the complex administrative difficulties and hard work in bleak and often dangerous conditions were recognized by the appointment of Major Radford to be a Member of the Order of the British Empire (MBE) and for the award to Flight Sergeant E. K. Tumman, RAF, of the Medal of the Order of the British Empire (BEM).

The Royal Air Force, throughout the immediate post-war years, reflected very closely the manpower problems and tasks of the Royal Engineers as described above. At the end of the war the Royal Air Force bomb disposal organization within the United Kingdom had been vigorously cut down to provide qualified manpower and specialist equipment for more urgent tasks overseas—in particular the disarmament of the Luftwaffe described in the previous chapter. Thus in 1945 it consisted of a HQ Bomb Disposal Wing based at Doncaster with under command three Bomb Disposal Squadrons commanding between them a total of nine Bomb Disposal Flights as shown below.

HQ BD Wing

5131 BD Squadron	5133 BD Squadron	5134 BD Squadron
6202 Flight	6215 Flight	6209 Flight
6204 Flight	6217 Flight	6226 Flight
6235 Flight	6219 Flight	
	6221 Flight	

On completion of the then-outstanding commitments (at that time gauged to be very few), it was the intention to practically disband the Royal Air Force bomb disposal organization on the grounds referred to previously—no more bombs were being dropped therefore why retain a bomb disposal capability? Only the Air Ministry Branch, Arm BD (Armaments and Bomb Disposal) and possibly one Bomb Disposal Flight were to be retained. However, HQ Bomb Disposal Wing, then commanded by Wing Commander R. W. Ackerman, MBE, RAF, managed to hang on until 1951 when the Wing HQ plus the headquarters of both 5133 and 5134 Bomb Disposal Squadrons together with 6202 and 6215 Bomb Disposal Flights were disbanded. There then remained one Squadron Head quarters (5131) and seven Bomb Disposal Flights. In 1952, 6209 Bomb Disposal Flight was transferred to Germany and then there were six.

These six Flights (6204, 6217, 6219, 6221, 6226 and 6235) were for the next thirteen years to carry out a wide range of bomb disposal tasks dealing with both Allied and ex-enemy bombs. Some bombs were dealt with individually, others were found on crashed aircraft in small groups and during bombing range clearance bombs of all sizes were found in huge numbers.

In June 1965 the Air Ministry gave authority for the disbandment of HQ 5131 Bomb Disposal Squadron and four of its Flights (6219, 6221, 6226 and 6235). The remaining two Flights, 6204 and 6217, were deployed to Royal Air Force Bicester and Dishforth respectively. Finally, on 16 January 1967, 6204 and 6217 Bomb Disposal Flights were absorbed into the establishments of 71 and 60 Maintenance Units with whom they had been living since 1965. Thus an era came to an end as the last two Flights of those established on 21 April 1943 faded into history. It was, however, only the name or number which had disappeared, the personnel remained and continued with the apparently never-ending task of bomb disposal.

As with the Royal Engineer units, the Phoenix rose again and today the Royal Air Force has explosive ordnance disposal units equipped to meet any eventuality.

During these changes bomb disposal work continued and in the relatively stable period between 1952 and 1965 vast quantities of dangerous items were disposed of. We have already considered the perils of the German No 17 long-delay clockwork fuze but the Royal Air Force bomb disposal units still had to face the British and American chemical action long-delay anti-removal bomb pistols and fuzes. These, like the German long-delay fuzes, did not become inert with time and were generally speaking more difficult and more dangerous to deal with than their German counterparts. The German SD2 butterfly bomb fuze, having a purely mechanical action, also retained its lethal capacity. Probably the last person in the United Kingdom to be killed by a butterfly bomb was Flight Lieutenant F. H. Derrington, RAF, the officer commanding 6221 Bomb Disposal Flight. His unit was responsible for operating the Royal Air Force Bomb Cemetery near Upminster, Essex, and it was in this area that much of the investigatory work was carried out on bombs both during the war and up to the 1960s when it was eventually closed down and cleared. Flight Lieutenant Derrington was working on a butterfly bomb on 27 November 1956 when it exploded and he died from the injuries he received. He was not alone, however, in dealing with these nasty little souvenirs of the war. No 6219 Bomb Disposal Flight dealt with some at Haltham in Lincolnshire in April 1954, 5131 Bomb Disposal Squadron dealt with some more a year later at Legbourne, also in Lincolnshire, and 6235 Bomb Disposal Flight dealt with more at Fitling, Hornsea and Hedon, all in east Yorkshire, during the period April 1957 to June 1958. But bigger bombs too caused their problems.

Above *Catloss bomb, July 1946. From left to right: Flight Lieutenant K. Price, RAF, Flight Lieutenant D. Bishop, RAF, Warrant Officer W. J. Preston, RAF, Squadron Leader T. Clark, RAF, and Squadron Leader J. Cotton, RAF.*

Below *Catloss bomb, July 1946. Warrant Officer W. J. Preston, RAF, and personnel of 6204 BD Flight, RAF, who did the digging.*

In July 1946 a 250 kg (550 lb) German bomb was discovered at Royal Air Force Catfoss in East Yorkshire. The bomb was found to be fitted with a simple No 15 direct impact fuze and a No 17 long-delay fuze with probably a ZUS 40 booby trap beneath it. The work of recovery was handled by 6204 Bomb Disposal Flight with specialist assistance from two Air Ministry officers, Squadron Leader T. M. Clark, OBE, RAF, and Flight Lieutenant D. Bishop, GM, RAF. The Flight Lieutenant had received his George Medal for work in Malta as a warrant officer and the Squadron Leader had received his OBE for dealing with similarly fuzed bombs in the Steenockerzeel bomb dump near Brussels the previous February. The bomb was uncovered at a depth of 3 m (10 ft) and the Air Ministry specialists decided this would be an ideal opportunity to demonstrate the experimental technique for neutralizing and removing the ZUS 40 normally fitted below the No 17 fuze to prevent its extraction. The procedure was successfully completed with Squadron Leader Clark in the hole and Flight Lieutenant Bishop lying nearby listening in on the stethoscope headphones and recording every move made. As at Steenockerzeel the procedure worked. Upon inspection of the removed ZUS 40 it was noted that its striker had moved forward and its point had actually penetrated the detonator but, thanks to the technique used, not with sufficient force to fire it and so detonate the bomb. This was a narrow escape for all concerned but it adequately demonstrated the success of the new technique.

Some bombs did not pose these dangers and were only of interest because of their historic connections. Such a bomb was the one recovered at Royal Air Force Coxhill, near Hill, Yorkshire, in June 1948. Six years earlier in May 1942, 14 Bomb Disposal Squad had been called to Coxhill because a large unexploded German bomb had penetrated the main runway on the very day when the United States of America was flying in its first bombers to the United Kingdom to join Bomber Command. Many VIPs were present, including General Eisenhower, and while the squad went on digging for the bomb the secondary runway was forced into use. After several days' work, the task became hopeless as the bomb merely sank deeper into the mire as the airmen dug. So the shaft was back-filled and the runway resurfaced. In 1948, 5133 Bomb Disposal Squadron relocated the bomb and sunk a shaft where eventually the bomb was recovered from a depth of 10 m (32.8 ft). It was a 500 kg (1,100 lb) bomb fitted with a simple impact fuze.

Many German bombs were dealt with during this period but between 1945 and 1978 thousands of British and American bombs were also cleared, far too numerous to be recounted in detail. The use of the term 'thousands' smacks of exaggeration but looking at the works diary of 6226 Bomb Disposal Flight during a period of less than three years (September 1948 to May 1951) it can be seen that they dealt with 211 bombs ranging in size from 4,000 lb (1,814 kg) high capacity to 4 lb (1.8 kg) incendiary devices. Multiplying 211 by the period worked and the number of Flights all engaged upon similar work, the term 'thousands' no longer appears to be an exaggeration! Indeed, if to the individual bombs and the clearance of bombs from crashed aircraft, is added the work undertaken by those Flights engaged upon area clearance tasks, the term should more correctly be 'many thousands'.

As early as 1945 a list was compiled of Royal Air Force bombing and gunnery ranges which would have to be searched and cleared of unexploded ordnance and practice inert ordnance which might be mistaken for live items. This list showed a total of seventy locations, some of which would require a Flight for two or three weeks, while others would prove to require several years' work. Many were thought to have been used only for inert practice bombing and so were given a lower priority than those known to have been used for high explosive bombing either for experimental purposes or as jettison areas. Most of the original seventy locations were cleared during the late 1940s and early 1950s but more were added to the list as the years passed. Eventually the task of clearing ranges and other explosive areas was to keep the Royal Air Force bomb disposal units fully occupied (when not dealing with priority bomb tasks) until the present day, and still the work is not finished.

As with the Royal Engineer BAC teams, Royal Air Force bomb disposal Flights engaged upon area clearance tasks not only have to contend with the hazards always inherent in disposing of long-abandoned items of explosive ordnance, they also have to endure the full rigours of nature. By design, bombing ranges or live firing areas are generally in the more isolated areas of the United Kingdom.

Clearly it is impossible to describe each site, but the scope of the work can be judged from the fact that, in 1954, 5131 Bomb Disposal Squadron with its six Flights searched a total area of 912 hectares (2,250 acres) and recovered over 35,000 missiles. Ten years later in 1964, 988 hectares (2,439 acres) were searched and 31 major tasks were completed. It is impossible to give examples of typical tasks as no two are alike but three vastly different ones are mentioned below. The first was undertaken by 6235 Bomb Disposal Flight in 1964 at Jurby on the Isle of Man. This was a redundant air-firing and ground training area of 93 hectares (230 acres), heavily overgrown with ferns and gorse. Over 500 various items of land ordnance were recovered before the range was handed back to the Isle of Man government.

Braid Fell near Stranraer in south-west Scotland provided a totally different task. This was a large bombing range spread over 1,718 hectares (4,240 acres) of rough hilly country and moorland. It had several separate target areas, the largest being a simulated factory which had been heavily practice bombed during the war. The task started on 24 March 1960 and was completed by October 1961, the work being done by 6235 Bomb Disposal Flight, at that time commanded by Pilot Officer A. Bibbey, RAF. In 1961, in order to speed up the work, additional personnel were provided from 6217 Bomb Disposal Flight. The factory area alone produced over 16.25 tonnes (16 tons) of bombs including some as large as 4,000 lb (1,818 kg). In all, some 25.4 tonnes (25 tons) of bombs were recovered.

Probably the largest land clearance task in respect of the weight of ordnance recovered was that at Llanberis. Royal Air Force Llanberis was opened as an explosive storage unit in May 1941, close to the Snowdonian village of that name in north Wales. The site occupied a large complex of disused slate quarries and interlinking tunnels. Between 1941 and July 1956 when the unit closed it had been used as a bomb store, a demolition area and a burning pit.

The demolition and burning of explosives within the quarry area started in June 1943 when the Royal Air Force School of Explosives moved to the site. The school curriculum included the destruction of explosives, so large quantities of bombs and pyrotechnics were brought in for demolition or burning. The destruction of explosives continued until July 1956 when the unit was closed. Included in the destruction programmes were virtually every type of explosive item on the Royal Air Force wartime inventory. Unfortunately, as sometimes happens with mass demolition, a proportion of the items were not completely destroyed. Thus this large and practically inaccessible complex of quarries was known to contain quantities of explosive items. As such the site solicited a certain amount of indiscriminate dumping of unwanted or recently recovered explosive items. The shape of the site was such that much of the explosive material dumped ended up on ledges and slate outcrops, never reaching the quarry bottoms. More still had been dumped or fallen into the lakes which had formed in the quarries during the years of inactivity between 1956 and 1969.

It was in this latter year, 1969, that the decision was taken to clear the entire site of explosives and explosive debris. The task was given to 71 Maintenance Unit EOD Flight from Royal Air Force Bicester (later to be designated No 2 EOD Unit, RAF). By the time the task was completed in October 1975, the personnel of the Flight had become expert in lifting tons of explosives from the quarry pits and lakes and in the handling of special mechanical equipment. They had also learnt the arts of tunnelling and rock climbing, which in the earlier days had been the only ways of gaining access to some of the pits and their surrounding ledges. This must have been one of the few bomb disposal tasks carried out by any Service where members of the unit had first to be instructed by a Mountain Rescue Team. The various rock climbing techniques and rescue procedures taught were essential to enable members of the unit to reach much of the explosive ordnance with which they had to deal.

From 1969 onwards, the various pits and tunnels were progressively cleared. Members of the EOD Flight burrowed further and deeper into the debris and slate rubble to uncover such items as incendiary bombs and high explosive bomb detonators. The latter, together with the numerous bomb fuzes which were uncovered, were in an extremely hazardous

condition and required careful handling. With the help of the Royal
Engineers, roads were constructed into the more difficult pits and the 'fly
on the wall' approach became less frequent. However, at no time throughout the six years of the project was the task rated any easier than 'very difficult'. It was not a question of true grit and stamina, but rather an excess of
slate, grit and slime.

Royal Navy divers were co-opted to investigate the contents of a large
lake in one of the pits as it was suspected that it might contain some explosive items. The divers reported that the bed of the lake was littered with
explosive items including a number of large bombs. Subsequently, over
20,000,000 gallons (90,920,000 litres) of water and sludge were pumped
out. By April 1973 the lake was emptied revealing everyone's worst
fears—it took a further two years of hard labour to recover and dispose of
the explosive items revealed. Fortunately, this pit was one of those to
which 38 Engineer Regiment, RE, had constructed a road, otherwise the
task would have been impossible.

On completion of the task, 71 Maintenance Unit EOD Flight had moved
approximately 85,000 tons (83,364 tonnes) of slate and debris, recovered
and disposed of 352 tons (357 tonnes) of explosive items together with
1,420 tons (1,443 tonnes) of non-explosive ordnance debris. Many people
were involved in this task, too numerous to quote by name, but a few who
played a prominent part deserve to be mentioned. Those directly involved
at the work face were Flight Lieutenants E. S. T. Tout, W. Jones and
J. Thomson, RAF, all of whom successively commanded the EOD Flight

Left *Flight Sergeant Twine and Sergeant Andrews stacking 25 lb incendiary bombs at Llanberis.*

Right *Flight Sergeant Twine examining a two-inch mortar bomb.*

concerned. In the early days of the task the workforce consisted of an eight-man team headed by Flight Sergeant Russell, RAF, who was awarded the Medal of the Order of the British Empire (BEM) for his work during the initial opening up of this extremely hazardous operation. Other senior non-commissioned officers involved at some stage or other in the project were Flight Sergeant G. Twine, Flight Sergeant E. K. Tumman, BEM (who moved to Llanberis direct from the Maplin Sands task), Chief Technician D. Andrews, BEM, and Sergeant B. Rutter (who was later killed whilst clearing British cluster munitions following a trial drop).

Such, then, were some of the activities of the United Kingdom-based bomb disposal units/EOD units during the thirty years following the end of World War 2. However, some bomb disposal units still existed abroad and a number of overseas tasks were also undertaken by the United Kingdom-based units. Many of these involved only very small numbers of men but the dangers faced were frequently as great as any met during the war. A few examples are given below.

It was only seven years after the end of World War 2 when British forces were again involved in a shooting war—this time in Korea. During 1952-3 a Royal Engineer bomb disposal section formed a part of the British Commonwealth Engineer Regiment operating in both Japan and Korea in conjunction with US Army EOD squads. During this period incidents were occurring at a rate of about two a week which was not excessive but did provide some interesting tasks as new Soviet and Chinese weapons were uncovered. During 1952 the section was commanded by Lieutenant (later Captain) D. J. W. Dalby, RE, who was subsequently relieved by Captain

F. C. Smith, MBE, RE (ex-Army BD School at Horsham), in January 1953. Unfortunately, in April 1953 Captain Smith suffered serious injuries to his hands and eyes when a Soviet bomb fuze, which he was dismantling in readiness for despatch to the United Kingdom, exploded in his hands. Despite the permanent damage to his hands and eyes, by considerable personal effort he overcame his handicaps and was operating from Seoul, Korea, by the end of June 1953. It was during that month that the Truce was concluded and it became apparent that there was not enough work to justify the continuing full-time existence of the Royal Engineer bomb disposal section. There were already fifteen US Army EOD squads well able to handle any contingency, and so the Royal Engineer section was disbanded.

Three years later a Royal Air Force Bomb Disposal Flight was involved in work in an operational environment which was very similar in all but scale to the activities of 1944-5. In the summer of 1956, 6204 Bomb Disposal Flight, RAF, under the command of Flight Lieutenant A. Fenton, RAF, was withdrawn from its parent squadron (5131) and joined the Royal Air Force element of those forces assembling and preparing for imminent overseas deployment.

In October 1956 the Flight was flown to Malta where it embarked on the aircraft carrier HMS *Ocean* and set sail for Suez together with other British troops. At first light on 5 November 1956 the force started landing at Suez, and a small team from 6204 Bomb Disposal Flight was airlifted to the civil airport at El Gamil just outside Port Said, at that time behind the enemy lines (there was, however, a troop of parachute Sappers already in residence). Under considerable Egyptian counterfire the remainder of the Flight was set down on the beaches by landing craft. However, once the opposition was quelled and the road to El Gamil was opened they moved on to the airport.

Work started on 6 November 1956 to clear El Gamil Airport of battle-field explosives, including some unexploded British bombs. This completed, the Flight carried out general explosive clearance in the Port Said area. As usual this involved a wide range of bomb disposal-related tasks such as searching houses and other buildings for weapons and booby traps. They were also required to use explosives to open specified safes for the removal of selected papers. Political pressure brought the operation to a standstill in early December 1956 and 6204 Bomb Disposal Flight, RAF, embarked on the landing craft *Salerno*. After seventeen days on very rough seas they reached Plymouth in time for a well-earned Christmas leave.

Earlier in this chapter it was seen that in 1952, 6209 Bomb Disposal Flight RAF was moved to Germany thus providing a Royal Air Force bomb disposal unit in that country for the first time since the disbanding of 6210 Bomb Disposal Flight at Celle in 1948. This transfer ensured that, in 1959, 6209 Bomb Disposal Flight would have the honour—and accompanying dangers—of defuzing probably the largest bomb neutralized by any bomb disposal unit. The bomb, a British 12,000 lb (5,455 kg) deep penetration bomb known as a 'Tallboy', was dropped on the Sorpe Dam, near Dortmund, by Bomber Command aircraft on 15 October 1944. In late 1958 part of the dam was being drained for reconstruction purposes when the bomb was found in ankle-deep mud and snow at the base of this 695 m (760 yd) wide dam.

The responsibility for dealing with bombs discovered on West German soil other than within Allied bases, lay squarely upon the shoulders of the West German bomb disposal organization. This functioned on an area basis and consequently this particular bomb, over 3 m (10 ft) long and 1 m (3.2 ft) in diameter, was the responsibility of the North-Rhine-Westphalia bomb disposal teams. The leader of these teams was Herr Walter Mitzke who had joined the German Army in 1925 and became an Ammunition Technician. During the war he was an instructor at the Technical School for Air Armament in Halle, where he trained people to become bomb disposal operators. In 1943 he was the Senior Weapons Instructor with the rank of Captain but he was also engaged in active bomb disposal. After the war he continued in the same job and by 1958 was head of the North-Rhine-Westphalia bomb disposal organization. When he retired from government employment he claimed to have personally defuzed over 5,000 high explosive bombs of 227 kg (500 lb) and over, eleven per cent of which had been fitted with British or American long-delay fuzes or pistols.

Clearly, therefore, Herr Mitzke was an extremely experienced man when it came to dealing with Allied bombs and yet when he was called to the Sorpe Dam he was unable to identify the three fuzes or pistols fitted into the rear of the bomb. (It would perhaps be convenient at this stage to define the difference between a bomb fuze and a bomb pistol. Essentially a fuze is a complete item with a safety and arming mechanism, an activator system and finally a detonator or pyrotechnic device which directly causes the weapon to function. The pistol, on the other hand, contains no explosive or pyrotechnic material and its final action requires a separate detonator before it can make the weapon function. The main advantage of the pistol and separate detonator is that the often complex mechanism can be stored, checked and maintained in an area free of explosive.)

Herr Mitzke therefore approached the Royal Air Force, Germany, and asked for assistance. The only person with knowledge of the Tallboy bomb and able to assist was Flight Lieutenant J. M. Waters, RAF, the officer commanding 6209 Bomb Disposal Flight. From the detailed description given by Herr Mitzke he was able to identify the bomb and confirm that it was fitted with three No 47 half-hour chemical delay pistols. The mode of operation of these pistols was such that after the bomb had been released from the aircraft an ampoule of acetone within the pistol was broken and the acetone allowed to come into contact with a celluloid disc. This disc prevented a spring-loaded striker from hitting the detonator fitted beneath the pistol. After approximately half an hour the celluloid disc would be so softened and pliable that it would release the striker and so detonate the bomb. However, if the ampoule had only been cracked or the

Defuzing the 'Tallboy' at Sorpe Dam on 6 January 1959: Herr Walter Mitzke and Flight Lieutenant J. M. Waters, RAF.

celluloid disc had not quite collapsed any movement of the pistol after the bomb had landed could be disastrous.

Flight Lieutenant Waters offered to defuze, or more correctly de-pistol, the bomb on the following day, 30 December 1958. His offer, although accepted, could not be implemented quite so quickly as formal permission had to be sought at Air Ministry level and time had to be allowed for the evacuation of the entire population of the nearby village of Langscheid, for had the bomb exploded the village would have been destroyed and the dam severely damaged.

Finally, all was ready and on the morning of 6 January 1959, Herr Mitzke and Flight Lieutenant Waters, assisted by Corporals F. Smith and A. Mouat, both from 6209 Bomb Disposal Flight, neutralized this huge bomb. The first pistol was removed using a remotely operated extractor but the remaining two were taken out by hand with Herr Mitzke and Flight Lieutenant Waters working unaccompanied as a team. It was subsequently discovered that the probable cause of the bomb's failure was that water had entered the fuze pockets. This was hardly surprising considering that the bomb had been dropped into 30 m (100 ft) of water and had remained there for half an hour before it was expected to function. The water, having entered the pistols under considerable pressure, diluted the acetone and in one case, although the celluloid disc had been ruptured, the striker had not hit the detonator with sufficient force to cause it to detonate the bomb. The press gave huge coverage of the event, some informed but much misinformed. Just over two weeks later, on 22 January 1959, two more 12,000 lb (5,455 kg) Tallboys were discovered in the mud below the dam and dealt with by the German bomb disposal organization. Admittedly these two were fitted with less dangerous pistols (No 58 direct impact) but their removal received only scant attention in the local papers.

Flight Lieutenant Waters was congratulated by both the Minister of the Interior for Westphalia and by the British Prime Minister for a job well done.

Apart from activities which were newsworthy, such as the Tallboy at the Sorpe Dam or the massive clearance at Llanberis, many small but often interesting tasks were taking place all round the world. Two most hazardous overseas tasks were undertaken by Major H. P. Qualtrough, MBE, RE, and Sergeant J. Cooke, BEM, RE, of the Bomb Disposal Unit (UK), RE, between October 1965 and March 1966. Their main task was to clear explosives from the small island of Betio in the Gilbert and Ellice Islands. Their subsidiary task, to be undertaken en route to Betio, was to carry out a full reconnaissance of the Japanese mine and bomb dumps on Penang, an island off the north-west coast of Malaya. Part of the island had been cleared in 1950 but some nine storage tunnels and hidden pits on the eastern side of the island had still to be entered and details noted. Once the tunnels had been located and an entry forced, the vast collection of Japanese bombs and shells, many of which were oozing explosive, filled them with horror. They certainly did not envy the men who would eventually have to clear the area. Work went on in Penang until November 1965 when Qualtrough and Cooke set off to clear the explosives from Betio Island.

The bulk of the Betio explosives was contained in about fifty collapsed bunkers. The official task given to the team was to excavate the bunkers by hand, remove the high explosive for sea-dumping, re-inter any human remains found and finally to sweep the whole island with a mine detector. It was a formidable task even for two very experienced bomb disposal personnel. A preliminary reconnaissance was made on 30 November 1965 and it was found that there were a total of 42 bunkers which had been Japanese gun sites, bomb stores or command posts. The Americans had made a considerable effort to clear the island at the end of the war and, having evacuated the population, had blown up any loose ordnance and bulldozed in the entrances to the bunkers. However, the collapsed bunkers still contained unexploded and fuzed rounds for 203, 152, 127 and 76.2 mm guns together with other miscellaneous mines, bombs and ammunition.

Work started on 3 December 1965 with a labour force of fifteen prisoners (thanks to the co-operation of the local Chief Police Officer) augmented by locally employed and paid labourers. By 19 January 1966 all except one of the bunkers had been cleared—no mean achievement. The ammunition recovered had been severely distorted and the explosive fillings so deteriorated that they varied from a liquid which gave off toxic fumes to the equally dangerous metal picrates. (Picrates are crystalline substances formed by the chemical action of the deteriorating explosive and the metal of the ammunition and are extremely sensitive to friction and excessive heat.) The removal of these finds caused the team considerable concern because the civil labour force remained patently uninterested in safety

Left *Clearing Japanese bombs from Penang.*

Right *Major A. J. Loch, RE, with a Japanese 60 kg bomb recovered at Penang.*

precautions, and the local population, once the bunkers were opened, would nightly carry out private enterprise work to obtain free explosive for fishing.

The last bunker was the most difficult task as it had received several direct hits during the war. Excavation began on 29 December 1965 but on 3 February 1966, after almost twenty tons (20.3 tonnes) of high explosive had been removed, work was abandoned. It was decided by Major Qualtrough that burrowing (it could not be described as tunnelling) under collapsed sections was even more dangerous than the explosives being handled.

Most of the bunkers contained human remains and these were carefully collected and re-interred in a mass grave. The explosive finds were separated into those which were safe to transport and eventually sea-dump, and those which should be moved as little as possible and later destroyed by demolition. Sea-dumping was carried out from an elderly ship's lifeboat and an outrigger canoe. When loaded to the gunwales these were not ideal boats in which to venture, but with a lot of hard work the sea-dumping was completed by 3 March 1966.

In all, over a hundred tons of explosives were cleared from the island but, as on Penang, much still remained. As a result of the extremely hazardous

work carried out over a period of six months at Penang and Betio both Major Qualtrough and Sergeant Cooke were later awarded the George Medal.

The final clearance of the Penang sites was started a year later in February 1967 under the command of Major A. J. Loch, RE, later succeeded by Major M. J. V. Hoskins, RE, and work continued for just over two years until March 1969. Thousands of tons of Japanese explosives were dealt with either by sea-dumping or demolition, much of it in an extremely dangerous state having survived 21 years of corrosion and deterioration in a climate featuring ninety per cent humidity. At the same time, other bomb incidents were being handled by the twelve-man team under Major Hoskins in places such as Brunei and elsewhere in Malaya. For their part in these operations, Major Hoskins was awarded the George Medal and Staff Sergeants J. C. V. Wood and G. Duncan the Medal of the Order of the British Empire (BEM).

The second major clearance of Betio Island had to wait over ten years until 1977. In that year a Joint Service Team composed of eleven Royal Navy, one Army and one Royal Air Force member, all EOD-trained, took part in an operation covering most of the Gilbert and Ellice Islands. The Naval party was responsible for clearing a Second World War Naval minefield from Funafuti Lagoon and the Army/Royal Air Force element was responsible for recovering and sea-dumping a reported 250 to 300 projectiles which had been exposed on Nanumea Island, an outer island in the Ellice Group. They had also to investigate the bunker on Betio Island in the Gilbert Group which had been abandoned by Major Qualtrough's team eleven years previously.

The Army was represented by Sergeant J. M. Devine, RE, of 49 EOD Squadron, RE, and the Royal Air Force by Flight Sergeant D. Trafford, RAF; between them they recovered and sea-dumped eleven boat-loads of American Navy and Army shells from Nanumea. Together with other calibres this ammunition included 452 six-inch (152-mm) shells.

Subsequently, Sergeant Devine and Flight Sergeant Trafford, assisted by Fleet Chief Petty Officer V. Gibbons, RN, and Petty Officer A. Broadhurst, RN, searched a number of bunkers on Betio Island, its causeway and an offshore reef. They recovered a wide variety of American and Japanese ordnance, some of which was demolished and the remainder of which they sea-dumped. In all, during this operation Sergeant Devine visited Funafuti, Nanumea, Nanumanga and Vaitupu in the Ellice Islands Group, and Betio, Bairiki and Abemama (of R. L. Stevenson's *Treasure Island* fame) in the Gilbert Island Group. Certainly a far cry from his parent unit back in Kent and probably a great deal more dangerous.

Throughout the 1960s and 1970s the Army and the Royal Air Force EOD units, in addition to their United Kingdom commitments, were engaged in short, sharp and frequently dangerous overseas tasks. These included Indonesia in 1964, Malta in 1968-70, Sardinia in 1970, the Falkland Islands in 1975 (seven years before it hit the world headlines) and Cyprus in 1974.

During May and June 1974 a Royal Engineer team from 49 EOD Squadron, RE, led by Warrant Officer W. G. Kibble, RE, carried out the clearance of approximately 3.25 hectares (8 acres) of the Polemidhia Range at Limassol. Having disposed of a number of mortar bombs, rockets and other miscellaneous items, the team returned to the United Kingdom on 28 June 1974. As far as they were concerned this was just one month too soon, for in July 1974 the Turkish Air Force attacked Cyprus in support of its nation's invasion of the island. The Royal Air Force EOD team based at Akrotiri was called out to deal with unexploded ordnance delivered by Super Sabre, Starfigher and Thunderstreak aircraft of the Turkish Air Force. During a preliminary cease-fire on 27 July 1974, a team led by Flight Lieutenant E. Costick, RAF, and comprising Flying Officer D. Wilson and Chief Technician F. Knox, RAF, made a sweep of Larnaca and Famagusta and found two 750 lb (340 kg) bombs in Famagusta. One was located in mud under a church and the other was balanced across two single beds six floors up in the Venus Beach Hotel.

Under the eye of a Greek National Guard officer, the team excavated and exposed the fuze on the bomb under the church and after examination declared the bomb safe for removal. The one in the hotel was not so easy.

Members of the RAF EOD team working on a Turkish 750 lb bomb on Nicosia airport.

The hotel lifts were out of action and in the understandable absence of any civilian assistance, the team carried the heavy specialist bomb disposal equipment up the apparently never-ending flights of stairs until they came to the room occupied by the uninvited guest. After carefully cutting away the bed-clothes which had become entangled around the bomb and fuze, the fuze was identified as American with a cocked striker mechanism which was armed and very susceptible to jarring or rough handling. Flight Lieutenant Costick arranged for the evacuation of the area and ordered the remainder of his team to leave. He then successfully removed the fuze using the specialist equipment which had so laboriously been carried up the stairs. With the aid of the local Royal Engineers the bomb was swung through the hole in the bedroom wall and lowered to the ground.

The International Airport at Nicosia had been a prime target for the Turkish Air Force and consequently, the EOD team made a full sweep of the airfield. They found one 750 lb (340 kg) bomb and a number of unexploded rocket heads, all of which were removed and later destroyed. This team included Flight Lieutenant E. S. T. Tout, MBE (he received his MBE for his work at Llanberis), Flight Sergeant L. McDermott, Junior Technicians Daly and Wood and Senior Aircraftsman Dennis, RAF, all of whom contributed significantly to the success of one or other of the tasks undertaken.

What of the Royal Navy during the post-war years? With the end of the war the Navy, like the other two armed Services, underwent a major contraction in numbers, particularly in those branches responsible for explosive ordnance disposal. Since most of the Bomb Safety Officers and the officers of the Land Incident Sections were RNVR they returned, in some cases reluctantly, to their lives as civilians.

During the early part of the war it had been considered that the disposal of bombs was distinct from and in no way related to the disposal of mines, miscellaneous missiles and projectiles. This was totally disproved following the invasions of Italy and Normandy and the subsequent port and harbour clearance tasks undertaken by the Royal Navy referred to in Chapter 9. In early 1944 the Director of the Naval Unexploded Bomb Department (DUBD), Captain L. E. H. Llewellyn, RN, expressed the view that it was seldom known what was buried after an attack, particularly in an attack where Naval bombardment was combined with bombing. He was sure that certain fundamental precautions and methods of disposal were common to all forms of unexploded weapons and that it was only in particular fuzes and fitments that the differences and difficulties really arose.

For the above reasons, and in view of the almost total cessation of bombing of the United Kingdom, it was proposed that the duties performed by the DUBD and his staff should be taken over by the Department of Torpedoes and Mining (DTM). This amalgamation took place in September 1944 and the duties performed by DUBD were taken over by DTM, the new department thus formed being known as DTM (Bombs and Mine Disposal Section); it was directed by Commander E. O. Obbard, DSC, GM, RN. This new branch thus controlled the BSOs, the Rendering Mines Safe personnel (who were already an integral part of DTM) and the Land Incident Section.

Thus, at the end of the war all the Royal Navy explosive ordnance disposal sections (although this term was not yet in use) were under one command. HMS *Vernon* continued to exit and maintained a centre of knowledge on all aspects of Naval underwater weapon disposal, although in 1946 it was said that no instructional courses would be required for some years. From here the Royal Navy followed the same path as the Army and the Royal Air Force but, as in the other Services, it was quickly appreciated that just because no one was firing or laying weapons it did not mean that these weapons would not turn up in the most inconvenient places. Thus the Mine Clearance Diving Officer and his Clearance Divers were established as the Naval explosive ordnance disposal units. As recommended by Captain Llewellyn, the Royal Navy Clearance Diving Teams can today deal with all aspects of explosive ordnance disposal whether on land or underwater.

During many of the thirty years following the end of the Second World War (1945-75) EOD units had, in the main, been engaged in clearing the United Kingdom and elsewhere of the debris of war. The incidents quoted above can only show a typical cross-section of the countless actions, many heroic, many just hard work followed by a few moments of excitement or, in the case of BAC tasks, years of what to many would be considered pure boredom. Yet at any point a momentary lack of attention could be, and on occasions was, fatal.

To all those men whose actions were equally heroic, interesting, unusual or exciting, but who have not been included in this chapter, the author apologizes. Within the EOD community they are known and will not be forgotten.

During the latter part of the above period attitudes began to change and policy with them. EOD policy and teaching began to look to the future, not unfortunately to a debris-free country with beaches unlittered with the jettisoned pyrotechnics of the world's shipping, but rather to the threats of the future. International terrorism had become a major threat to security as had the many sophisticated weapon systems being developed, not only by the super-powers but also by the smaller countries. How these threats were dealt with are considered in the next chapter.

11

Today and tomorrow

During the 1970s and 1980s, when the press announced that a bomb had exploded in Beirut, Belfast or Berlin, the general public immediately thought of a terrorist weapon, an improvised explosive device (IED). Yet twenty years earlier the first thought would have been of the traditional aerial bomb perhaps left over from the Second World War. Thus has thinking changed as international terrorism has resorted to the bomb and explosive ambush to make its demands or political aspirations better known. The terrorist bombs can vary from a few grams of explosive in a letter to a hijacked fuel tanker packed with hundreds of kilograms of explosives, usually home-made.

The use of explosives to make a political point is not a phenomenon purely of the twentieth century. There was a certain Guido (Guy) Fawkes whose protest over the penal laws against Catholics resulted in an attempt to blow up King James I and the Houses of Parliament in November 1605. Nearly 300 years later, in 1894, Colonel N. D. Majendie, His Majesty's Chief Inspector of Explosives, visited Paris to learn how the French were dealing with improvised explosive devices, then referred to much more descriptively as 'infernal machines'. On his return he wrote a detailed report which included this extract:

'The enormous area of London as compared with Paris renders it much less easy to find suitable sites remote from thickly populated places in which to deposit, examine and destroy the bombs. Moreover, there is the difficulty that the conditions which may arise are so various, the nature of the suspected packages to be dealt with are so uncertain, the charges (if any) which they may contain are liable to differ so enormously that it is impossible to prescribe anything like a uniform method of treatment or to say that a plan which would be suitable for the examination of one class of infernal machine would be suitable for all. After a very careful consideration of the whole matter I am of opinion that what is wanted is as follows:

a. Some place readily accessible with suitable arrangements for effecting a preliminary examination (and in some cases when necessary, the explosion) of a small parcel or bomb without public risk or observation.

b. Some place reasonably accessible with suitable arrangements for effecting theexamination(andinsomecaseswhennecessarytheexplosion)oflargerparcels or infernal machines.

c. Some more distant place for effecting the safe destruction of any very formidable machine, the removal of which could be undertaken with reasonable safety.

It may, I think, be taken that we have two centres of possible Anarchial activity to provide for.

a. The district of which the Home Office and Scotland Yard may be regarded as the centre and in which are collected the more important public buildings and places of probable attack, and

b. The City district which comprises St Paul's Cathedral, the Bank, the Mint, the Guildhall and Mansion House, the Tower and other places of importance.

At the present moment if a bomb or infernal machine is found whetherin either these two districts or elsewhere there is no place whatever provided at which the same can be properly deposited and dealt with.

Having regard to the fact that it is important to minimize the distance through streets or crowded thoroughfares, that a suspected infernal machine should be conveyed, I think it would be desirable that independent provision should be made for each of the two districts above indicated, and with this view I would suggest:

First: That if possible some place be provided in the vicinity of the Home Office and Scotland Yard to which a small bomb or machine could be taken for examination and that an apparatus (in the shape of shields, etc) be provided and kept at such place which would enable such examination to be carried out without undue risk.

Second: That similar provision be made in the City District.

Third: That for the deposit, examination (and in those cases in which it might be absolutely necessary the destruction) of larger infernal machines some site or sites should be assigned remote from houses accessible without undue traversing of public streets and from which the public could be excluded and which indeed could be so arranged as to withdraw it from public notice or observation and that at this place suitable provision should be made (by means preferentially of a sunken or half sunken bomb-proof cell) where the necessary measures for dealing with infernal machines could be carried out and in case of necessity the explosion of the machine be effected without risk.'

As a result of this report a half-sunken bunker fitted with the latest 1895 remote handling equipment was constructed by the Royal Engineers on Duck Island in St James's Park, London. The bunker, used during the Second World War, was finally dismantled in 1985 and the bomb handling equipment delivered to the Royal Engineer Museum in Chatham, Kent. Those trained today to deal with improvised explosive devices will recognize many of the basic assumptions and principles as formulated by Colonel Majendie in 1895.

In addition to the well-identified threat at the turn of the nineteenth century, the Mafia in the 1920s also utilised the improvised explosive device, in their case as a murder weapon placed in a victim's car, not unlike similar actions of the 1970s and 1980s. Thus the idea and use of these devices is by no means new, but it was not until 1970 and later that their use became established and publicized in Northern Ireland and throughout Europe.

After the end of the Second World War and prior to 1970, explosive devices had been used against British Forces and interests in such places as Palestine, Hong Kong, Cyprus and Aden. Initially these bombs tended to lack complex fuzing systems, the most common type being a few sticks of plastic explosive with an electric detonator and a simple clock to complete the electrical firing circuit.

For many years one of the responsibilities of the Ammunition Technicians and the Ammunition Technical Officers of the Royal Army Ordnance Corps has been the disposal of bulk explosive which has become unsafe due to storage conditions or old age. Thus when packets of unsafe explosive were discovered it seemed natural, at that time, that the Royal Army Ordnance Corps should be responsible for their disposal, even if this lack of safety was solely man-made. Thus the Royal Army Ordnance Corps accepted the responsibility for the disposal of improvised explosive devices, a responsibility which in Northern Ireland in the early 1970s was to cost them many lives and earn them the respect and admiration of the remainder of the Armed Forces of the United Kingdom.

Initially the improvised explosive devices (IED) used by terrorists in Northern Ireland were crude, but effective and frequently lethal. They were in practice grenades or mines consisting of perhaps two of three sticks of commercial explosive surrounded by 6 in (152 mm) nails and activated by a detonator and a length of safety fuze. Other fragmentation bombs were constructed from lengths of metal pipe, capped at each end, filled with home-made explosive and again initiated with a safety fuze and a plain detonator. The problem with this sort of device was that it required the bomb layer or thrower to be present or very near to the scene of the explosion, thus increasing his or her own risk of detection.

Consequently, timing devices were soon incorporated into the bombs and electric detonators and batteries used, thus allowing bombs to be placed in position and detonated at a preset time after the bomber had left the area. The early timing devices showed little imagination and were similar to those used by the anarchist of the last century. A length of cord would be wrapped round a clock winder so that, as the key turned, the cord pulled an insulator from a simple switch and so completed the firing circuit. Some used the key as an electrical contact but these methods were quickly replaced by mass-produced units consisting of 60 or 120 minute timers normally used to remind drivers when their parking meter requires more money. A simple contact was attached to the timer and after a preset time of up to a maximum of 120 minutes the electrical circuit was completed and the bomb detonated. However, these devices could be temperamental and a number of bomb layers were killed by their own bombs, so an arming device was incorporated enabling the bomb to be safely handled and placed in position before it was armed. This arming was usually completed by removing a short length of dowel rod.

Thus the improvised time bomb had come of age and could also be modified to become a booby trap such that almost any action by the security forces, whether it be moving a vehicle, picking up a weapon found in a suspect building or even investigating a body, could trigger an explosion.

In addition to explosive devices, incendiary devices frequently concealed in a tape cassette were manufactured and hidden in furniture or clothing shops. If these devices went off whilst being handled severe injuries could be expected and on occasions occurred.

It was in this dangerous environment that the Royal Army Ordnance Corps Ammunition Technical Officers (ATO) and Ammunition Technicians (AT) of 1970 and early 1971 worked. However, conditions quickly became worse! On 9 August 1971 the British government introduced internment under the Special Powers Act of 1971 and very shortly after the improvised explosive devices, as well as being aimed at the security forces in general, were turned directly towards the IED operators of the Royal Army Ordnance Corps. The first of these bombs was discovered at Castlerobin on 9 September 1971 and while the young ATO, Captain D. Stewartson, RAOC, was dealing with it, it exploded, killing him instantly. He was the first of seventeen IED operators to be killed in Northern Ireland whilst dealing with terrorist devices between 1971 and 1985.

The new device named the 'Castlerobin' had to be defeated. A number were quickly reported but all had been pulled or moved remotely and so caused to detonate with no casualties. None had so far been recovered intact. Finally one was recovered undamaged and the secrets of its complex electrical circuits were revealed. The circuitry included an arming device and micro-switches at the top and bottom of the box in which the bomb was built such that if the box was lifted, tilted or the lid opened the bomb would explode. This bomb, together with the X-rays of the other bombs, enabled a possible render-safe procedure to be devised. The dubious honour of converting the theory into practice against a live bomb fell to Major S. G. Styles, RAOC, the Senior Ammunition Technical Officer (SATO) in Northern Ireland, assisted by Captain A. Clouter, RAOC, and Captain R. Mendham, RAOC.

At 16:00 hours on 20 October 1971 a box had been discovered in a telephone booth in the Whip and Saddle Bar of the Europa Hotel in Belfast. Captain Clouter X-rayed the box and confirmed it was a 'Castlerobin'. The three officers, having evacuated the area, rendered the electrical circuits safe to move in accordance with the previously prepared plan. They then carefully dragged the box from the hotel into the street where it was successfully dismantled.

Two days later a second bomb was found in the Europa Hotel, but on this occasion it had a much larger charge and apparently even more complicated wiring. After carefully analysing the X-rays it was realized that the bomb had the same circuits as the other 'Castlerobins' but in this box had been placed a mass of meaningless wire and micro-switches to confuse the

IED operator. Again Major Styles took charge and after nine hours' intensive and dangerous work the bomb was rendered safe and dismantled.

Major Styles left Northern Ireland in 1972 and retired from the Army as a Lieutenant Colonel in 1974. For his work at the Europa Hotel he was awarded the George Cross and received a great deal of media publicity. (The problems of publicity for IED operators are considered later in the chapter.)

Two days after the last incident at the Europa Hotel another bomb in a wooden box was delivered by four masked and armed men to a club in Belfast. They gave the occupants of the club five minutes to clear the building—which they did! When the IED team arrived they inspected the box and returned to their vehicle for equipment. It was while they were with their vehicle that the bomb exploded. It was subsequently discovered that the bomb was similar to the 'Castlerobin' but fitted with a timing device which precluded the long render-safe procedures used previously. Clearly the bombers had noted the time taken to clear the two bombs from the Europa Hotel, seven and nine hours respectively, and had responded accordingly.

This new type of bomb posed a very real problem for the IED teams but luckily at this time a special item of equipment was being developed by a research establishment in England. The first prototype arrived in Northern Ireland in time to be used against a similar bomb placed in the Midland Hotel in Belfast. This new equipment enabled a controlled explosion to be used to disrupt most IEDs then being found. The disruption took place with very little risk of the main charge exploding. The equipment was used with complete success in the Midland Hotel and the secrets of the new device were laid bare. This type of bomb was thereafter known as the 'Midlander'.

The advent of the disrupter reduced the time spent by the IED operator in close contact with the explosive device and so reduced his exposure to danger. It did not, however, preclude the necessity for the operator to approach the bomb at least twice, once to place the equipment and later to determine the effect of the disruption, confirm that the device had been rendered harmless or take any secondary action which might be necessary.

December 1971 saw the advent of the first remote-controlled EOD vehicle. This was capable of moving a bomb and in some cases of disrupting it whilst the operator remained at a safe distance. It was quickly followed by a more sophisticated vehicle known as 'Wheelbarrow'. This was capable of carrying a TV camera, firing a shotgun, lifting a bomb, moving a car and a host of other options as it developed through its successive marks. This equipment was certainly needed as during 1971 there were over 600 explosions in the province and the IED teams were recovering several hundred pounds of explosives each month.

As the campaign in Northern Ireland continued the bombs became more sophisticated, frequently larger and, as with all bomb disposal, the bomb and fuze designer had the initial advantage. Following the con-

Demolishing a terrorist car bomb in Northern Ireland using a Wheelbarrow remote surveillance and handling device.

tinued and successful use of the disrupter the terrorists started placing their devices in milk churns, domestic gas bottles, cars, fuel bowsers and even trains. They started to use remote control to fire their buried charges either via a long firing cable or by using a radio transmitter. They designed powerful mortar bombs which could be fired remotely against security forces' barracks or strongpoints. They began to use electronic timers rather than clockwork mechanisms and maintained a close liaison with other terrorist groups. Thus the ATO and AT of the Royal Army Ordnance Corps were continually fighting a battle of technology and wits against the terrorists. It was a battle like all other bomb disposal battles where one small mistake or lack of attention could be one's last.

The scientists came to the aid of the IED operators as they had to the bomb disposal operators in the Second World War. As devices were discovered so were countermeasures designed, manufactured and proved on the ground. As in the Second World War, the designers tried out their own equipment. Two very well known scientists from research establishments repeatedly donned combat kit (to avoid notice) and proved their equipment in the streets and fields of Northern Ireland. The same two scientists were also seen at different times in the Falkland Islands helping to solve conventional bomb disposal problems.

The equipment designed to cope with these later generations of terrorist bombs and the names of the brave men who carry out this work cannot and should not be revealed. Combating terrorists and dealing with their explosive devices is a dangerous activity at any time. If an individual operator is identified or given unnecessary publicity in the media there is always the risk that he or his family will become specially selected targets and thus increase still further the risks undertaken. In the early years publicity was given to those men who received gallantry awards for dealing with terrorist bombs. Their citations frequently described in some detail the actions they had carried out, thus enabling individual men to be publicly linked to particular incidents. Today and for the past ten years IED operators have quite rightly shunned publicity, and citations when published often state merely, 'For gallant conduct whilst undertaking EOD operations in Northern Ireland'.

To give an indication of the gallant work undertaken by the IED operators of the Royal Army Ordnance Corps in Northern Ireland it is worth noting that during the period 1969 to 1985 they have been awarded: one George Cross, 27 George Medals, 39 Queen's Gallantry Medals, 16 British Empire Medals and 74 Mentioned in Despatches. In addition, twelve have been appointed Officers of the Order of the British Empire (OBE) and fifteen appointed Members of the Order of the British Empire (MBE). The two scientists from the research establishment referred to earlier have both been appointed Members of the Order of the British Empire.

Before leaving Northern Ireland credit should also be given to the many members of the Royal Engineer Search Teams, who are specially trained to search for booby-traps. It is they who clear the route to a suspect car, building or body, etc, to enable the IED teams to reach their objective.

Although the Royal Army Ordnance Corps is responsible for the clearance of all improvised explosive devices in Northern Ireland, elsewhere the responsibility is not so clearly defined. In Great Britain the Royal Navy and the Royal Air Force are, in conjunction with the civil police, responsible for improvised explosive device disposal on their own property, and the Royal Engineers also have responsibilities in respect of these devices. Similarly, the Metropolitan Police have their own explosives officers trained to deal with terrorist devices. Consequently, in addition to the Royal Army Ordnance Corps; the Royal Navy, the Royal Air Force and the Royal Engineers, EOD units all have trained IED operators equipped with the latest countermeasures and may be called at any time to support the civil powers.

Turning once again to conventional explosive ordnance disposal, each time an EOD unit deploys to deal with a live bomb it is working under active service conditions. However, the last time that EOD units from all three Services deployed in action in a truly hostile environment was in 1982 during the Falklands' conflict. No history of British bomb disposal would be complete without reference to the work carried out by the EOD units during that campaign.

The Task Force which sailed from the United Kingdom towards the Falkland Islands comprised more than 100 ships and over 28,000 men and women, yet of these personnel fewer than fifty were EOD operators. The history of the Falklands' conflict is well-documented and this chapter will only consider those actions in which unexploded bombs formed a major factor. Thus, although Royal Navy or Royal Fleet Auxiliary vessels which had unexploded bombs on board are referred to, those sister ships which had no unexploded bombs on board but were present and either survived the fighting or were tragically lost will not be mentioned. The outline map of East Falkland indicates where the various incidents took place.

The main landings on the Falklands took place during the night 20/21 May 1982. Under cover of darkness the troopships and their escorts entered San Carlos Water on the north-west coast of East Falkland and began what proved to be an unopposed landing once the danger from a strong observation post had been overcome. However, it was not until 26 May that the British forces were ready to advance from the bridgehead. During that period Royal Fleet Auxiliary (RFA) vessels were off-loading essential stores and equipment, protected by vessels of the Royal Navy. Whether off-loading stores or providing protection these vessels were subjected to a series of fierce air attacks whilst in the restricted waters of San Carlos Water. Similarly, the troops ashore were subjected to frequent air attack and it was these various attacks which produced many of the unexploded Argentinian bombs.

The first ship to report an unexploded bomb on board was a destroyer, HMS *Antrim*, on 21 May 1982. Fleet Chief Petty Officer (Diver) M. G.

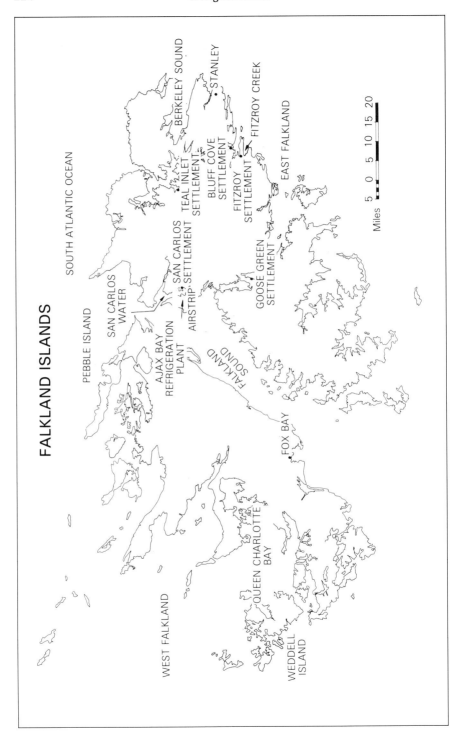

FALKLAND ISLANDS

SOUTH ATLANTIC OCEAN

BERKELEY SOUND

STANLEY

FITZROY CREEK

TEAL INLET SETTLEMENT

BLUFF COVE SETTLEMENT

FITZROY SETTLEMENT

EAST FALKLAND

SAN CARLOS SETTLEMENT

SAN CARLOS WATER

AIRSTRIP

GOOSE GREEN SETTLEMENT

PEBBLE ISLAND

AJAX BAY REFRIGERATION PLANT

FALKLAND SOUND

FOX BAY

WEST FALKLAND

QUEEN CHARLOTTE BAY

WEDDELL ISLAND

Miles

5 0 5 10 15 20

Fellows, BEM, RN, a memberr of the Fleet Clearance Diving Team No 1 (FCDT-1), together with a party of ratings from the team, discovered that a 1,000 lb (453.6 kg) bomb was lodged close to the Seaslug missile magazine. The bomb was damaged so that the state of the tail fuze could not be determined and it was decided that the safest course of action was to attempt to free it from its location and lift it on to the deck whence it could be lowered into deep water.

The operation was hampered by frequent air attacks during which the team had to stay close to the bomb to prevent it from being jarred. Smoke from burning materials forced them to wear breathing apparatus and to carry out fire fighting tasks to protect the bomb from the heat. Finally, after ten hours' hazardous and extremely difficult operation the bomb was safely extricated from the magazine, lowered into a rubber boat and subsequently sunk in deep water. As this was the first unexploded bomb dealt with during the conflict no precedent had been set and FCPO(D) Fellows and his team displayed considerable courage dealing with an unexploded bomb whilst under fire.

On the same day, 21 May 1982, HMS *Argonaut*, a 'Leander' Class frigate, also in San Carlos Water providing protection to the amphibious forces, was attacked repeatedly. On one occasion whilst in Falkland Sound she was attacked by six aircraft and so seriously damaged that she was forced to anchor. In addition, two unexploded bombs were lodged in her, one in the forward magazine and the other in her boiler room. HMS *Argonaut* remained in her location for nine days, unable to move, while damage was repaired and the unexploded bombs were dealt with. Throughout this period the battle raged around her and her air defence weapons continued to engage the enemy.

FCDT-1 under command of Lieutenant Commander B. F. Dutton, QGM, RN, was tasked to deal with the two unexploded bombs. The one in the magazine had caused extensive damage and had finally come to rest between two Seacat missiles, surrounded by damaged and extremely dangerous ordnance. This was clearly going to be a long and dangerous task and Lieutenant Commander Dutton decided that the bomb, a 1,000 lb (453.6 kg), was too dangerous to attempt to defuze *in situ*. Instead he decided to clear away the damaged munitions, lift the bomb from the magazine and hoist it overboard. The second bomb, in the boiler room, was also a 1,000 lb (453.6 kg), but on inspection it was found to be damaged and the only way to deal with the fuze was to remove it from the bomb. The only EOD team readily available that had the necessary equipment was a detachment from 49 EOD Squadron, Royal Engineers. This team, consisting of Warrant Officer Class 2 J. H. Phillips, RE, and Staff Sergeant J. Prescott, RE, was therefore tasked to the bomb in the boiler room. Working in extraordinarily cramped conditions and in very unfamiliar surroundings, Warrant Officer Class 2 Phillips and Staff Sergeant Prescott successfully removed the damaged fuze from the bomb, thus rendering it safe. The bomb was later removed from the ship.

Meanwhile the Naval team was still having difficulties with the bomb in the magazine. The task was proving extremely complex and hazardous as the surrounding munitions were removed and holes were cut through sections of the ship's structure to allow the passage of the bomb. The operation took the team seven days during which time HMS *Argonaut* came under attack a number of times. The slightest jar or disturbance to the lifting angle could have resulted in an explosion which would almost certainly have caused the loss of the ship, as was fully realized by the whole team following the tragic loss of HMS *Antelope* on 24 May 1982. In spite of the difficulties and dangers the bomb was successfully removed on 28 May and great credit must be given to all concerned.

On 23 May 1982, the Royal Engineer EOD team having successfully dealt with the bomb in the boiler room of HMS *Argonaut* on the previous day, was tasked to deal with two unexploded bombs in a Type 21 Frigate, HMS *Antelope*. HMS *Antelope*, like the other Naval vessels, had entered San Carlos Water to provide anti-aircraft protection to the amphibious force. She was subjected to heavy air attack including one aircraft which had crashed into the ship's foremast. During these attacks HMS *Antelope* was hit several times and sustained a number of casualties. She also received two unexploded bombs. The first bomb could not be approached until extensive clearance of debris had taken place. The second, situated amidships, was seen by the Royal Engineer EOD team to have a damaged fuze and was assessed as being in a dangerous condition. It was therefore decided to deal with this bomb first. The Captain of HMS *Antelope* (Commander N. J. Tobin, RN) had anchored his ship and moved the ship's crew away from the area of the unexploded bomb. Warrant Officer Class 2 Phillips and Staff Sergeant Prescott then attempted to render the bomb safe. They made three attempts to remove the fuze remotely, returning to the bomb after each attempt, but on none of these occasions could the fuze be withdrawn. On the fourth attempt, using a different type of equipment, the bomb exploded. Despite the preparation of a blast route of open doors and hatches up through the ship, a fully fastened steel door at the forward end of the passageway where the two men were standing was completely blown off. Staff Sergeant Prescott died instantly and Warrant Officer Phillips was seriously injured.

Following the detonation of the bomb, the ensuing explosions ripped the ship apart and started uncontrollable fires. The ship was abandoned with minimum casualties and finally sank following a massive explosion on 24 May 1982.

One of the Landing Ships Logistic (LSL) disembarking troops and equipment for the initial landing force was RFA *Sir Galahad*. She had been under repeated air attack since her first arrival in San Carlos Water on 21 May 1982, and on the evening of 25 May 1982 was struck by a 1,000 lb (453.6 kg) bomb. The bomb failed to explode and FCDT-3 under the command of Lieutenant N. A. Bruen, RN, was tasked to deal with it. The bomb was lodged in an awkward position surrounded by broken batteries which had splashed acid around the compartment. It was decided to lift the bomb to the vehicle deck and then dispose of it overboard. Work started immediately and the team was greatly assisted by Chief Engineer Officer C. K. A. Adams, Royal Fleet Auxiliary, who was able to advise on the best removal route for the bomb and provide general engineering assistance. The bomb was finally disposed of in the early hours of 26 May 1982. Following the removal of the bomb the full crew returned to the *Sir Galahad*, repaired the damage and continued operations in support of the troops ashore. On 8 June RFA *Sir Galahad* was attacked by Argentine aircraft during troop disembarkation in Fitzroy Creek which resulted in heavy casualties and the loss of the ship.

Sir Galahad's sister ship RFA *Sir Lancelot*, whilst operating in support of the land forces, was also hit by a bomb which failed to explode. Again FCDT-3 was tasked to deal with the bomb and in this case Chief Petty Officer (Diver) G. M. Trotter, RN, was in charge of the team responsible for the removal. In this instance the bomb was located in a film store amongst a large quantity of debris, all of which had to be removed before the EOD operations could take place. The removal of the bomb was further hindered by air attacks and fierce squalls, both of which tended to cause the bomb to move and during the actual removal to swing against the bulkheads. Despite these problems the bomb was finally disposed of on 29 May 1982.

Other unexploded bombs dealt with on board Royal Navy ships included two on the 'Rothsay' Class frigate HMS *Plymouth* and another on HMS *Broadsword*, a Type 22 frigate.

Onshore life was equally hectic and EOD teams were very much in demand especially in the days immediately following the formal surrender of General Menendez and his forces on 14 June 1982.

The Royal Air Force EOD Team, consisting of eleven all ranks commanded by Flight Lieutenant A. J. Swan, RAF, and drawn from No 1 EOD Unit, Royal Air Force, disembarked on 25 May 1982. The team on board RFA *Sir Bedivere* arrived in San Carlos Water at 10:00 hours on 24 May 1982. The *Sir Bedivere* anchored some 400 m (437 yd) from HMS *Antelope*. HMS *Antelope* was burning fiercely and the Royal Air Force team was told that this was the result of a bomb exploding during an EOD render-safe procedure—hardly a welcoming sight. For the next 36 hours the team remained on board while the Naval force was repeatedly attacked from the air. The RFAs *Sir Bedivere*, *Sir Galahad* and *Sir Lancelot* were all hit by unexploded bombs although the one on *Sir Bedivere* exited through the fo'c's'le into the sea and so presented no problem.

Flight Lieutenant Swan pressed to be allowed to take his team ashore where he felt they could be of more use than aboard *Sir Bedivere*. Eventually the team was disembarked in darkness at 22:00 hours on 25 May 1982. They landed with a 4-tonne load carrier and two Land Rovers on a rocky beach in Ajax Bay.

At dawn the Royal Marines of 45 Commando were surprised to find the

EOD team on their patch and even more surprised to see the vehicles complete with blue lights and red wings—the beach went straight into rocky hills with no exit roads! However, the team quickly dug itself in and began EOD operations using only that equipment which they could carry.

After two days of air raid alerts and attacks the Commando Logistic Mobile Surgical Unit based in the Ajax Bay Refrigeration Plant was hit. Two bombs exploded at the rear of the complex causing 31 casualties. Two unexploded bombs were located outside the hospital and were demolished by the team. However, some two hours later a further two unexploded bombs were discovered inside the hospital adjacent to the operating theatre.

The bombs were of a type unknown to either Flight Lieutenant Swan or his Warrant Officer (Warrant Officer D. Trafford, RAF) and lay within 30 ft (9.1 m) of each other. One was embedded in the side of a steel refrigeration unit and the other was lodged in the roof space immediately above the operating theatre. Since the bombs were of an unknown type there was a very real risk of them exploding should a render-safe procedure be attempted. There was, therefore, a need to evacuate the hospital before the attempt was made, but this was quite impossible. Personnel in the hospital could not be evacuated because of the operations being carried out on casualties. Medical personnel could not leave the patients and patients could not be moved outside because of the freezing temperature (-10°C).

After consultations between Flight Lieutenant Swan, Warrant Officer

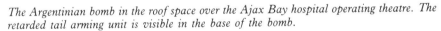

The Argentinian bomb in the roof space over the Ajax Bay hospital operating theatre. The retarded tail arming unit is visible in the base of the bomb.

Trafford and Lieutenant Bruen of the FCDT-3, who was ashore at that time, the Flight Lieutenant formed the opinion that providing the bombs were left alone it was unlikely that they would explode. He therefore advised the Commanding Officer of the hospital of his view and to reassure the patients and staff he billeted himself in the hospital and slept within a few feet of the bombs.

When these two bombs were eventually defuzed by Major G. S. Lucas, RE, they were found to have most peculiar fuzes, being a mixture of sophisticated fuze components and what looked like improvized components. They were certainly unlike anything previously seen by the United Kingdom EOD fraternity. Having rendered them safe Major Lucas sent them to the United Kingdom for scientific evaluation.

During the same attack on the hospital a nearby ammunition dump had been hit and the hospital helicopter landing ground was strewn with unexploded ordnance which had been damaged by the explosion and subsequent fire. The Royal Air Force EOD team manually cleared the landing ground of its extremely dangerous contamination and so made it available for further operations. This took some two hours of hazardous work, but it took a further three days before the whole area around the hospital had been cleared of over 250 items of damaged and dangerous ordnance.

On 30 May 1982 the team heard that Goose Green settlement had been taken by 2 Parachute Regiment and that the airstrip there needed to be cleared for further operations. It had been an Argentinian air base and therefore was protected by minefields and littered with unexploded and undropped bombs, damaged aircraft and the usual assortment of battle debris.

The Royal Air Force team, assisted by a Royal Engineer Search Team and an Ammunition Technical Officer of the Royal Army Ordnance Corps, started the task of clearing Goose Green airstrip and settlement. One priority task was the removal from the village centre of a quantity of Argentinian weapons thought to contain napalm. On inspection the weapons were confirmed as containing napalm; in some cases the filling was found to be weeping from the containers and they were considered to be in a dangerous condition. Flight Lieutenant Swan and Flight Sergeant D. W. Knights, RAF, moved the weapons to the airstrip where Warrant Officer Trafford demolished them, together with another seventeen tonnes of similar weapons found on the airstrip.

Throughout this period unexploded bombs were being discovered and were either destroyed *in situ*, or if in a critical position defuzed. As soon as the cease-fire occurred the Royal Air Force EOD team moved to Port Stanley airfield where it carried out a preliminary surface search for unexploded items of ordnance. It also searched a number of Argentinian aircraft which were suspected of being booby-trapped. The team had no search instruments and was operating in intense cold, high winds and the beginning of a snowstorm. The search was therefore of a very basic nature and only adequate to allow the preliminary repair work to take place and so allow the first aircraft to land.

Following the loss of the advance element of 49 EOD Squadron, Royal

Assorted unexploded ordnance recovered in the Falklands.

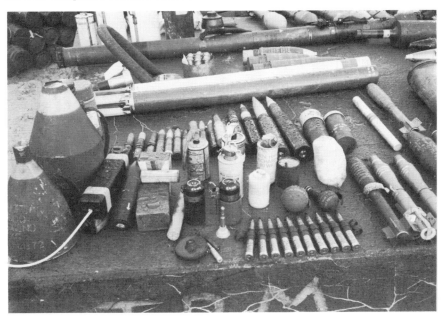

Engineers, on HMS *Antelope* on 23 May 1982 a full EOD team from that squadron was flown to Ascension Island on 28 May 1982 and finally arrived in the Falklands area on 15 June 1982, the day after the formal surrender of the Argentinian forces. The team commander, Captain B. Lloyd, RE, moved his team directly into a relatively undamaged house in Port Stanley. The whole of the town was a squalid mess of discarded weapons, ammunition and general filth. In addition to a general clean up there was an urgent requirement for a co-ordinated and planned ordnance clearance operation. Captain Lloyd established an *ad hoc* Joint Service EOD Operations Cell and the initial clearance began.

On 23 June 1982 Major G. S. Lucas, RE, the squadron commander of 49 EOD Squadron, Royal Engineers, arrived in the Falklands having travelled with the Governor of the islands on the first Hercules passenger flight into Port Stanley. Major Lucas' main task was to establish a Joint Service EOD Operations Centre (JSEODOC) to plan and co-ordinate all aspects of EOD work on the Falklands Islands. The scene which greeted him was, from the EOD point of view, most unsatisfactory. Exocet and Roland missiles were lying in the ditches alongside the track to the airfield. Mortar bombs, grenades and shells of all sizes were strewn everywhere, as were all natures of small-arms ammunition. Stanley itself was a vast ammunition dump, garages and houses being packed with missiles, shells and mines. Many of the mines were not immediately familiar to the EOD teams as they originated from such diverse countries as Argentina, Italy, Spain and Israel. In some of the other settlements a similar picture existed.

A priority for clearance was soon established as first, all inhabited areas, followed by areas immediately around the settlements and areas to which access was considered essential by the military and civil administration and finally those areas, including the high ground, over which battles had been fought or which were suspected to contain land mines.

By early July 1982 much of the clearance work was hindered by snow which was up to 18 in (457 mm) deep in places. However, the clearance of bombs, missiles and larger weapons was carried out, and this included the rendering-safe of the two Argentinian bombs in the hospital site at Ajax Bay. On 13 July 1982 a full instrument search of Port Stanley airfield was begun by the Royal Engineers and a large number of unexploded bombs and bomblets were discovered and dealt with. One member of the Royal Engineer team writing back to the United Kingdom at this time said, 'This is real bomb disposal. Today I was tasked to a 1,000 lb (453.6 kg) bomb at Stanley airfield. On arrival I was met by a very happy Corporal Sanderson whose section had just found another 1,000 lb bomb only 10 in (254 mm) below the surface. In this bomb, after removing the pistol by remote means, the striker was found to have been in contact with the detonator and therefore very dangerous.'

In addition to straightforward bomb disposal, as just described, there was also the clearance of booby traps, some set in the vacated slit trenches, some among the huge heaps of ammunition, some even in the homes of the

Major G. S. Lucas, RE, dealing with a booby trap on the Darwin road.

Stanley residents and one large one on the Darwin road. The latter could have caused many casualties had it not been reported by an Argentinian prisoner-of-war just before he was repatriated in early July 1982. Major G. C. Lucas, RE, and Staff Sergeant D. W. Clarke, RE, went to investigate and discovered two charges approximately 30 ft (9.14 m) apart. Each charge consisted of an anti-tank mine connected to 25 lb (11.3 kg) of TNT and a 130 kg (286 lb) aircraft bomb. The charges were connected so that they could be fired either from a command wire or by a heavy vehicle running over either mine.

The clearance of Stanley was finally completed on 1 September 1982, the detailed search having been carried out by a Royal Engineer EOD Section, a Royal Engineer Search Team and an Infantry Search Team from the Queen's Own Highlanders. Once ammunition, whether boxed or lying loose on the ground, had been declared free from booby traps it was handed over to the Ammunition Technicians of the Royal Army Ordnance Corps, who disposed of it in accordance with instructions from the Director of Land Service Ammunition. Some was recovered for shipment to the United Kingdom, but the majority of it was repacked for demolition or disposal. This was no mean feat when it is remembered that there were over seven million rounds of small-arms ammunition recovered from the streets of Stanley alone. The same problems existed in the settlements and

Demolition in a Falklands minefield.

to an even greater extent on each of the sites where a battle had taken place.

When Captain B. Lloyd, RE, returned to the United Kingdom in September 1982 his team had, between his arrival in the Falklands on 15 June and his departure on 22 September 1982, dealt with over 10,000 items of unexploded ordnance excluding small-arms ammunition. These included aerial bombs and bomblets, rockets and missiles, shells, mortar bombs, grenades and deliberate booby traps.

The minefields in the Falklands pose a quite different problem. A vast proportion of the mines laid have no or very little metal content and so are undetectable by the usual mine detectors which are designed to react to a metallic mass. The peat and rock conditions in which many of the mines are laid make other types of detectors less than 100 per cent effective. Consequently, those minefields containing plastic mines have been securely fenced and will be cleared when a completely safe method has been determined. The difference between an operational breaching of a minefield to allow the infantry or tanks to pass through in a combat situation and the clearance in a peacetime situation must be understood. In the first case the use of explosives, ploughs or flails will achieve perhaps a 98 per cent clearance rate, which would be acceptable in battle. In the Falklands, however, the clearance must be such that the soldiers would be prepared to play football with the local children on the cleared area, ie, 100 per cent clearance. For this reason some minefields must await the advent of the necessary technology before they can be cleared.

When it is considered that at the time of writing in 1986, the Falkland Islands have, with the exception of certain minefields, been very largely cleared of the dangerous debris of war, it reflects great credit upon the EOD officers and men of all three Services who often whilst under fire, co-operated to the full and who after the shooting stopped continued their dangerous work in close co-operation and harmony.

Many of the officers and men referred to in the above account were honoured for their gallantry but one award deserves special mention. That is the posthumous award of the Conspicuous Gallantry Medal (CGM) to Staff Sergeant J. Prescott, RE, who was killed on HMS *Antelope* whilst attempting to defuze an unexploded bomb. The CGM is a very rare Naval award for Petty Officers and men of the Royal Navy and Sergeants and men of the Royal Marines; it may also be awarded to equivalent ranks in the Army and the Royal Air Force. It is awarded for conspicuous acts of gallantry which do not merit the award of the Victoria Cross. Since its inception in 1855, only 245 medals had been awarded previously. The award to Staff Sergeant Prescott was the first to be made to either the Army or the Royal Air Force and the first in the reign of HM Queen Elizabeth II.

*   *   *

What of tomorrow? One only has to read the commercial defence journals to appreciate the wide range of weapons being manufactured and sold on a world-wide basis. In today's uncertain world a potential enemy cannot always be defined or recognized, or expected only to use weapons of his own manufacture. The Falklands' conflict and the war between Iran and Iraq have adequately demonstrated that an EOD operator must be prepared to face an unexploded weapon originating from almost any country in the world. Thus weapons produced by the east or the west are frequently offered to the highest bidder and what one nation has today any nation might have tomorrow.

Thus the days of the heroic dedicated amateurs such as filled the bomb disposal units of all three Services at the beginning of the Second World War have gone. Today the EOD operator faces up squarely to the three roles which confront him—the clearance of the debris of past conflicts, the combating of the terrorist device wherever it is found and finally the ability to meet any future conflict with a sound knowledge of the weapons likely to be used by both sides. There just won't be time to learn by luck or trial and error as sometimes occurred in the past.

So what exactly is the EOD operator who goes about his tasks of today and plans and trains for his role of tomorrow—which hopefully never comes. He has the characteristics already described in the introduction to this book. In addition he will have reached a high level of professional training in all aspects of explosive ordnance disposal (including working in a

'. . . including working in a hostile environment.' A Royal Engineer EOD operator dressed in a full Chemical Protection Suit.

hostile environment) together with a detailed knowledge of those specialist skills relevant to his single Service responsibilities. Thus whether he is working on an unknown mine at the bottom of the Red Sea, a bomb in the middle of an anti-personnel minefield in the Falkland Islands or involved in the clearance of bomblets from an airfield, the task will always be done with courage and dedicated professionalism.

(To the large number of professionally trained and exceedingly competent female EOD operators in the US Forces and the increasing number in the Royal Air Force, please read 'he' and 'his' in the above paragraph to include 'she' and 'her' where relevant.)

Tail piece

The story of bomb disposal will never end whilst nations continue to wage war or continue to train for war with live ordnance, but this book must end. The author is sorry about all the heroic men whose stories he knew but omitted from the book. He assures them or their relatives that no slight has been intended. They include such men as Captain K. Revis, MBE, RE, who has probably displayed more courage and determination since he was blinded removing booby-trapped mines from the West Pier at Brighton in September 1943, than he did during his operational bomb disposal career. Or Captain H. C. L. Barefoot, GC, RE, and his work in Essex during 1940, or Captain M. F. Blaney, GC, RE, who died with eight others and whose lasting memorial is Blaney Crescent in East Ham, London. The greatest omission is of the many thousands of soldiers, sailors and airmen who spent years in bomb disposal digging holes or carrying out the other laborious work necessary for the recovery of mines and bombs. They were exposed to constant danger but were rarely recognized for their prolonged courage. As an ex-bomb disposal officer it is to them that I say 'Thank you'.

Annex A
Important documents

Home Security Circular No 88/40—Disposal of Unexploded Bombs *(Issued by the Ministry of Home Security on 11 May 1940)*

I am directed by the Minister of Home Security to refer to Air Raid Precautions Department Circulars 233/39 and 239/39 and to pages 32 and 33 of ARP Training Manual No 2, and to inform you that it has now been decided that the duty of dealing with unexploded bombs and ammunition except where they have fallen on Admiralty or Air Ministry property shall remain the responsibility of the War Office. Circular No 239/39 is therefore cancelled. The Minister hopes shortly to be in a position to communicate detailed guidance to local authorities as to the procedure to be followed when the specialist parties to be provided by the War Office to undertake this duty, are called upon. Meanwhile, RE parties will continue as before, to be available in an emergency and the procedure indicated in Circular No 233 for calling them out, will continue to be followed. The responsibility of the local authority will be limited in the first instance to reporting the presence of unexploded bombs, indicating which bomb should be tackled first as, eg likely to cause most obstruction, and ensuring the immediate safety of the public by preventing their approach to the site. It will no longer be necessary to hold in readiness personnel and material for sandbagging, and paragraph 2 of Circular 233 is, in consequence, cancelled.

Conference held at Air Ministry, 27 August 1940, on the Unexploded Bomb Disposal Organization

Present:

Major General C. J. S. King; Chairman — Home Forces (Chief Engineer)
Major General K. M. Loch — War Office
Brigadier C. G. Ling — War Office (SD)
Major F. G. Clouth — War Office (AA4(b))
Commander Henry S. H. Ellis — Admiralty (D of L D Bomb Section)

Brigadier General C. C. Lucas	Ministry of Home Security
Mr H. C. Emmerson	Ministry of Home Security
Mr R. J. P. Harvey	Home Defence Executive
Commander Stephen King-Hall	Ministry of Aircraft Production
Air Marshall Sir Arthur	
S. Barratt, KCB, CMG, MC	Air Ministry
Air Vice-Marshall R. H. Peck	Air Ministry (ACAS(G))
Group Captain McGregor	ADWO, Air Ministry
Wing Commander J. A. Easton	AI1(g), Air Ministry
Squadron Leader E. L. Moxey	AI1(g), Air Ministry
Squadron Leader Heap	T Arm 4, Air Ministry

1. In accordance with the instructions issued by the Chief of Staff on the morning of the 27th August, a Meeting was held at 3.30 pm on the same afternoon, which was attended by representatives of the Ministry of Home Security, Home Defence Executive and Air Production and of the three Services. The existing organization was reviewed and certain proposals to improve and expand the organization were formulated.

2. Responsibility

It was agreed that the responsibility for dealing with unexploded bombs should be as follows:

(a) The Admiralty will be responsible for unexploded bombs on Admiralty property.

(b) The RAF will be responsible for unexploded bombs on RAF property.

(c) The Army will be responsible for all other unexploded bombs, with the exception of the special cases detailed below.

(d) The provision of a suitable 'Bomb Cemetery' is the responsibility of the Local Authorities.

Special Cases.

(a) The RAF will be responsible for unexploded bombs on aircraft.

(b) Any organization required for islands such as the Scillies will be provided by one Service only, irrespective of the fact that the other Services may have property or installations in the island. The acceptance of the responsibility for the provision of the organization will be by arrangement between the Services concerned.

3. Technical Information.

The means by which technical information is collected and distributed is not satisfactory. The distribution is slow, there is overlapping in some directions and lack of liaison in others.

The formation of a central clearing house in which the three Services and any interested Ministries are represented is necessary. The duties of this central office will be to ensure the most rapid collection and distribution of technical information as follows:

(a) To receive information from any one of the three Services and distribute it to the other two. This type of information will be largely 'hot news' which must be distributed immediately to all Bomb Disposal Sections and to the Research Department.

(b) To transmit to the Research Department all technical information regarding new types of bombs. To distribute information from the Research Department on the methods of dealing with bombs.

(c) To receive suggestions from the Bomb Disposal Sections for improvements in equipment etc, and to arrange for the necessary experiments through existing experimental establishments.

(d) To provide Home Security with weekly summaries of such technical information as may be useful to Regional Commissioners.

It is recommended that the central office should be established at GHQ Home Forces and should have a sufficient staff to provide a continuous duty officer.

4. Number of Bomb Disposal Sections.
The scale of provision was discussed at some length and the difficulties of arriving at any conclusion were stressed. It was agreed that a total of 1,200 to 2,000 delay action bombs might be dropped in a day if this form of attack were developed to the utmost. This estimate was based on the carrying capacity of aircraft; no consideration was given to the production aspect.

While this estimate can only be very approximate it will serve as a basis for estimating the probable increase required.

The position is as follows:

(a) Admiralty. 18 Bomb Disposal Parties for Shore Establishments exist. Proposals for increase are under consideration.

(b) Army. 110 Bomb Disposal Sections exist, though they are not complete in every respect. Proposals have been submitted to the War Office to double the strength of the Sections with no increase in Officers. This will provide the quickest means of providing an immediate increase.

(c) RAF. 80 Bomb Disposal Sections exist. These are being increased.

It is recommended that a programme of expansion of the number of Army Bomb Disposal Sections to double the existing number should be accepted; the rate of expansion must be co-ordinated with the output of equipment.

5. Equipment.
The present distribution of equipment is:
1/5th to Admiralty
2/5ths to Army
2/5ths to RAF

No change in this proportion is recommended at present, but the necessity for the highest possible priority for the production and issue of equipment is very strongly emphasized.

6. Training.
The training of personnel for all Services is carried out at the RAF School. Its output is forty per week. It is recommended that arrangements for an output of eighty should be made as quickly as possible.

The scale of trained personnel of three per Section is recommended.

It was also recommended that an Instructor from the Royal Navy and the Army should be posted to the School in order to assist in providing extra staff and to emphasize the fact that it is a combined School for the three Services.

7. The necessity of a guide on the order of priority was discussed. The representative of the Ministry of Home Security agreed to refer the GHQ draft to the Minister of Home Security.

8. The disposal of unexploded shells was discussed. The undesirability of adding to the task of the Bomb Disposal Sections was recognized. It was agreed, however, that the formation of a separate organization for dealing with shells would be quite unjustifiable and would lead to many difficulties. It was therefore decided that the Bomb Disposal Sections should be responsible for the disposal of shells as well as bombs.

9. Arising from this, the necessity for providing the necessary instruction at the Training Centre was recognized.

10. The Committee was informed of the Prime Minister's wish that suitable recognition should be taken of meritorious service in this dangerous work.

11. Mr Emmerson was asked to investigate reports in daily papers which were alleged to be injudicious.

Annex B
Technical aspects of bomb disposal

This Annex is written to give more details of the bombs, fuzes and bomb disposal equipment referred to in the main text of the book. It is divided into two sections: Section One—German high explosive bombs; Section Two—German bomb fuzes and their methods of immunization.

Section One—German high explosive bombs

The German high explosive general bombardment bombs dropped on the United Kingdom and her forces overseas during World War 2 ranged in weight from 50 kg (110 lb) to 1,800 kg (3,960 lb). There were, additionally, various high explosive anti-personnel bombs, some as small as 0.5 kg (1.1 lb). The most notorious of these anti-personnel bombs were undoubtedly the 2 kg (4.4 lb) SD 2s, or butterfly bombs, but these could not be classified as general bombardment bombs.

Initially, the German high explosive bombs were divided into two principal types: the 'Spreng Cylindrisch' (SC), the thin-walled general purpose bombs, and the 'Spreng Dickenwand' (SD), the thick-walled armour-piercing or semi-armour-piercing bombs. In 1942 the Germans renamed their genuine armour-piercing bombs (as opposed to the merely thick-walled bombs designed to penetrate buildings and then explode, producing heavy steel splinters) as the Panzerdurchschlags Cylindrisch (PC).

The SC general purpose bombs had an explosive charge of approximately fifty per cent of their total weight and their destructive quality was used primarily for general demolition purposes. The bomb was usually of a three-piece steel construction with the nose, body and base being welded together. The tail fin was made of sheet steel or a light alloy and was attached to the bomb body by screws or rivets.

The SD bombs, whether true armour-piercing or merely splinter bombs, had an explosive charge of approximately thirty per cent of their total weight, although in some bombs it could be as low as sixteen per cent. These bombs were used primarily against ships or fortifications and their bodies were usually of drawn or forged steel and made in one piece. They were always more streamlined than the SC bomb and in one case (the SD

250 kg) a tail extension with a dummy fuze head was fitted to add still further to the streamlined appearance.

All SD bombs had one fuze pocket, whereas in the SC range the 250 kg (550 lb) and 500 kg (1,100 lb) could have one or two fuze pockets. The need for two fuze pockets was demonstrated in the main text where it was seen that a No 50 anti-disturbance fuze was frequently fitted to protect a No 17 long-delay fuze.

Shown below is a sketch of ten typical SC/SD bombs as used during World War 2. Under the German nomenclature serials six and nine were classified as PC and their streamlined shape can be seen. Less obvious is serial 8 which is also a PC bomb.

Sizes of the above bombs are shown in the table below:

It must be emphasized that the above list is only a cross-section of those bombs dropped during World War 2; there were a number of other high explosive bombs used and a number of variations or marks of those listed. For example, there was a parallel-sided version of the SD/PC 500 kg (1,100 lb) which was only 380 mm (15 in) in diameter and which was later converted into one of the rocket-assisted bombs.

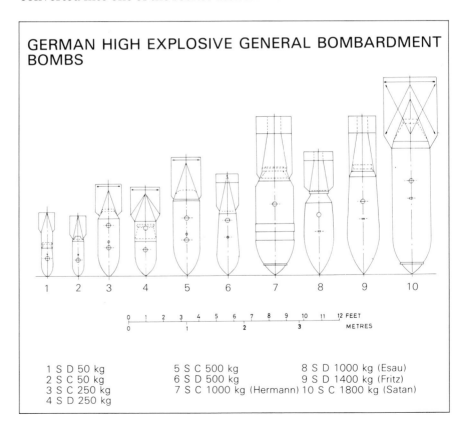

GERMAN HIGH EXPLOSIVE GENERAL BOMBARDMENT BOMBS

1 S D 50 kg	5 S C 500 kg	8 S D 1000 kg (Esau)
2 S C 50 kg	6 S D 500 kg	9 S D 1400 kg (Fritz)
3 S C 250 kg	7 S C 1000 kg (Hermann)	10 S C 1800 kg (Satan)
4 S D 250 kg		

Designation	Bomb diameter mm (in)	Bomb body length (excluding tail) mm (in)	Overall length (including tail) mm (in)	Number of fuze pockets	Charge/weight ratio %
(a)	(b)	(c)	(d)	(e)	(f)
SD 50 kg	203(8)	596(23.5)	1,092(43)	1	30
SC 50 kg	203(8)	787(30.6)	1,096(43.2)	1	44
SC 250 kg	368(14.5)	1,194(47)	1,638(64.5)	1 or 2	51
SD 250 kg	368(14.5)	874(34.4)	1,638(64.5)	1	30
SC 500 kg	457(18)	1,411(55.7)	1,961(77.2)	1 or 2	48
SD 500 kg	445 (17.5)	1,375(54)	2,286(80)	1	36
SC 1000 kg (Hermann)	660(26)	1,905(75)	2,781(109.5)	1	52
SD 1000 kg (Esau)	502(19.8)	1,486(58.5)	2,172(85.5)	1	16
SD 1400 kg (Fritz)	559(22)	1,922(75.7)	2,815(110.8)	1	21
SC 1800 kg (Satan)	660(26)	2,718(107)	3,738(147.9)	1	56

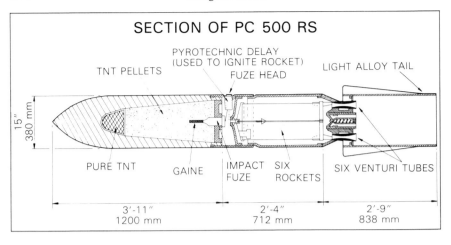

The first recovery of a rocket-assisted bomb was made in Malta and the incident is described in Chapter 5. This bomb, a PC 500 RS (Panzer-durchschlags Cylindrisch 500 kg Raketensatz) or armour-piercing 500 kg rocket-assisted bomb, was intended for the attack of warships or other heavily protected objectives. It consisted of three sections, a converted PC 500 kg bomb 1,200 mm (47 in) long filled with TNT, a container for six rockets 712 mm (28 in) long, and six venturi tubes and a tail 838 mm (33 in) long. There was a Rheinmetall fuze head for charging two fuzes, one with a pyrotechnic delay to light the rockets three seconds after the bomb had left the aircraft, and the other in the base of the bomb itself. This latter fuze was designed to function with a slight delay after impact thus allowing the bomb to penetrate its target before detonation. A diagram of the 500 kg (1,100 lb) bomb is shown below. Larger bombs of a 1,000 kg (2,200 lb) bomb were also used but the basic design was similar to the smaller version except that it contained eight rockets.

Section Two—German bomb fuzes and their immunization

A large variety of bomb fuzes were fitted to the German aerial delivered weapons dropped on the United Kingdom between 1939 and 1945. By the end of the war over 50,000 high explosive German bombs of 50 kg (110 lb) or over had been dealt with by the bomb disposal units of the three armed Services. Yet with a few exceptions the fuzes in those 50,000 unexploded bombs could be grouped into three principal types. Once the problems caused by these types had been solved, variants of them presented few additional problems to either the research scientists or the bomb disposal operators. The three types were represented by the Nos 15, 17 and 50 fuzes referred to frequently in the main text. All were Rheinmetall electric fuzes which received a charge into their reservoir capacitors at the moment of dropping from the aircraft. As the bomb fell, the charge on the reservoir capacitor leaked through a high resistance to a firing capacitor, thus arming the fuze.

The No 15 fuze was a direct impact fuze with either an instantaneous or short-delay action. A sketch of the fuze head as seen by the bomb disposal operator and an electrical circuit diagram are shown below.

The electrical circuit had two independent parts. That charged from plunger A gave an arming time of eight seconds and instantaneous action on impact. That charged from plunger B had two firing capacitors with arming times of two and eight seconds, with igniters firing pyrotechnic delays of eight seconds and 0.05 seconds respectively. The aircraft's bomb aimer could by a simple switch arrange for the bomb to detonate with or without a delay on impact, either by charging plunger B only, or both plungers A and B.

If a bomb with a No 15 fuze was dropped from less than about 20 m (65 ft) the fuze would not operate on impact as none of the firing capacitors would have become sufficiently charged. The bomb was 'dud' but still dangerous because the firing capacitors continued to receive a charge and any movement of the bomb could close the switches and cause the bomb to detonate. This fuze could be made safe merely by depressing the plungers to make a contact with the reservoir capacitor and then earthing for sufficient time to discharge both the reservoir and firing capacitors. A

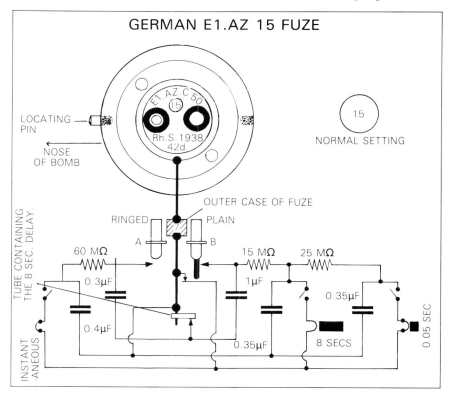

GERMAN E1.AZ 15 FUZE

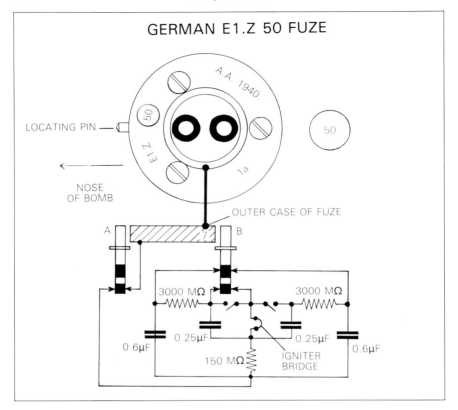

simple tool for this purpose--the 'Two-Pin Plug Discharger' was produced in April 1940 and issued to all bomb disposal units.

The No 50 fuze was first encountered in September 1940 and was
designed to act as a booby trap and anti-handling device. Its circuit diagram is shown below.

This fuze was very similar to the No 15 fuze except that its arming time
was increased from seconds to minutes by using a very high leakage resistance, so that the fuze became live only after the bomb had come to rest in
the ground. The trembler switches were extremely sensitive and any
slight movement or vibration of the bomb would cause detonation. If the
charging plunger B was depressed after the fuze was armed this short-cir-
cuited one or both of the trembler switches so detonating the bomb. Thus
the use of the two-pin discharger on this fuze would be fatal. The
sensitivity of the trembler switches not only precluded any form of violent
attack upon the fuze head but also limited the nature of any excavation to
get to the bomb. This was particularly important as normally excavation
was carried out as rapidly as possible. The Road Research Laboratory
carried out a series of tests using concrete breakers, automatic spades and
even heavy vehicles driving past a bomb fitted with a No 50 fuze, and all
caused the experimental fuze to function. The sensitivity to vibration was

determined quantitatively and it was found that a movement of 0.006 in (0.15 mm) in a time of 0.025 seconds was sufficient to close the trembler switches.

A method of immunization was therefore sought which did not require the depressing of either plunger or risk any movement of the bomb. The Royal Aircraft Establishment showed that steam could be injected past the plungers without depressing them and, when condensed inside the fuze, would slowly and safely discharge the condensers. A 'Steam Fuze Discharger' was developed and issued to Royal Engineer bomb disposal units. This equipment was used frequently and successfully to immunize live No 50 fuzes. It consisted essentially of a small steam boiler heated by an electrical element connected to a battery (the same battery as those used with the magnetic clock stopper).

Simultaneously with the development of the steam discharger, experiments were made using a slightly-conducting liquid forced past the plungers. After a series of experiments carried out in various laboratories a combination of alcohol, benzine and salt was evolved. A measured quantity of the liquid was forced into the fuze under a controlled pressure using a bicycle pump and left for thirty minutes, by which time the fuze was completely discharged. Evacuation of the fuze prior to injection of the liquid was investigated but found to be unnecessary. This equipment, when perfected, was known as the 'BD Discharger' and became a

BD discharger.

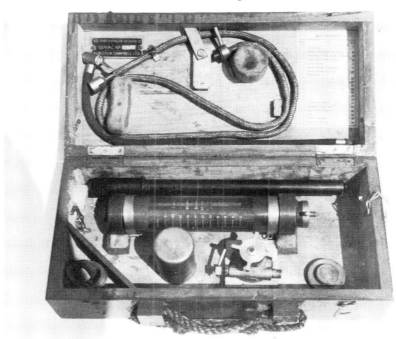

standard store issued to BD units of all three Services. It was used not only on the No 50 fuze but on all types of direct acting short-delay fuzes and superseded the two-pin discharger.

The No 17 fuze was a clockwork long-delay fuze as described in the main text. It consisted of two main parts. The top half was an electrical portion similar to the instantaneous action portion of the No 15 fuze except that when the electrical igniter fired, it ignited not the detonator but a small tube of thermite. The heat was either conducted through the casing to the lower part of the fuze where it melted a wax pellet freeing the clockwork

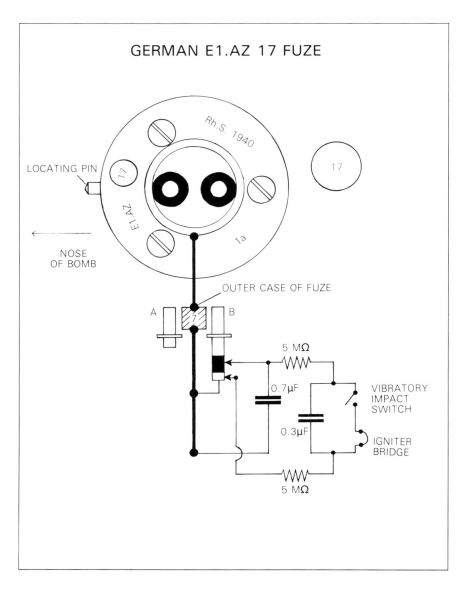

GERMAN E1.AZ 17 FUZE

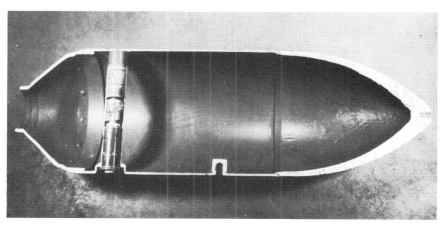

German 250 kg SC Bomb with a single fuze pocket. A ZUS 40 anti-withdrawal device can be seen beneath the fuze.

mechanism or, in the earliest models, the heat was transferred via a pyrotechnic train which burnt a plug thus freeing the clockwork mechanism. Shown opposite is the electrical circuit diagram of the No 17 fuze.

There was no opening of any sort connecting the upper electrical part of the fuze with the lower encased clockwork portion situated deep in the fuze pocket. It was useless to attack the electrical portion as that had served its purpose once it had freed the clockwork mechanism. The essential and difficult problem faced by those having to deal with this fuze was to find a method of stopping the clock. The obvious answer and one that was used successfully on many occasions was to remove the ticking fuze from the bomb. This method was quickly countered by the fitting of a ZUS 40 anti-withdrawal device under the No 17 fuze. This was a simple mechanical device with a spring-loaded striker prevented from striking a detonator by the presence of the No 17 fuze gaine. Any attempt to remove the No 17 fuze and its attached gaine freed the ZUS 40's striker which under the power of its spring struck the detonator, causing the bomb to explode.

Thus the only method of dealing with a No 17 fuze was to stop the clock. When a bomb was reached and the fuze identified as being a No 17 it was essential to know if the clockwork mechanism was ticking. The clock might not be working because it had accidentally stopped before the preset time or because for some reason it had never started. It was, therefore, equally essential to know when a stopped clock began to tick. A medical stethoscope applied to the fuze head or the bomb case could just detect the ticking clockwork mechanism under ideal conditions of near total silence. An electrical stethoscope was therefore quickly developed which enabled the fuze to be monitored from a distance of 50 m (164 ft).

It was well known that certain watches were affected by magnets whereas those fitted with non-magnetic hairsprings were not. On investigation it was found that the hairspring and most of the components of the clock in the No 17 fuze were non-magnetic, but two spindles and bushes were found to be made of steel. There was, therefore, a chance that a strong electromagnet might stop the clock, but to stop a clock deeply buried in a massive steel casing by this means was no simple problem. The Royal Aircraft Establishment (RAE) produced the first working model using an air-cooled coil working from batteries. This electromagnet, however, required 200 amperes and the current could only be passed for a few seconds before the coil overheated. This initially stopped the clock but it might start again as soon as the power was switched off. The General Electric Company (GEC) finally produced an electromagnet which only required 25 amperes and could be used continuously for an hour under full load. This electromagnet, although a great improvement upon the earlier model, still weighed 81.5 kg (180 lb). Finally, RAE and GEC jointly developed a light-weight electromagnet of the same power as the 180 lb one but weighing excactly half (40.75 kg (90 lb)).

The magnet, although it stopped the clock, did not render the fuze permanently safe and research continued to find an alternative. A lot of work was done to try and follow the basic immunization concept of pumping in some form of jamming fluid. It was the Air Ministry Bomb Disposal Technical Branch (under the command of Wing Commander J. C. Stevens, OBE, RAF) which was the first to demonstrate successfully that, after evacuation, a liquid of sufficient viscosity to stop the clock and hold it stopped could be introduced into fuzes of the No 17 type. Detailed experiments were then put into action to determine the safe minimum vacuum and subsequent pressure to ensure that the liquid reached all the vital parts of the clock, the necessary viscosity to keep the clock stopped and the effect of the liquid on the explosive train. As a result the final apparatus was perfected and known as 'The Stevens Stopper'. The magic liquid was a sugar solution!

When the Stevens Stopper came into use it was found that the ZUS 40 as well as the clock became filled with the sugar solution. If the No 17 fuze was then extracted, the solution so slowed down the ZUS 40 striker that the detonator was not pierced, although the striker was left pressed against it—a very uncertain state of affairs for the bomb disposal operator. It was then arranged that the fuze extractor injected some dental impression powder into the fuze pocket as the No 17 fuze was removed. This powder mixed with the sugar solution set so hard that the ZUS 40 could not possibly function.

Not one of the three main types of fuze, but worthy of comment, was the Y fuze. The discovery of this fuze and its method of defeat is told in Chapter 6. One other fuze should be mentioned; although never used in a bomb, its discovery had long-lasting effects upon bomb disposal equipment. When the bomb dumps of Sicily were searched immediately after their capture an entirely new type of fuze, the No 57, was discovered. This was a chemical long-delay fuze with a built-in mechanical anti-

Above left *German bomb fuze, showing gaine withdrawn from top picric acid ring and remaining pellets.*

Above right *Typical German transverse bomb fuze with gaine attached.*

withdrawal device which fired the fuze if any attempt was made to loosen the fuze locking ring. None of the existing immunization techniques were suitable as the fuze contained no clocks, capacitors or batteries. The long-delay action was obtained, as in many British and American bomb pistols and fuzes, by the softening action of acetone on a celluloid disc, finally releasing a spring loaded striker on to a detonator. The final operation of both the delay action and the booby trap depended on mechanical working parts, and if these could be prevented from moving the problem was solved. Using this approach a technique was developed of completely filling the fuze with a quick-setting synthetic resin, thus totally and permanently jamming the mechanical movement. Entry to the fuze was obtained by either removing a screw from the fuze head or drilling a hole in the fuze head. To ensure the complete filling of the fuze the Stevens Stopper technique of creating a high vacuum in the fuze and then forcing in the solution under pressure was employed. This technique was subsequently used on many types of mechanical action fuzes.

Annex C
A brief history of the Army Volunteer Bomb Disposal units

The Territorial Army (TA) has existed in some form or other for many years. The 'Terriers' were the first reinforcements for the British Army in the early months of the First World War. Similarly, in the dark days of 1939 and early 1940 it was the Territorial County Regiments which provided the first influx of trained and semi-trained men to Britain's Regular Army.

At the end of the war and during the late 1940s many men missed the comradeship experienced within their wartime units and sought it in civilian life by joining the TA units normally based at their local Drill Halls (hence their name). Others, however, had experienced more than enough of war and could not wait to shed their uniforms and forget about the Army as quickly as possible and certainly gave no thought to joining a TA unit. Thus, the Volunteer Army then as today was either enthusiastically supported or totally ignored. The major difference between then and now is that today the need for a fully trained and equipped volunteer Army is fully appreciated among both politicians and senior Service officers. It is now totally integrated into the modern order of battle and not looked upon as a pool of reserves to be called upon as required.

As the post-war TA included most Arms and Services it is not surprising that Royal Engineer bomb disposal was well represented. In 1951 there were six independent TA bomb disposal squadrons:

243 BD Sqn, RE (TA), located at Paisley, Scotland;
272 BD Sqn, RE (TA), located at Shipley, Yorkshire;
290 BD Sqn, RE (TA), located at Birmingham, Midlands;
572 BD Sqn, RE (TA), located at Camborne, Cornwall;
579 BD Sqn, RE (TA), located at Chatham, Kent; and
583 BD Sqn, RE (TA), located at Dover, Kent.

These squadrons were at full war strength, not because of a host of volunteers but because they had, in addition to the genuine volunteers, a large number of 'Z' reservists. These men had a mandatory Reserve Army commitment to undergo two weeks' training a year so in most cases they joined the TA squadrons just for their annual camp and took no other interest in the unit. This problem had been foreseen and a year earlier, on 1 October 1950, the Army Emergency Reserve (AER) had been established. This was similar to the TA except that its units were not based in a Drill Hall or any other fixed location, and consequently undertook no weekend training or regular 'drill nights' and had no centre for social activities. Instead their commitment was to come together for an annual training camp. In this way recruiting for an AER unit could be on a nation-wide basis.

With the formation of the AER there was also formed HQ 137 Bomb Disposal Regiment, RE (AER) with, under its command, 346 Bomb Disposal Squadron, RE (AER). The first commanding officer of the regiment was Lieutenant Colonel R. O. St J. Marshall, OBE, RE, who promptly wrote a letter to the *Daily Telegraph* inviting ex-bomb disposal officers to volunteer for service with the AER bomb disposal units. The response was immediate and volunteers far exceeded the vacancies available. By 1952 the regiment had grown from one squadron to four, having absorbed three newly formed AER bomb disposal squadrons (347, 348 and 549).

Although the AER bomb disposal units thrived, it became increasingly apparent that some of the TA bomb disposal units were not entirely successful. There were many and varied reasons for this. The three most often quoted reasons were, first, that the units had very few fully qualified bomb disposal instructors and therefore it was difficult to maintain the interest of newly joined soldiers. Second, not every would-be volunteer really wanted to carry out live bomb disposal since training on occasions involved genuine unexploded bomb disposal. Finally, due to the units' wide dispersion, the various Engineer commanders under whom they came had difficulties in directing the technical training of these small specialist units.

It was therefore decided to disband some of them and re-form them as AER units. Thus in 1953 HQ 142 Bomb Disposal Regiment RE (AER) was formed to command:

290 BD Sqn RE (AER)—converted from 290 BD Sqn, RE (TA);
551 BD Sqn RE (AER)—a new unit; and
547 BD Sqn RE (AER)—a new unit.

The first Commanding Officer of this Regiment was Lieutenant Colonel W. G. Parker, MBE, GM, RE.

The reorganization continued as units established their identities and underwent realistic and strenuous training. By 1955 the reorganization had been completed. On 1 January 1955 three new AER bomb disposal squadrons were created:

546 BD Sqn, RE (AER), from the old 243 BD Sqn, RE (TA);
548 BD Sqn, RE (AER), from the old 272 BD Sqn, RE (TA); and
550 BD Sqn, RE (AER), from the old 572 BD Sqn, RE (TA).

On 1 August 1955 these three squadrons were given a Regimental Headquarters and became 144 Bomb Disposal Regiment, RE (AER). This regiment was also commanded by Lieutenant Colonel W. G. Parker, who moved from 142 Bomb Disposal Regiment, RE (AER). Thus on 1 August 1955 there were three AER bomb disposal regiments (137, 142 and 144) commanded by Lieutenant Colonel P. J. Hands, MBE, RE, Lieutenant Colonel B. S. T. Archer, GC, RE, and Lieutenant Colonel W. G. Parker, MBE, GM, RE, respectively. All three names feature several times in the main text of the book and it would be difficult to find three more experienced and dedicated bomb disposal commanders. This reorganization still left two independent TA bomb disposal squadrons (579 and 583 based at Chatham and Dover respectively).

During this reorganization realistic training continued, two examples of this being quoted below. In 1940 a flight of Luftwaffe bombers were chased by Royal Air Force fighters and to assist their escape the bombers flew very low and ditched their bombs, all of which fell in an isolated field in Marlow, Buckinghamshire, and failed to explode. There they lay until 1953 when, throughout the summer, a bomb disposal troop from each of the AER squadrons worked in succession to locate, recover and dispose of these bombs. By the end of the summer all explosive had been removed from the field and excellent training on live bombs had been received by all involved.

A year later in 1954 a large unexploded bomb had been located near Fareham in Hampshire by the regular bomb disposal troop based at Fort Widley, Portsmouth. The work of recovery was so arranged that 290 Bomb Disposal Squadron, RE (AER), would be in camp at Fort Widley when the excavation was close to the bomb. Thus during their camp personnel of the AER squadron completed the excavation and discovered a German 500 kg (1,100 lb) bomb with one fuze. Lieutenant D. Woodbridge, RE (AER), successfully dealt with the fuze. This received considerable press attention and gave welcome publicity to the AER.

From 1955 until 1 April 1967 there were twelve years of relative stability for the three AER bomb disposal regiments and two independent TA bomb disposal squadrons. On 1 April 1967 there was a major reorganization of the Volunteer Army which at the time was considered by many to foreshadow the end of such forces. The old style TA disappeared as did the AER and in its place was formed the Territorial Army and Volunteer Reserve (TAVR). This was a very much smaller force that was to be better equipped and more closely integrated with the Regular Army. Its units were again to be based on a Drill Hall and recruiting was by necessity on a regional basis. However, units had to be justified by the need for them within the overall Army order of battle rather than the policy of 'if we can recruit we will form a unit'. In 1967 bomb disposal was not very high on the priority lists and from that date the only reserve bomb disposal unit remaining was 590 Specialist Team, RE (EOD) (V), which was formed on 1 April 1967. (The symbol (V) was the replacement for TA or AER and

Lieutenant D. Woodbridge, RE (AER), and his team from 290 BD Squadron, RE (AER), with their 500 kg bomb.

represented the TAVR.) No 590 Specialist Team, RE (STRE) (EOD) (V) was followed by the formation of a second STRE in 1973 when 591 STRE (EOD) (V) was established.

On 1 March 1975, 590 and 591 STRE (EOD) (V) amalgamated to form 590 EOD Squadron, RE (V), which, upon becoming effective on 1 September 1975, became the first volunteer squadron to be a sub-unit within the regular 33 Engineer Regiment (EOD). This new squadron was commanded by Major A. J. Spark, TD, RE (V).

On 1 April 1979 a second squadron was formed, 591 EOD Squadron, RE (V). This also formed a part of 33 Engineer Regiment (EOD) and on formation was commanded by Major J. Ford, TD, RE (V). It is interesting to note that just three weeks after its formation, personnel from 591 EOD Squadron, RE (V), joined their sister squadron (590) in excavating and recovering two 500 kg (1,100 lb) German bombs from Epping Forest, Essex. The officer in charge of this investigation and subsequent disposal of the bombs was Captain S. K. J. Henry, TD, RE (V), then second in command of 590 EOD Squadron, RE (V).

The formation of 591 EOD Squadron, RE (V), was followed by the formation of two more EOD (V) squadrons (579 and 583) on 1 April 1981. This was the rebirth of the two original independent TA bomb disposal squadrons just fourteen years after their disbandment on 31 March 1967.

Thus from 1951 when there were six independent TA bomb disposal squadrons dispersed between Scotland and Cornwall, many of which were not totally dedicated to bomb disposal, we come forward 35 years to today. Now there are four volunteer EOD squadrons which form part of a regular EOD regiment and which are trained by experienced regular staff and equipped with identical equipment to that used by their regular counterparts. There is no question of these volunteers being a pool of trained or semi-trained reinforcements. They are part of an operational unit and are firmly established in the order of battle as trained and effective EOD units.

Annex D
German bomb disposal

Having considered the actions of the British bomb dispoal organizations during the Second World War, what of those of the (then) enemy? During the war little thought was given to German bomb disposal personnel other than to make the Allied bombs as difficult as possible to deal with by fitting anti-disturbance, long-delay and anti-removal fuzes. (For the sake of simplicity the term fuze will be taken to include pistol where appropriate.) In fact, the problems and dangers that the British bomb disposal personnel were facing were almost identical to those faced by their opposite numbers in Germany.

Today in the 1980s the Federal Republic of Germany and the United Kingdom, as fellow members of the NATO alliance, work closely together in all aspects of bomb disposal and in preparing and perfecting methods of defeating modern weapons of war. Indeed, very many bomb disposal officers and men are personal friends of their fellow NATO bomb disposal colleagues. The camaraderie of the NATO EOD community today transcends all national boundaries. For that reason it is important to consider some of the problems faced by the German bomb disposal operators during the Second World War and to recognize that their problems and undoubted bravery were very similar to those in Great Britain.

Whereas in Great Britain most bomb disposal within the towns and cities was carried out by the Army with the Navy and Royal Air Force being responsible for their special areas of interest, in Germany the main bomb disposal service was provided by the Luftwaffe. The German Navy and Army also had their responsibilities but by far the largest force was the Luftwaffe. Like the Royal Air Force, the Luftwaffe made their armourers (*Feuerwerker*) responsible for bomb disposal. Prior to 1939, officers and senior non-commissioned officers attended a two-year armourers' course at Halle near Leipzig. This was an extremely technical course dealing with both the theoretical and practical aspects of being an aircraft armourer. It also included a section on bomb disposal. By 1940 the course had been reduced to seven months which included some time at both the *Waffen-technische Schule* (Technical Weapons School) and the *Feuerwerkerschule* (Armourers' School) both at Halle. At a later stage in the war, armourers who had gained practical experience on airfields were examined by senior officers and, if found proficient, were qualified as Feuerwerkers after an eight-week course at Halle. By 1944 there was no regular Feuerwerker training and new Feuerwerkers were appointed after examination, from men who had learned their job by experience through working in the field under trained men.

The fully qualified men were officers or *Oberfeuerwerker* (senior non-commissioned officers). There were also *Munitionsverwalter* who were equivalent to the Royal Air Force Corporal Armourers and could only do operational bomb disposal if they had attended a special course and obtained a '*Sprengerlaubnis*' (explosives certificate).

There was also a civilian bomb disposal organization within the German equivalent of the British Civil Defence organization. This was, however, formed very much earlier than its British equivalent. In the early 1920s the German Defence Minister, Gustav Noske, established under the command of General Hampe an Air Protection Service known as the *Technische Nothilfe* (Technical Emergency Organization). This organization formed bomb disposal groups in each city and major town consisting of a leader, a second in command and four trained men. The leaders of these groups were normally ex-World War 1 senior non-commissioned officers of the Army or Navy. Bomb disposal at this stage, as described in the training manuals of the late 1920s, consisted of carrying the bombs away from the built-up areas to a place where they could be safely destroyed. Later, in 1938-9, these civilian bomb disposal groups were put under the command of the SHD (*Sicherheits* und *Hilfsdienst*)—Security and Assistance Service—a para-military organization under the control of the German Air Ministry.

Once the war started and the first Royal Air Force raids had taken place the civilian groups went into action and either destroyed the unexploded bombs *in situ* or carried them away as earlier instructed. Nor surprisingly many of the group leaders began to take an interest in the bomb fuzes in an effort to understand how they worked. At this stage, unlike the Luftwaffe groups, no instructions were given concerning the operation of enemy (Allied) bomb fuzes. The great change occurred in late 1940 when most of the civilian groups were put under the command of young Luftwaffe artificer armourers (*Feuerwerker*) who had received a full technical training at Halle. The old leaders either became assistants and supervised excavation operations or were transferred to other posts within the SHD (later to be known as the *LS Polizei* (Air Protection Police)). A few continued to command auxiliary bomb disposal teams whose members were known as *Hilfsfeuerwerker*.

Thus, initially, the German bomb disposal operator was generally better qualified than his counterpart in Great Britain. He certainly was in 1939 when, it must be remembered, none of the British forces received any formal training in bomb disposal and there was still some doubt as to whether a threat actually existed.

In Britain, as soon as bomb disposal training began, bomb disposal units were formed which included officers, senior and junior non-commissioned officers and the junior ranks who provided the muscle when digging was required. Whether it was a Section, Company, Squad or Flight, in each unit or sub-unit there was a sense of belonging and mutual respect for the shared dangers. In Germany the basic bomb disposal team was the *Sprengkommando* consisting of a leader (an officer or *Oberfeuerwerker*) and three or four *Feuerwerker*. When digging or other labour intensive work was required it was done by convicts from civil prisons or German political prisoners from the concentration camps. Towards the end of the war authority was given for members of the Germany Army undergoing punishment to be used also. Prisoners-of-war were never used for this type of work, although in the occupied countries local nationals were used. It is difficult to determine whether they were forced labour or paid volunteers. Certainly many of these nationals continued with bomb disposal in their own countries after the war.

Although the *Feuerwerker* organization was well trained and an elite dedicated body of men, the use of prisoners or unwilling workers must have put an additional strain upon the morale of the force. Yet this is denied by *Feuerwerkers* who were involved at the time. They claim that relationships between the Luftwaffe members and the political prisoners were especially close and mutually supportive. Two instances tend to support this contention. The first occurred at Mainz when *Oberfeuerwerker* Kurt Engelhard was punished for having allowed five political prisoners to

The Mainz Sprengkommando in 1943, consisting of one officer, four Feuerwerker, prisoners and two guards. Oberfeuerwerker Kurt Engelhard is in the back row fourth from the left.

work unguarded on a farm preparing vegetables for the rest of the group to eat. The second instance concerns Hauptmann (Captain) Heinze Schweizer of the Luftwaffe, who towards the end of the war received information that the SS were going to execute certain political prisoners. He, together with his assistant *Oberleutnant* Werdelmann (an army officer) went immediately to the camp and, on the grounds that he needed a large work force to clear very quickly a number of unexploded bombs, managed to secure the release of the endangered prisoners to his custody. He took the prisoners to his headquarters at Kalkum in the Ruhr Valley and later hid them until the arrival of the American Army.

It is equally true that many *Feuerwerkers* did not like working with criminal prisoners. It is interesting to note that at bomb disposal reunions held in Germany after the war many ex-political prisoners attended and were made welcome, whereas the ex-criminal prisoners did not attend, nor were they invited. Whatever the full story, the use of prisoners was, of course, a military necessity to save uniformed manpower and in this respect was successful. At the height of the Allied bombing of Germany it was estimated that the Luftwaffe deployed 600 officers and 1,800 senior non-commissioned officers on active bomb disposal throughout Germany and the occupied territories. At the height of the blitz the Royal Engineers had just under 10,000 men deployed throughout Great Britain, a large proportion of whom were junior ranks involved in the less technical tasks.

Initially Allied bombs were either destroyed *in situ* or, if possible, allowed to stay for up to three days before any form of render-safe action was attempted. This meant that in towns and cities the usual practice was to destroy the bombs *in situ*. However, as the intensity and frequency of air attacks increased it became impractical and bad for morale to add still further to the damage. Instructions were, therefore, given to all German bomb disposal personnel that fuzes were to be identified and dealt with accordingly. Thus by 1942 casualties among the *Feuerwerkers* began to increase as Allied anti-removal and anti-disturbance fuzes took their toll. This was exactly the reverse to what was happening in Great Britain. During the German attacks of 1941 there was a tendency among British bomb disposal personnel to immunize or remove fuzes to prevent damage to buildings, but sometimes at the cost of those same bomb disposal personnel. This put a considerable strain upon the organization and finally an instruction was issued stating that unexploded bombs should wherever possible be detonated *in situ*. The only exception was those which were threatening a military target or any aspect of the war effort.

In Germany as more casualties occurred the newspapers began to explain the need for this more heroic approach. The excerpt shown below is taken from the *Münchener Neuste Nachrichten* in southern Germany.

'*Oberfeuerwerker* Walter Heyl, of a German Air Force bomb disposal unit (*Spreng-kommando*) has been killed in Munich while removing the fuze from a time bomb.

In the fight against the enemy terror bombers, the German Air Force bomb disposal units are in the front line. Their work demands great courage and exacti-

tude. Whereas formerly unexploded bombs and time bombs were generally
exploded, they must now, since the enemy began his heavy raids, always be
defuzed, in order to avoid further unnecessary destruction. The bomb disposal
units work under a technically trained officer and consist entirely of experts. The
additional helpers allocated to them work under the directions of the Sergeant
Artificer, partly at the laborious digging out and exposure of the bomb, and are
then withdrawn. The Sergeant Artificer then begins his dangerous work alone in
an area cordoned off for a considerable distance. Detailed knowledge of every type
of enemy fuze is essential. Even then, the possibility of an accident cannot be
entirely ruled out, as the fuze of a time bomb may run out while the work is in progress. A large number of these artificers have already lost their lives, and members
of this service were recently decorated in recognition of the difficult work it does.'

The second extract is taken from the *Hamburger Fremdenblatt* of 23 April
1943, again a similar view but this time from northern Germany.

'Comprehensive technical knowledge and *sang froid* are necessary in dealing with
unexploded missiles dropped from the air. The bomb may go off at any moment
until it is rendered safe—be it a 'dud' or a delayed action bomb, both are
dangerous; not merely to those who at the risk of their lives have to handle the
bomb, but also to life and property of every kind in the neighbourhood. Immediate action by technically qualified personnel is therefore of the utmost
importance.

In most cases an attempt is made to render the bomb safe for removal so that it
can then be transported, without risk, to a place where 'for sake of interest' its
contents may be examined. If this attempt cannot be carried out, the bomb is
destroyed on the spot having first taken all necessary technical precautions to
avoid any considerable damage. All this has to be carried out during a time in which
there is no certainty as to why the bomb has not exploded, or whether it is going to
explode at all and if so, when. Many hours' work are frequently necessary before
one can approach the bomb.

During this time, the delayed action fuze runs on—how soon it will run out no
one knows. In any case the Kommandos are all the while sitting on a 'Powder-
barrel'. It may well be understood that in such circumstances things do not always
end happily, and already many a comrade ordered to this service has given his
life . . .

A few hours later the people of the area are again in their undamaged dwellings,
the traffic has resumed, and on a heavy vehicle, an English bomb, intended for the
destruction of homes and lives has been borne away. It attracts no further
attention. The men who had recovered it have quietly and unobtrusively done
their duty. Their way leads to the next bomb . . .'

Any of the above quotations could be describing the actions of bomb
disposal operators almost anywhere. One disadvantage the Germans had
was the lack of any organization similar to the British Unexploded Bomb
Committee. Thus specialist tools and equipment were developed by individual officers or *Sprengkommando* resulting in some cases in a considerable duplication of effort. There was an exchange of ideas between
the more experienced *Feuerwerker* but no central research and development organization existed in respect of bomb disposal equipment.

This may have been due to political doctrine since Marshal Goering,
Commander-in-Chief of the Luftwaffe, had very early in the war stated

that no enemy bombs would be dropped on the Fatherland. Thus to make preparations for dealing with a heavy concentration of unexploded bombs would be to express doubts on the veracity of the Marshal's statement. Whatever the reasons no central research organization was ever established.

One of the better-known bomb disposal officers of the Luftwaffe was *Hauptmann* Heinz Schweizer who, at the beginning of the war, was the officer commanding the bomb disposal school at Halle. Within two years, although still nominally based at the school, he had established his headquarters in the Ruhr Valley at Kalkum where enemy (Allied) bombs were freely available, as was an almost endless supply of prison labour. His work as both the *'Führer des Sprengkommandos Kalkum'* (Chief of the Kalkum bomb disposal team) and his inventiveness in designing bomb disposal equipment resulted in his becoming one of the most decorated men in the *Sprengkommando* organization. His highest award was that of the Knights Cross for gallantry, and from accounts of his exploits written by his contemporaries he certainly earned his decorations. After the Royal Air Force attack against the Möhne, Sorpe and Eider dams during the early hours of 17 May 1943, Hauptmann Schweitzer personally directed the recovery and exploitation of the only unexploded bomb recovered. He was thus responsible for revealing the secrets of the Barnes Wallis bouncing bombs.

Although less well-known outside the German bomb disposal fraternity, there were many other brave men such as *Hauptmann* Griessl, *'Führer des Sprengkommandos Stuttgart'* (Leader of the Stuttgart bomb diposal team), Oberfeuerwerker Leyendecker, an Armourer Sergeant Major in the Kalkum bomb disposal team, and Oberleutnant Emil Braunweiler, who perfected the freezing technique for dealing with the British No 845 anti-disturbance battery-operated fuze.

The development of equipment, although in many ways fragmented, produced pieces of equipment very similar to those made in the United Kingdom. For example, the freezing technique developed in Britain to combat the German Y fuze was very similar to that developed by Oberleutnant Braunweiler to combat the British No 845 fuze. The German method was either to build a trough of clay around the nose of the bomb and fill the trough with a mixture of water, alcohol and solid carbon dioxide, or use plaster of paris to fix a metal tube to the nose of the bomb through which the same mixture could be poured. In either case, within about fifteen minutes the fuze reached a temperature sufficiently low not only to make the battery inert but also to freeze solid the minute drop of mercury in the mercury tilt switch, thus enabling the bomb to be moved.

Other techniques were designed to remove remotely nose or tail fuzes so quickly that they were clear of the bomb before the anti-disturbance mechanism within the fuze had time to operate. One such device was the 'Marine Turbingerät' (Marine Turbine Device). This was invented and first used by the German Navy. A charge of black powder was inserted into the head of a cylinder which was then fixed to the fuze. The powder charge

German bomb disposal techniques — freezing. **Above** *Preparing a British bomb fitted with an 845 anti-disturbance fuze.*

Below *Using Plaster of Paris, a metal tube has been fitted over the nose fuze.*

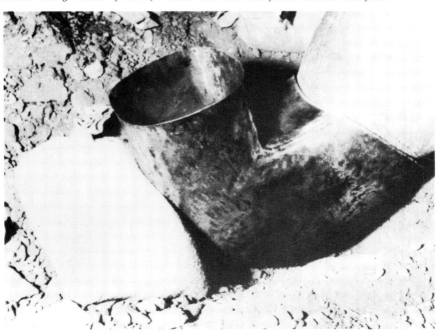

Above *A freezing mixture is prepared and pouring begins.*

Below *The freezing process is completed. Hauptmann Griessl, leader of the Stuttgart bomb disposal team, is shown on the left.*

The Marine Turbine Device, also known as the DM Device (Drehmomentgeräte) fitted for experimental firing on the remains of an Allied 1,000 lb MC bomb and tail fuze.

was ignited electrically from a distance of approximately 200 m (218 yd). The gas produced by the burning powder was allowed to escape through obliquely set holes in the cylinder so causing the cylinder and the attached fuze to rotate at a speed of 3,000 revolutions per minute and thus unscrew the fuze before its striker or other firing device had time to operate. This equipment was so much in demand that a German Ammunition Bulletin dated February 1945 forbade bomb disposal units from ordering this equipment direct from the manufacturers and directed them to use the proper supply channels.

However, this type of equipment was held on a 'need to know' basis and those bomb disposal teams based in the occupied countries or the remaining Hilfsfeuerwerker teams in Germany did not have access to it and so were forced to design and improvize their own specialist equipment. An example of this was the Raketen Gerät or rocket device which, based on a French design, was found to be cheaper and better than the Marine Turbineugerät. Indeed, it is upon this equipment that the American and later the British rocket wrench for unscrewing a wide range of nose or tail fuzes was based.

Other methods of unscrewing Allied fuzes used compressed air driven turbines or consisted simply of winding a cord round the fuze and then pulling from a distance. The latter method was, however, reported to produce a detonation in about a third of all attempts.

One other similarity between the British and German bomb disposal operators was that, although both knew their enemy's bombs and fuzes, with certain exceptions neither had free access to information on their own

German bomb trepanner, for gaining access to the explosive content of Allied bombs.

bombs and fuzes until very late in the war. The main text shows examples of problems caused by the delay in releasing to the Army details of Allied bombs and fuzes. The same thing occurred in the German forces, but here very few bomb disposal teams, other than those based on Luftwaffe airfields, had any knowledge of German bomb fuzes. Over the years some knowledge was acquired but a considerable number of Germans were killed attempting to recover their own bombs. A well-documented case concerns Leutnant Bube of the Luftwaffe serving with the Köln (Cologne) bomb disposal team. He was a very experienced officer having dealt with over 800 British and American bombs, but he had little information relating to German bombs. He was sent to Schleiden, a small town in the Eiffel region, to deal with a bomb and on arrival he found it to be the remains of a V1 flying bomb. He removed the No 80a fuze, but was unaware that it was a sensitive all-ways-acting fuze and, as he unscrewed the gaine, it exploded and a fragment entered his head and killed him.

Nations may fight nations and scientists and engineers may design more complex fuzing systems but when it comes to the problem of bomb or mine disposal there will always remain for either side three positive options. One, to risk all and remove the unexploded weapon as it is; two, to destroy it without getting involved with the fuzing system; or three, to use equipment, skill and courage to render the weapon safe to move. The work of these personnel whether friend or foe will always deserve respect and admiration.

Annex E
Bomb disposal units of the Royal Air Force and the Royal Engineers mentioned in the text

The following bomb disposal units are referred to in the text. It must be emphasized that this list does not attempt to show all the bomb disposal units or sub units which have existed or still do exist. It is merely an extension of the main index to assist those readers who may be interested in a particular unit or sub unit.

UNITS	PAGES	UNITS	PAGES
THE ROYAL AIR FORCE		6208 BD Flt RAF	115
HQ BD Wing RAF	115, 177, 198	6209 BD Flt RAF	115, 198, 199, 206-208
No 1 EOD Unit RAF	227	6210 BD Flt RAF	115, 186, 206
No 2 EOD Unit RAF	203		
5130 BD Sqn RAF	115, 181	6211 BD Flt RAF	115, 184
5131 BD Sqn RAF	115, 198, 199, 202, 206	6212 BD Flt RAF	115, 186
		6213 BD Flt RAF	115
		6214 BD Flt RAF	115, 177, 178, 185
5132 BD Sqn RAF	115, 181		
5133 BD Sqn RAF	115, 198, 201	6215 BD Flt RAF	115, 198
		6216 BD Flt RAF	115
5134 BD Sqn RAF	115, 198	6217 BD Flt RAF	115, 198, 199, 202
5135 BD Sqn RAF	115, 181		
5137 BD Sqn RAF	154, 177, 181, 184	6218 BD Flt RAF	115, 184
		6219 BD Flt RAF	115, 198, 199
5138 BD Sqn RAF	154, 177-179, 181		
		6220 BD Flt RAF	115, 177, 184
5139 BD Sqn RAF	154, 177, 180	6221 BD Flt RAF	115, 198, 199
5140 BD Sqn RAF	181, 185	6222 BD Flt RAF	115
6201 BD Flt RAF	115	6223 BD Flt RAF	115, 182
6202 BD Flt RAF	115, 198	6224 BD Flt RAF	115
6203 BD Flt RAF	115, 186	6225 BD Flt RAF	115, 177, 184
6204 BD Flt RAF	115, 198-201, 206	6226 BD Flt RAF	115, 198, 201
6205 BD Flt RAF	115	6227 BD Flt RAF	115
6206 BD Flt RAF	115, 180, 182	6228 BD Flt RAF	115, 177-179
6207 BD Flt RAF	115	6229 BD Flt RAF	115, 182

Index

19/12/45

Dear Ted,

I enclose more press cuttings of the Croydon job, this closes the incident & there is nothing further appearing in the papers.

Love

DAD.

No.14.89.0023......DRIVER....Rank

Name MILLER. E. QUARTERS

This Pass entitles the abovenamed soldier to be absent
from his quarters from after duty until 23.59 hours
daily within the London district.

DOUBLE QUARTERS

N8. 2 BOMB DISPOSAL COY, R.E.

ROYAL ENGINEERS

The lads on Power Linesman course
at Seamans – Woolwich.

g,' says Walter Weisspfenni

FIRED AT

S

CROYDON BOMB HAS A RIVAL

The sappers working on Hermann, Croydon's 4½-year-old 2000lb. unexploded bomb, are likely to be beaten by a short head by their colleagues who are extracting the 1100lb. bomb which is lodged beneath machinery in the Greenwich works of Redpath Brown and Co., Ltd., structural engineers.

The bomb at the Redpath Brown works is about 30ft. down, and the sappers are already within five feet of it. They expect to bring it out next Wednesday, after 23 days' work.

But the smaller bomb is a delicate job: it is believed to contain a delayed-action fuse which, even though the bomb fell five years ago, may still become active.

When asbestos tubes carrying detectors were being used to probe into the earth near the bomb, Captain G. F. Holsall, the officer in charge, had to take his men away from the site for four days because of the danger that one pipe might have touched the bomb and set the fuse working.

Work on Hermann at Croydon has been held up for the last few hours by a breakdown of the pumping machinery used to drain off the 24,000 gallon-an-hour flow of Croydon "Woe Water." New machinery has been brought up to pump it out.

Geneva
ing five
king of
chine-
vas so

at was
wreckage
by air-

were com-
tains such
and Hoff-

North Atlantic
much, as the
there was well
South Atlantic
uld only steam
night — chicken
aissance—would
The moral and
would be pretty
months' cruise

of a journey
nander might
e added.

tended

he Vatican
whole of
vinces of
este, and
he Post-
to-day.

sa
Go

Evenin

The
M
agrou
off De
Late
was r
of W
mot
Go
tr
a
fr

str
m
a
su
Cl

less' iellies